INTRODUCTORY COLLEGE PHYSICS

INTRODUCTORY
COLLEGE PHYSICS

BY

OSWALD BLACKWOOD, Ph.D.

Professor of Physics
The University of Pittsburgh

NEW YORK
JOHN WILEY & SONS, Inc.
London: CHAPMAN & HALL, Limited

To My Friend and Colleague

ARCHIE G. WORTHING

PREFACE

In the past generation, physics has done more to affect the life of man than in all previous history. Although it earlier made important contributions, in later years physics has given abundantly to the physical well-being of man; and has, as well, influenced his manner of approach to the world of the intellect. For example, the industrial applications of physics have at last made it possible, by working hand in hand with the old crafts, to provide food, clothing, and leisure for everyone. Besides, philosophy has been profoundly modified by the work of Einstein and Heisenberg. And too, the psychologist no longer relies on introspection, but rather upon experimentation by physical methods.

Physics has guided progress in the social world. Sectional and cultural barriers have been broken down. The motion picture and the radio, products of the physics laboratory, are binding the world together into a more closely integrated organism. Pictures on the screen, music, and voice from the air have added to everyone's knowledge of everyone else, and with knowledge will come understanding.

Herein arises a challenge to the teacher. Thousands of students crowd our colleges. Most of them have not studied physics in high school and are not well grounded in mathematics. Living in a technological age, they would profit greatly by an acquaintance with the great concepts of physics and with the part it plays in modern life. Should we bar the doors of our classrooms against these students? If not, how shall we meet their need without neglecting those who want physics as a tool subject or as a foundation for further study? Can future lawyers, clergymen, and business men achieve a reasonable degree of success in the same classroom with students preparing for the professional schools of medicine and engineering? If so, how should the usual treatment be modified to serve the dual need?

The first requirement of such a course is that it shall stimulate the interest of the general student who has had little scientific training. To him, the illustrative material must be familiar and of vital concern. That triumph of technology, the automobile, is probably the best source of such illustrations. It may be drawn upon for every part of physics, but provides especially good illustrations in mechanics. The skidding of automobile tires on the road, and the streamlining of its body to reduce air friction are well known to every driver. Almost every student can recall the forces that arise when the speed of the car increases, when it goes around a curve, or when the car runs into a telephone pole. Such experiences give the teacher excellent material. They are readily correlated by appropriate equations, typical examples may be solved, and the equations may be derived.

The world of sport also supplies effective teaching material. Queries may be raised over why a sprinter starts from a crouching position, over what his acceleration is during the first second, and over how far he travels. Or the national game can provide problems on the force that a ball exerts on the catcher's mitt, and how a baseball must spin in order to curve downward sharply.

Physics as a vital, ever-growing science may be presented through the oft-told stories of Archimedes and the bathtub, of Copernicus avoiding a martyr's crown, of Galileo, Newton, Franklin, Faraday, and Becquerel. Then, too, there is the wonder world of modern physics where a glimpse is had of present-day scientific scouts, equipped with atom guns and fog-trail detectors, who spy out the secrets of the protons, positrons, neutrons, and cosmic rays.

Not only must the student's interest be aroused, but also he must be guarded against discouragement, especially during the first few weeks of school. To this end, the journey may well begin slowly, with wide consideration given to the meaning of physics and to its place among the sciences. The important concepts of physics should, in the writer's opinion, be introduced one at a time in a carefully studied sequence. For instance, the meaning of mass may well be deferred until the student is familiar with the concept of force. Simple harmonic motion, though logically part of mechanics, can be postponed until the second half year, when it is needed in discussing vibrations.

This book, devised to meet the needs of a non-technical course taught by the writer, has been used for five years by more than 700 students. Care has been exercised to present the material as simply as possible, yet with such precision and rigor that there will be little to unlearn later on.

Numerous illustrative examples are worked out in considerable detail. These problems are stated with units, principally because experience has shown that the distinctions between physical quantities, such as velocity and acceleration, are clarified. Important statements are printed in bold-faced type. The legends of the figures are unusually complete so that the figures themselves may teach as much physics as possible. Summaries, review questions, and problems are given with each chapter, and a table of algebra and geometry aids in the Appendix.

Criticisms of this book and suggestions for its improvement will be appreciated.

OSWALD BLACKWOOD

Pittsburgh, Pa., June 30, 1938

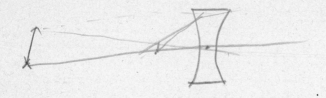

ACKNOWLEDGMENTS

It is a pleasure to acknowledge the direct assistance of many friends. Among my colleagues, Dr. A. G. Worthing has spared no pains in criticizing the work at several stages of its development. Dr. Millard Manning, Dr. A. H. Croup, Dr. Robert Osborne, and Mr. Paul M. Dysart have carefully read the manuscript, including the problems, giving much aid in improving its form and content. Dr. Elmer Hutchisson has made many suggestions. Other helpers include Dr. Thomas Carroll of New Rochelle College, Dr. Forest Shollenberger of Mt. Union College, Professor E. R. Bordner and Dr. L. K. Van Velzer of Pennsylvania State College, Mr. Jennings Hammer, Mr. Leonard Schwartz, and Mr. Jasper Shriner. Lastly, I mention the two Gertrudes, my wife and my daughter, who have toiled at the preparation of the manuscript.

parallel forces

torque

work + power

simple machines

Resultants

coef of friction

$s = \frac{1}{2} g t^2$ (in rectang. motion)

K.E. + P.E. energy

general gass law

paskals law

Temp. scales ✓

coef. of linear expansion

change of state

Inertia

Newtons laws

Torque $= I \alpha$ or inertia × ang. acc. ✓

$\omega = \alpha T$

$s = \frac{1}{2} a t^2$

$ym = \dfrac{\dfrac{F}{a \text{ or (cross section area)}}}{\dfrac{\Delta L}{L}}$

$C.F. = \dfrac{m v^2}{r}$

accel. ✓

Kalametry ✓

CONTENTS

MECHANICS

CHAPTER   PAGE

I. Science and Measurement 1
II. Forces in Equilibrium 10
III. Levers and Torques 19
IV. Work, Power, and Machines 25
V. Friction 37
VI. Rectilinear Motion 47
VII. Force and Acceleration 55
VIII. Curvilinear Motion 63
IX. Energy, Impulse, and Momentum 74
X. Rotary Motion 84
XI. Gravitation 93

MOLECULAR PHYSICS AND HEAT

XII. Atoms and Molecules 105
XIII. Molecular Forces in Liquids 111
XIV. Molecular Forces in Solids 119
XV. Pressures in Liquids at Rest 126
XVI. Pressures in Gases 141
XVII. Fluids in Motion 153
XVIII. Molecular Motions 159
XIX. Temperature 166
XX. Expansion of Solids and Liquids 176
XXI. Calories and British Thermal Units 182
XXII. Heat Transfer and Radiation 188
XXIII. Change of State 198
XXIV. Heat, Work, and Engines 215
XXV. Physics of the Weather 228

VIBRATIONS, WAVE MOTIONS, AND SOUND

XXVI. Vibrations 242
XXVII. Wave Motion and Sound 248
XXVIII. The Physics of Musical Sounds 258

LIGHT

CHAPTER   PAGE

XXIX. ILLUMINATION 269

XXX. THE SPEED OF LIGHT 276

XXXI. REFLECTION AND REFRACTION 280

XXXII. LENSES AND CURVED MIRRORS 291

XXXIII. OPTICAL INSTRUMENTS 303

XXXIV. THE SPECTROSCOPE—A MASTER DETECTIVE . . . 314

XXXV. COLOR, DIFFRACTION, AND INTERFERENCE 324

XXXVI. POLARIZED LIGHT 336

ELECTRICITY AND MAGNETISM

XXXVII. ELECTRIC CHARGES 342

XXXVIII. AMPERES, COULOMBS, AND OHMS 352

XXXIX. POTENTIAL DIFFERENCES 359

XL. ELECTRIC CIRCUITS 366

XLI. ELECTROLYSIS AND VOLTAIC CELLS 373

XLII. ELECTRICAL ENERGY AND POWER 383

XLIII. ELECTRICAL HEATING—THERMOELECTRICITY . . . 387

XLIV. MAGNETISM 394

XLV. ELECTROMAGNETISM 403

XLVI. INDUCED CURRENTS 413

XLVII. GENERATORS AND MOTORS 424

XLVIII. RADIO 433

THE NEW PHYSICS

XLIX. IONS AND ELECTRONS 447

L. X-RAYS AND PHOTOELECTRICITY 455

LI. RADIOACTIVITY AND COSMIC RAYS 462

APPENDIX 473

ANSWERS TO PROBLEMS 475

INDEX 481

INTRODUCTORY COLLEGE PHYSICS

MECHANICS

CHAPTER I

SCIENCE AND MEASUREMENT

The truth shall make you free.

The Slow Progress of Civilization. Two hundred centuries ago, the cave men were able to use simple tools such as levers, hammers, and flint knives. They knew how to carve, on the walls of their dwellings, pictures which have artistic merit. Then, more than 160 centuries

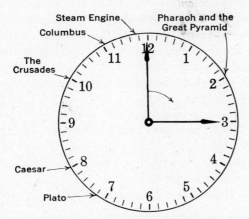

FIG. 1.—A slow-ticking clock.

passed before the beginnings of history and the rise of civilization in Egypt and Mesopotamia. Imagine a clock driven so slowly that 6,000 years are required for a single revolution of the minute hand (Fig. 1). By this slow-moving timepiece, the cave men carved the pictures three hours ago. Fifty minutes have crept away since the great pyramid was built in Egypt. Twenty minutes ago, Julius Caesar was born, and the

1

Roman Empire extended its law and order to the boundaries of the known world. Four minutes have ticked away since Columbus discovered the New World. Less than two minutes ago, two very important events happened: the writing of the Declaration of Independence and the invention of the steam engine.

During the last century the changes have crowded so closely that they can be followed only on the second hand of our clock. About 60 seconds have passed since Faraday invented a toylike dynamo which was the forerunner of those giant generators that supply energy to light our houses and actuate our radios. This was followed by the electric telegraph, and the motor. The last 40 years, 24 seconds on the imaginary clock, bring the radio, radium, and the dream of the alchemist, the transmutation of the elements. Less than 10 seconds have slipped by since Lindbergh made his lonely flight across the ocean.

Why this sudden increase in the knowledge of and the control of the physical world? Is it not surprising that the ancient Greeks, with their highly developed civilization and culture, made so little progress in the physical sciences? One reason that our advance is more rapid than theirs is that in modern times men have learned to use a very effective technique called the *scientific method*. In the words of Huxley:

The introduction of this method with its dispassionate, objective analysis of material forces and with the constant testing of theories by experiment, is one of the most valuable achievements of the ages.

1. What is the Scientific Method? A competent physician uses all the successive steps which characterize the complete scientific method. These are as follows:

1. *Observation.* He determines the patient's temperature, pulse, respiration rate, blood pressure, and other relevant "symptoms."

2. *Organization.* He carefully considers the results of his observations and compares them with the knowledge of diseases which has accumulated through the centuries.

3. *Hypothesis.* He makes a diagnosis or a hypothesis as to the nature of the disease.

4. *Verification.* He prescribes a treatment and by experimentation finds out whether or not his hypothesis was correct.

Thus by trial and error the physician gradually increases his own skill and also adds to the knowledge of his profession.

An example of long-established, crude use of the scientific method is provided by a market gardener as he tries to find out in which part of his land beans will grow best. He plants the seed in several plots. By trial and error, in the course of a few years, he learns where beans flourish, and this information he gives to his children.

Most of our knowledge of the times of planting, the choice of seeds, fertilizers, and the like was garnered through the ages by the slow and painful method of trial and error, and progress was very tedious. The gardener's son attacks the same problem, having had the advantage of training in an agricultural school. There he has learned that beans thrive in soils which are slightly acid, and he uses this knowledge in testing his fields. By simple methods he determines the acidities of the different parts of his land and gets information in a few hours instead of years. Both men use the scientific method, yet one does so more effectively than the other.

It should be emphasized that the scientific method was practiced before the dawn of history. The primitive "medicine man," trying various vile concoctions, was practicing a crude form of scientific method. Why was he less successful than the modern physician? For this failure, several reasons are worthy of mention.

The World Has Greater Faith in the Uniformity of Nature. In primitive societies, disease was regarded as the result of the wrath of some offended witch, hobgoblin, or demon. The question asked was not what caused the disease but rather who caused it. The medicine man tried to placate the evil spirits, whereas today the physician zealously observes symptoms, and performs experiments, assuming that nature's laws do not vary.

Scientific Men Have Greater Skill and Knowledge. Because of the increased leisure made possible by machinery, the scientist nowadays has an abundant formal education. Research formerly was done principally by amateurs, but today thousands of well-trained workers are devoting their lives to scientific research.

The Scientist Has Better Libraries, Tools, and Instruments. Franklin performed his famous experiments on electricity using a few pieces of fur and cloth, some bits of wax, some needles, and the like. He had no worthy library, and communication with friends in Europe required many months. Today, Millikan and Compton have great libraries to use. They have intricate instruments and—best of all—the encouragement of other zealous workers.

The increasing control of nature made possible by scientific research and the development of machinery has brought great blessings to humanity. Often we belittle these achievements and advocate the return to a simpler way of living. When we do, it is helpful to remember that the wise and good Greek philosopher Plato once justified slavery, saying that without it there could be no leisure class of cultivated people. In his day, to gain the most meager subsistence required unending toil. Today the machine has brought a great amount of leisure, and work is looked upon as something desirable because of the rewards it brings. The machine has freed the slave and has provided possibilities of culture for the common people.

In recent decades the scientific method has been applied to the study of man and of society. The results in historical research in psychology and in sociology give promise of greater security and freedom for all.

2. What is a Science? The word *science* is used in many ways. It is derived from the Latin word *scire* meaning *to know,* and might, therefore, be applied to all kinds of knowledge. Usually it is restricted to those highly organized fields in which there is an incessant search for the relationships between cause and effect. Some divisions of knowledge are partly included in the limits of science although they extend beyond its borders. For example, as will be seen later, there is a well-developed science of musical sounds, in which are studied the physical differences between musical sounds and noises, the laws of harmony, and the methods of tone production. Yet few singers or violin players are scientists. Though skilled in the techniques of producing musical sounds, they are ignorant of the science behind their art.

3. Meet the Sciences. Scientific knowledge in olden times was so limited that one man could be an expert in many fields. Scientists called themselves natural philosophers rather than physicists, chemists, or astronomers. For instance, Franklin's experiments with lightning made him famous, yet he found time to interest himself in studies of the weather, of ocean currents, of water films, and of dietetics. He wrote treatises on economics and politics and was an eminent statesman. Franklin was an amateur in science; his great achievements were in diplomacy.

After Franklin, came the age of specialization in which we live. The term "natural philosophy" was abandoned about seventy-five years ago and "physics" was adopted. This word is derived from a Greek expression meaning nature, which might well be applied to all the natural sciences. Actually the physicist usually limits his attention to the general and fundamental aspects of matter and energy, while other scientists have taken over the more specialized fields. Thus we have:

Physics—the fundamental science of matter and energy.

Astronomy—the science of the stars.

Chemistry—the science of the properties of atoms and molecules.

Geology—the science of the earth.

Biology—the science of living organisms.

4. The Subdivisions of Physics. The foundation part of physics is mechanics, in which the effects of forces in producing motion are studied and the meanings of such terms as mass and energy are made clear. Afterward the mechanics is applied in the study of heat, sound, light, and electricity. Thus, we shall consider

Mechanics—the effects of forces in producing motion and the meaning of mass and energy.

Heat—the motions and energies of molecules and atoms.

Sound—the properties of the waves by which we hear.

Light—the properties of the agency by which we see.

Electricity and magnetism—the motions and energies of electrons, protons, and other charged particles.

5. Measurement. Since physics concerns itself almost exclusively with measurable quantities, it is very important to know precisely what this term means. When any quantity is measured, we determine **the ratio of that quantity to a chosen unit.** For example, in measuring the width of a room, we find the number of yardsticks which, placed end to end, would reach from one wall to the opposite side.

It is interesting to consider the development of weights and measures from the earliest times. In primitive societies there was little commerce outside the village, and very crude and simple units of measure were used. The yard was often defined as one-half of the distance from finger tip to finger tip of the king's outstretched arms, and the pound as the weight of a certain number of "grains of barley chosen from the middle of the ear." Simple, inexact units served well enough for barter among friends and neighbors, but trouble arose when commerce developed between the cities and towns of a country. To meet the needs of traders, some of the commonly used units of measure were made legal throughout an entire nation. As no attempts were made to interrelate them, the result was a hodgepodge. In America, the system of measures, inherited from Great Britain, has as units of volume the foot, gill, pint, quart, gallon, and the bushel. Every schoolboy finds it hard to remember that 1,728 cubic inches equal 1 cubic foot or that 5,280 feet equal 1 mile. Most of the tables are quickly forgotten; few people are certain which is larger, the troy pound or the pound avoirdupois. The difficulty increases when a national boundary is crossed. A citizen of Detroit taking an automobile trip into Canada supposes that gasoline is more expensive than it is in Michigan. The explanation is that the imperial gallon of Canada is about 20 per cent larger than the gallon which is legal in the United States.

6. The Metric System. The French Revolution in the latter part of the eighteenth century caused a pronounced tendency to abandon customs and usages. Scientific men had been greatly hindered by the absence of an international system of weights and measures, and they introduced a new metric system which is so convenient that it is used everywhere for scientific work. It has been adopted commercially by all excepting the English-speaking nations, and even by them, it is being gradually accepted. One great advantage of the metric system is that all the units for measuring a quantity are decimally related. To change centimeters to meters is as easy as converting cents into dollars. All that is needed is to shift the decimal point. For instance, 1.23 meters = 123 centimeters; 3.456 kilograms = 3,456 grams. A second advantage is that the metric system is a truly international language of measurement and it is understood by educated people everywhere.

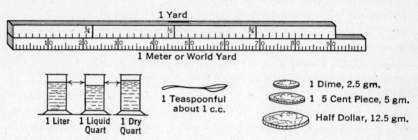

FIG. 2.—Metric and British units of length, volume, and mass.

7. Metric and British Units of Length—the Meter and the Yard. The metric standard of length is the **meter** (sometimes called the world yard) which is defined as the distance between two scratches on a certain platinum-iridium bar, at the temperature of melting ice. This bar is kept at the International Bureau of Weights and Measures at Sèvres, near Paris. Replicas of the standard meter are deposited at Washington, London, Berlin, and other capitals.

In establishing the meter, it was desired to choose some object as a standard which could not be lost or damaged, and which would not shrink or expand. The object chosen was the earth. Originally the meter was defined as the one ten-millionth part of the distance from the equator to the north pole, on a line through Paris, and a platinum bar was constructed whose length was as near as possible to this. The "meter stick" was later found to be a hair's breadth too short, and in 1872 the platinum-iridium bar itself was adopted as the primary standard. It is also kept at the International Bureau of Weights and Measures.

The yard, legal in the United States, is defined as a certain fraction (3,600/3,937) of the standard meter. Thus 39.37 inches equal 1 meter, which is about 10 per cent longer than a yard. Also 2.54 centimeters equal 1 inch, and 30.5 centimeters equal 1 foot (Fig. 2).

Table I, of metric and British units, will show the advantage of the metric system.

TABLE I

METRIC UNITS OF LENGTH AND THEIR APPROXIMATE BRITISH EQUIVALENTS

1 megameter = 1,000,000 meters
1 kilometer = 1,000 meters = 5/8 mile
1 meter = 1.1 yard
1 centimeter = 1/100 meter = 1/2.54 inch = 1/30.5 ft.
1 millimeter = 1/1,000 meter
1 micron = 1/1,000,000 meter

1 KM = .6 Mile
1 M = 39.37 in
1 in = 2.54 cm

BRITISH UNITS AND THEIR APPROXIMATE METRIC EQUIVALENTS

12 inches = 1 foot = 30.5 centimeters
3 feet = 1 yard = 0.91 meter
5 ½ yards = 1 rod
40 rods = 1 furlong
8 furlongs = 1 mile
5,280 feet = 1 mile = 8/5 kilometer
3 miles = 1 league

1 L = 1000 cm³
1 L = 1.06 qt.

8. What is Mass? Another very important unit is that of mass by which is meant the amount of matter in a body. One way to compare the masses of two bodies is to exert equal forces on them and to see which is easier to "get going." Suppose that two pasteboard boxes are lying on the pavement, one empty, the other containing a brick. If a boy kicks first one and then the other, he quickly determines which box has the

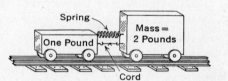

FIG. 3.—The more massive body acquires the smaller speed.

greater mass and is harder to "speed up." A more precise application of this method of comparing masses is as follows: Place two cars on a level table, and compress a spring, tying the two by a cord (Fig. 3). Burn the cord, releasing the cars, and the spring will exert equal forces on each of them. Then, if the masses are the same, the cars will travel equal distances in equal times. If they are not the same, the car of smaller mass will acquire the greater speed. (The measurement of masses will be discussed more completely later.)

9. Units of Mass. The Gram and the Pound. The metric unit of mass, the gram, is **the one-thousandth part of the quantity of matter in a certain platinum-iridium cylinder which is kept with the standard**

meter. One gram is nearly equal to the mass of a cubic centimeter of water at 39.2° Fahrenheit or 4° Centigrade. A new five-cent piece has a mass of 5 grams; the mass of a dime is one-half as great. The pound-mass equals 454 grams (more exactly 453.6 grams), so that 2.20 pounds equal 1 kilogram, approximately.

SOME METRIC UNITS OF MASS AND VOLUME AND THEIR
APPROXIMATE BRITISH EQUIVALENTS

1 metric ton (1,000 kilograms)	= 0.98	long ton
	1.10	short tons
1 gram	= 1/454	pound = 1/30 ounce
1 kilogram	= 2.20	pounds
1 liter (1,000 cubic centimeters)	= 1.06	liquid quarts
	= 0.91	dry quart

(See Appendix for other equivalents.)

10. Units of Time—the Mean Solar Day and the Second. From prehistoric epochs the apparent motions of the heavenly bodies have served to measure time. The apparent motion of the sun gives us our day, that of the moon measures off the months, and the positions of the stars tell us the passing of the year. About 7,000 years ago Egyptian scholars first noticed that in the spring the star Sirius was barely visible on the eastern horizon at sunrise, and thus they marked the beginning of their year. Today the years and days are measured by the apparent motion of the sun. The **mean solar day** is the average time from noon to noon, as measured on a sundial. This day is divided into 24 equal hours, and each of these into 3,600 seconds. The solar second is the 1/86,400 part of a mean solar day.

11. Derived Units. These units of length, mass, and time are called the **fundamental** units, and all other units of mechanics can be derived from them. For example, as units of area in the two systems we have the square centimeter and the square foot, respectively, and as units of speed the centimeter per second and the foot per second.

The set of units derived from the **centimeter, gram,** and **second** is known as the C. G. S. system. The British units derived from the **foot, pound,** and **second** constitute the F. P. S. system.

REFERENCES

LOEB and ADAMS: "Development of Physical Thought," Chap. I.
HUXLEY: "Essays and Addresses."
LIBBY: "History of Science."
Encyclopædia Britannica, article on Measurement.

SUMMARY

The complete scientific method comprises (1) observation, (2) organization, (3) hypothesis, and (4) verification.

A science is a highly organized body of knowledge, developed by the scientific method, characterized by an incessant search for relationships between causes and effects.

To measure a quantity means to find the ratio of that quantity to its unit.

The metric system is convenient because its units are decimally related and because it is used internationally.

The meter is the distance between two scratches on a certain platinum-iridium bar when it is at the temperature of melting ice. One meter = 39.37 inches; 2.54 centimeters = 1 inch.

The kilogram is the mass of a certain platinum-iridium cylinder. The avoirdupois pound is a certain part (approximately 1/2.20) of the kilogram.

REVIEW QUESTIONS

1. Why is scientific progress more rapid now than it was a century ago? (Can you find other reasons in addition to those cited in the text?)

2. What are the four consecutive steps in the scientific method? Illustrate by a practical problem.

3. Define "science," and name several sciences not mentioned in this chapter.

4. Define "measurement," and give illustrations of things which cannot be measured.

5. Define "meter," "kilogram-mass," and "mean solar second."

6. Define "derived unit," and cite several examples.

7. Express your height in meters and your mass in kilograms.

8. In short-distance running, the "440-yard dash" is used. How many meters is this?

CHAPTER II

FORCES IN EQUILIBRIUM

Our first ideas of the nature of force are derived from muscular sensations. A child soon becomes acquainted with various pushes and pulls which act upon him. Among these are the forces due to the attraction of the earth. Lift a 1-pound mass of sugar in a market basket and your arm will experience a down-pull. Add another pound, and the down-pull or down-force will be increased. Thus we see that the earth's attraction for a body—that is, the weight of the body—increases with its mass.

The weights of different bodies can be found by using a spring balance, which is a spiral spring, fitted with a pointer and scale to

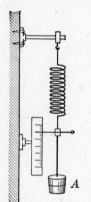

FIG. 1.—A spring balance, to measure forces.

indicate its elongations (Fig. 1). Suspend a body of 1 pound mass from the spring, and the pointer will move to a certain position on the scale. Add a second body of equal mass, and the spring will be stretched twice as far. In this way the scale can be marked off so as to indicate the weight of any body suspended from it.

A spring balance can be used to measure other forces besides the weights of bodies, for example, the pull necessary to drag a sled along a sidewalk.

12. Units of Force—the Pound-Weight, the Gram-Weight, and the Dyne. * The pull of the earth on a body whose mass is 1 pound is called a pound-weight (represented by lb. from Latin *libra* meaning pound). In the metric system the gram-weight (written gwt.) is defined as the pull of the earth on a body whose mass is 1 gram. The weight of a body, or the earth-pull on it, is not the same at all parts of the earth's surface. Hence to define the pound-weight and the gram-weight exactly it would be necessary to specify the point where the weighing was done. However, the variations of weight with position on the earth are so small as to be

---

* It is extremely important that forces be distinguished from masses. To this end the following abbreviations will be used.

1 gwt.	= gram-weight.	1 lb.	= 1 pound-weight.
1 gram	= 1 gram-mass.	1 pound	= 1 pound-mass.

negligible in many problems. Later it will be made clear how the difficulty is avoided in precise measurements.

A small unit of force, the dyne, is widely employed in scientific work. It is 1/980 of a gram-weight, approximately, and hence is slightly larger than the weight of a milligram.

13. Resultants of Forces. Forces acting in the same direction are added arithmetically. For example, suppose that 10 sophomores pull northward on a rope, each exerting a force of 40 lb. The total north-pull is 400 lb. This single force which is equal to the others is called their **resultant.**

The resultant of several forces is the single force which is equivalent to them.

Two forces acting in opposite directions are subtracted from each other. In a tug of war, let the sophomores pull northward with a force of 400 lb. while the freshmen pull southward with a force of 360 lb. Then the resultant force is 40 lb. directed north.

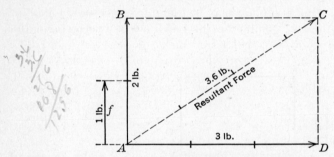

FIG. 2.—The force represented by AC is equivalent to those represented by AB and AD.

14. The Parallelogram Rule. When two forces are not parallel, their resultant is found by the **parallelogram rule.** The first step is to represent the forces by arrows or "vectors" of proper directions and lengths. For example, the arrow f (Fig. 2) (of any desired length) represents 1 lb.; then AB, two times as long, represents a force of 2 lb. directed north, and AD, three times as long, is a force of 3 lb. directed east. Observe that the two arrows are placed tail to tail. Complete the parallelogram $ABCD$. The arrow AC, which is the diagonal of the parallelogram, represents the resultant of AB and AD. It is 3.6 times as long as f, hence the resultant is 3.6 lb.

The parallelogram rule is as follows:

The resultant of two forces is represented by the diagonal of a parallelogram of which the two force arrows are adjacent sides.

The Resultant of Two Forces May Be Greater or Less in Magnitude Than Either of Them. The resultant of two forces depends upon the angle between them. In Fig. 3*A* the two forces are oppositely directed, and their resultant equals the difference between them. In *B* and *C*, the resultant increases as the angle becomes smaller, and in *D* it equals the sum of the two. Thus, the resultant of two forces may be greater or less than either of them.

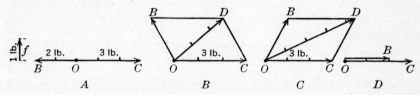

FIG. 3.—The resultant of two forces may be greater or less in magnitude than either force.

15. The Resultant of Three or More Forces. The resultant of three or more forces acting at a point may be found by successively applying the parallelogram law, combining the resultant of two forces with a third force, and so on.

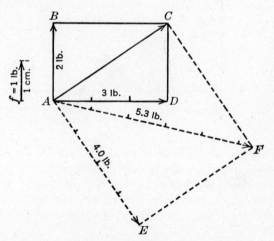

FIG. 4.—Finding the resultant of three forces.

Example. Combine the forces, 2.0 lb., 3.0 lb., and 4.0 lb., represented in Fig. 4 by *AB*, *AD*, and *AE*.

A parallelogram is drawn as before, letting 1.0 cm. represent a force of 1 lb. The force *AC* is the resultant of the forces *AB* and *AD*. Next a second parallelogram is constructed with *AC* and *AE* as sides, and its diagonal *AF* is the single, resultant force which is equivalent to the three. The length of the arrow is 5.3 cm., and hence the resultant force is 5.3 lb.

16. Equilibrium. In a tug of war, when the two opposing teams pull equally, the forces balance each other, their resultant is zero, and no motion is produced (Fig. 5). In general, **when the resultant of several forces acting on a body is zero, the body is said to be in equilibrium.**

The force which will balance one or more other forces is called their

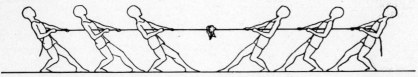

FIG. 5.—When forces are in equilibrium no motion is produced.

equilibrant. In Fig. 6, the downward pull AE of the weight W is equilibrant of the forces AB and AD which are exerted on the cords by the two spring balances. The **resultant** AC of these two forces, found by the parallelogram method, *is equal and opposite to the equilibrant force AE.*

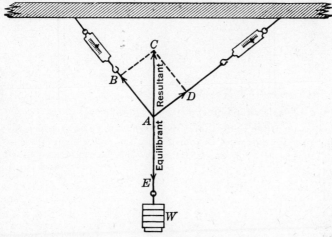

FIG. 6.—The down pull of the load. W is the equilibrant of the two forces exerted by the spring balances.

When several forces are in equilibrium, any one of them is the equilibrant of all the others.

Example 1. The forces AB and AD, Fig. 7, are 20 lb. and 22 lb., respectively. Find their resultant and equilibrant.

By the parallelogram method, the force AC is found to be 25 lb. The equilibrant, equal and opposite to the resultant, is represented by AE.

Example 2. A stone weighing 15 lb. is suspended from the midpoint of a clothes line (Fig. 8). Find the pull of the rope along AB.

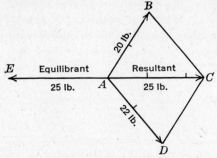

FIG. 7.—The force AE is the equilibrant of AB and AD.

Let the arrow f represent a force of 10 lb.

The down-force AE is 15 lb., and is the equilibrant of the other two forces. Their resultant must be the **equal** and **opposite** force AF. Lines are drawn from F so as to complete the parallelogram $ABFD$. The arrow AB represents the pull of the rope. Since AB is 2.7 times as long as f, the force is 27 lb. The equal pull of the other part of the rope is represented by the arrow AD.

Example 3. A sign weighing 30 lb. is supported by a wire attached at the end of a wooden bar (Fig. 9). Find the pull of the wire along AC, neglecting the weight of the bar.

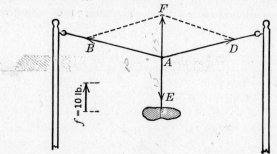

FIG. 8.—AE is the equilibrant; AF the resultant of the forces AB and AD.

Three forces act at the point A: one, the weight of the sign; another, the unknown pull of the wire; and the third, the out-push of the rod. Construct a separate force parallelogram (Fig. 9B). Let the weight of the sign be represented by OF, 3 units

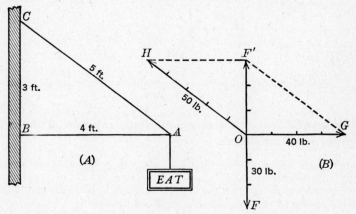

FIG. 9.—The three forces acting at A are in equilibrium.

long. Next, draw two lines *OH* and *OG*, parallel to the pull of the wire and to the push of the bar. *OF* is the equilibrant of the two unknown forces; hence, *OF'*, equal and opposite, is their resultant. Complete the parallelogram, drawing *F'H* and *F'G* parallel to the two respective forces.

By measurement, as in previous problems, the magnitude of the pull *OH* is found to be 50 lb. It can also be determined by similar triangles as follows:

The triangles *GOF'* and *ABC* are similar, hence their corresponding sides are proportional.

$$F'G/OF' = CA/BC$$
$$F'G/30 \text{ lb.} = 5 \text{ ft.}/3 \text{ ft.}$$
$$F'G = 50 \text{ lb.}$$

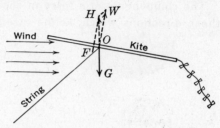

FIG. 10.—Three forces act on the kite.

Three forces act on the kite represented in Fig. 10. One is the pull *OF* of the string; another, the push *OW* of the wind. The resultant of these two forces, *OH*, is equal and opposite to the third force, the weight of the kite. Hence it is in equilibrium.

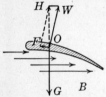

FIG. 11.—Forces acting on an airplane wing.

The forces on a wing of an airplane flying horizontally are diagrammed in Fig. 11. The propeller exerts a forward force *OF*, and the wind a force *OW*. Their resultant, *OH*, is equal and opposite to the down-pull *OG*, and the three produce equilibrium.

17. The Components of a Force. When a sled is dragged over a frozen pond by means of a rope (Fig. 12), the pull tends to drag the sled forward and also to lift it from the surface. Using the parallelogram law, the force *AC* is found to be equivalent to the vertical

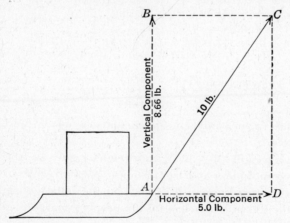

FIG. 12.—The forces *AB* and *AD* are the vertical and horizontal components of the force *AC*.

force AB (8.66 lb.) and the horizontal force AD (5.00 lb.). Thus the effect on the sled is just the same as if one rope pulled it horizontally and another exerted a vertically upward force. These two equivalent forces are called the horizontal and vertical **components** of the force AC.

The components of a force in specified directions are the forces in those directions which, acting together, are equivalent to that force.

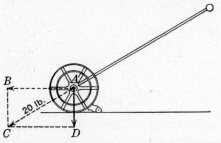

FIG. 13.—AB and AD are components of AC.

Example 1. A force AC of 20 lb. is exerted along the handle of a lawn mower (Fig. 13). What are its vertical and horizontal components?

The force AC is equivalent to AB and AD, acting together. By measurement the components are found to be 17.3 lb. and 10.0 lb., respectively.

Example 2. What force parallel to the roadway is required to keep an automobile weighing 2,000 lb. from starting down a uniform incline which is 100 ft. long and 20 ft. high?

In Fig. 14 the weight of the car is represented by the arrow OG and is equivalent

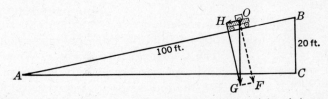

FIG. 14.—OH is the down-hill component of the weight of the car.

to the component forces OH and OF. The two right-angled triangles ABC and GOH are similar for the corresponding angles are equal.

Therefore

$$OH/OG \qquad = BC/AB$$
$$OH/2,000 \text{ lb.} = 20 \text{ ft.}/100 \text{ ft.}$$

The "down-hill" component is: $OH = 400$ lb.

SUMMARY

Forces may be measured by the elongations which they produce in a spiral spring.

The pound-weight (lb.) and gram-weight (gwt.) are the weights of bodies of 1-pound-mass and 1-gram-mass, respectively.

Forces are directed quantities and can be represented by arrows, parallel to the forces, whose lengths are proportional to the magnitudes of the forces.

The resultant of several forces acting at a point is the single force that is equivalent to them. The resultant of two forces acting at a point may be found by means of the parallelogram law.

Several forces are in equilibrium when their resultant is zero and no motion is produced.

The components of a force in specified directions are forces in those directions which, acting together, are equivalent to the given force.

REVIEW QUESTIONS

1. Define "pound-weight," "gram-weight."
2. Define "resultant," "equilibrant," and "component."

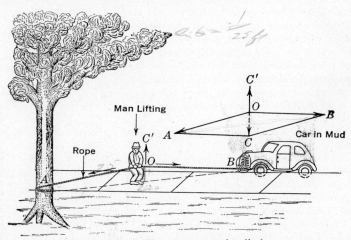

FIG. 15.—Pulling a car out of a ditch.

3. If given a long spiral spring, a pound-mass, and a bag of sugar, how could you determine the weight of the sugar?

4. In Fig. 6, find the equilibrant of the forces AB and AE. The load is 20 lb.

5. When a barrel is pushed up an inclined plane, how does the vertical component of the force vary with the steepness of the incline?

6. When telephone wires are loaded with sleet, is there more danger of their breaking when they are taut or when they sag?

PROBLEMS

NOTE: The problems are graded as follows: the more difficult problems are primed, as Problem 2; the most difficult ones are double-primed, as Problem 4.

1. Find the resultant of the following forces acting at right angles to each other. 8.0 lb. N.E., 8.0 lb. S.E.

2'. The ends of a rope 10 ft. long are tied to a rafter, the ends being 6 ft. apart. A stone weighing 48 lb. is suspended from the midpoint of the rope. Find the tension or pull in the rope.

3. What is the magnitude of the force that will balance the following three forces, producing equilibrium: 10 lb. N.E., 5.0 lb. E, 3.0 lb. S.?

4″. A man, wishing to drag an automobile out of a ditch, attaches a 50-ft. rope to the car and to a tree (Fig. 15). By exerting an up-force of 40 lb., he raises the mid-point of the rope 1.00 ft. Find the pull produced in the rope.

5. A boy weighing 50 lb. sits in a swing. With what force must he pull on a horizontal rope to keep the swing at an angle of 30° with the vertical?

6′. A boy weighing 100 lb. hangs from a horizontal beam, his arms being parallel. (*a*). What is the pull exerted by each arm? (*b*). What would the pull be if each arm were at an angle of 60° with the vertical?

7. A bag of cement weighing 30 lb. is suspended from one end of a light horizontal rod 4.0 ft. long, the other end of which rests against a vertical wall. The rod is supported at its end by a wire 5.0 ft. long attached to the wall. Find the pull of the wire.

8′. The propeller of an airplane exerts a horizontal force of 200 lb., and the plane weighs 2,000 lb. Find the equilibrant force exerted by the wind against the wings of the plane. (Draw a force parallelogram.)

9′. A stone weighing 2,000 lb. is attached at the end of a pole which makes an angle of 45° with the horizontal. A horizontal rope is attached to this end of the pole. Find the pull of the rope, neglecting the weight of the pole.

10′. A stone weighing 1,000 lb. is suspended by two wires each making an angle of 30° with the horizontal. Find the tension or pull in each wire.

11″. A ball which weighs 30 lb. is suspended by a cord which would be broken by a force of 50 lb. What horizontal force must be applied to the ball in order to break the cord?

12. A southwest force has a westward component of 71 lb. Find the magnitude of the force.

13′. A block of wood weighing 20 lb. rests on an inclined plane 6.0 ft. high and 10.0 ft. long. Find (*a*) the force pushing the block against the plane, and (*b*) that tending to make it slide downhill.

14′. A ball weighing 2.0 lb. on a 30° inclined plane rests against a brick lying on the plane. Find the force exerted on the brick by the ball.

15′. A telephone pole is braced by a cable 50 ft. long, one end of which is attached at the earth's surface, the other at a point on the pole 40 ft. above the level ground surface. The pull of the cable is 200 lb. What are the vertical and horizontal components of this force?

16′. The handle of a floor-polishing mop makes an angle of 30° with the vertical. (*a*) What is the vertical component of a force of 2.00 lb. directed along the handle? (*b*) If this force is a push and the mop weighs 3.00 lb., find the total down-force.

17″. Three ropes *A*, *B*, and *C* are attached together in a three-sided tug of war producing equilibrium. The pulls of two of the ropes, *A* and *B*, are 100 lb. each. What is the pull of the third rope, *C*: (*a*) if *A* and *B* are parallel; (*b*) if they are at right angles to each other?

CHAPTER III

LEVERS AND TORQUES

Give me a place on which to stand and I will move the world.—Archimedes.

A lever is a rigid bar or rod which can rotate on a pivot or **fulcrum** (Fig. 1). Levers have been used since prehistoric times, and the cave men, like children of today, learned that the force should be applied to

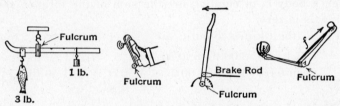

Fig. 1.—Familiar examples of the lever.

a lever at a large distance from the fulcrum. Archimedes, a famous Greek scientist, first stated the rule in a quantitative way. He showed that when two bodies are suspended from opposite ends of a lever, balancing each other and producing equilibrium, the weight of one body times its distance from the pivot or fulcrum was equal to the weight of the other times its distance. For instance, in Fig. 2, the body which weighs 3 lb. is suspended at a point on the lever ½ ft. from the fulcrum, and the 1-lb. body at a point 1½ ft. from the fulcrum. The products of the forces by their distances from the pivot are equal.

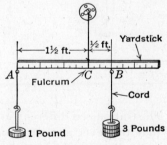

Fig. 2

18. The Lever Arm. In dealing with forces which produce rotations, it is convenient to speak of the **lever arm** of the force, which means **the shortest distance from the fulcrum or pivot to the line along which the force acts.** In Fig. 2, the lever arm of the force acting at B is ½ ft., and that of the force acting at A is 1½ ft.

19. What is a Torque? The effectiveness of a force in producing

19

rotation depends upon two factors, one the magnitude of the force, the other its lever arm. Experiments prove that a force of 1 lb. with a lever arm of 2 ft. is just as effective as a force of 2 lb. with a lever arm of 1 ft.

The product, **force times lever arm,** is called the **torque** or sometimes the **moment** of the force.

$$\text{Torque} = \text{Force} \times \text{Lever arm}$$

A force of 5 lb. having a lever arm of 4 ft. exerts a torque of 20 lb-ft.

Torques that tend to cause counterclockwise rotation are usually considered to be positive; those tending to produce clockwise rotation, negative.

The **principle of torques** is as follows:

When a body is in equilibrium, the sum of the torques about any chosen axis is zero.

In Fig. 2, the torques about C are:*

Clockwise: 3.00 lb. × 0.50 ft. $= -1.50$ lb-ft.
Counterclockwise: 1.00 lb. × 1.50 ft. $= +1.50$ lb-ft.
$$\text{Sum} = 0$$

20. Measuring the Lever Arm. In the levers which we have considered, the forces were directed at right angles to the lever. As an

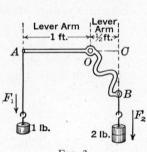

Fig. 3

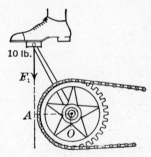

Fig. 4.—The lever arm OA is the shortest distance from the point O to the line along which the force acts.

illustration of a different situation, carefully examine Fig. 3. Remember that the lever arm of a force is the **shortest distance from the pivot to the line on which the force acts.** In Fig. 4 a down-force acts on the

---

* In stating problems the units of measure as well as the numbers will be given. These units may be multiplied and divided just like numbers, and the result tells the units of the answer. For example:

$$3 \text{ ft.} \times 4 \text{ ft.} \quad = 12 \text{ ft.}^2$$
$$40 \text{ mi.} \div 2.0 \text{ hr.} = 20 \text{ mi./hr.}$$

pedal of the bicycle. Its lever arm OA is the **shortest distance** from the pivot O to the line of action of the force.

21. The Two Conditions of Equilibrium. In the preceding chapter it was shown that, when a body is in equilibrium, the resultant of all the external forces acting upon it is zero, and now we find that the resultant of all the torques must also be zero. The two conditions for complete equilibrium are:

1. The resultant of all the external forces acting on the body must be zero.

2. The sum of all the positive and negative torques acting on the body must be zero about any chosen axis.

These two conditions of equilibrium are useful in solving problems.

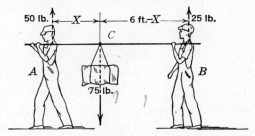

FIG. 5

Example. Two men A and B carry a sack of wheat weighing 75 lb. by means of a pole 6.0 ft. long (Fig. 5). At what distance from A must the sack be suspended so that he may carry two-thirds of the load?

The total up-force on the pole is 75 lb. (the first condition of equilibrium). The man supports two-thirds of the load, or 50 lb., and the boy carries 25 lb.

By the second condition, the resultant torque about C must be zero.

$$50 \text{ lb.} \times X - 25 \text{ lb.} (6.0 \text{ ft.} - X) = 0$$
$$X = 2.0 \text{ ft.}$$

22. The Center of Gravity of a Body. The weight of the lever itself can be neglected in many problems, but in others it must be taken into account. The difficulty is that there are trillions on trillions of molecules in the lever, each of which is attracted by the earth. The way out of this difficulty is to find the point where the resultant of all these tiny forces acts, and this point is called the **center of gravity** of the body.

The center of gravity of a body is the point where the resultant of the weights of its particles acts. It is that point where we may consider the mass of the body to be concentrated.

To locate the center of gravity of a yardstick, support it on a pencil and shift it to and fro to a position where it balances horizontally. Then the down-pull of the weight is equal to the up-push of the pencil, and the two forces act in the same straight line. Hence the center of gravity is vertically above the fulcrum.

The center of gravity of a wooden door is found as follows: First suspend it from a cord at A (Fig. 6). After it comes to rest, the center

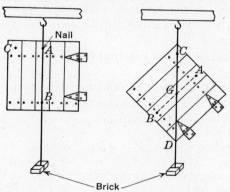

FIG. 6.—Locating the center of gravity of a door.

of gravity will be somewhere on the vertical line AB. Trace this line with a pencil, and then suspend the body at some other point, C. The center of gravity is on the line CD, and therefore it must be at G, where the two lines intersect.

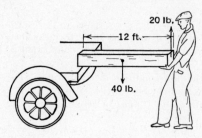

FIG. 7

To see how the center of gravity is used in lever and torque problems, suppose that a man supports one end of a uniform plank 12 ft. long weighing 40 lb., and that the other end rests on a truck (Fig. 7). Assume that the weight of the plank acts at the center of gravity (at the midpoint of the plank), and that the man exerts a force F. The torques about the point where the log rests on the truck are:

Counterclockwise: $F \times 12$ ft.
Clockwise: $- 40$ lb. $\times 6.0$ ft.

Hence

$$F \times 12 \text{ ft.} - 40 \text{ lb.} \times 6 \text{ ft.} = 0$$
$$F = 20 \text{ lb.}$$

SUMMARY

The tendency of a force to produce rotation about an axis is the **torque** of the force about that axis.

The lever arm of a force is the perpendicular distance from the axis of rotation to the line of action of the force.

Torque = Force × Lever Arm

The two conditions of equilibrium of a body are as follows:

1. The resultant of the forces acting on it must be zero.

2. The sum of all the positive and negative torques acting on it about any axis must be zero.

The center of gravity of a body is the point through which the resultant of the weights of all its particles acts.

REVIEW QUESTIONS

1. Define torque and lever arm.

2. State the two conditions of equilibrium.

3. Define *center of gravity of a body*, and show how it may be located.

PROBLEMS

1'. A man pushes downward on a horizontal pump handle at a point 2.0 ft. from the pivot, exerting a force of 20 lb. (*a*) What torque about the pivot is thus produced? (*b*) What is the torque when the handle makes an angle of 30° with the vertical?

2'. In a human jaw the distance from the pivots to the front teeth is 3.0 in., and the muscles are attached at points 1.0 in. from the pivots. What force must the muscles exert to cause a biting force of 100 lb.?

3. A dentist grips a pair of forceps exerting a force of 20 lb. at a point 4.0 in. from the pivot, and the tooth is gripped at a point 1/4.0 in. from it. Find the force on the tooth.

4. The radius of the steering wheel of a car is 9.0 in. The driver exerts a force of 2.0 lb., tangent to the rim of the wheel. What is the torque?

5'. A man exerts a downward force of 50 lb. on one of the pedals of a bicycle, the pedal being 12 in. from the axle about which it revolves. Find the torque about this axle when the pedal crank makes the following angles with the vertical: (*a*) 90°; (*b*) 60°; (*c*) 30°; (*d*) 0°.

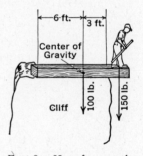

FIG. 8.—How far can the man venture safely?

6'. How far can the man depicted in Fig. 8 venture out on the 12-ft. log?

7'. A 100-lb. uniform log is 24 ft. long. It rests with one end projecting over the edge of a cliff, the length of the projecting portion being 8.0 ft. How far from the edge of the cliff can a boy venture on the log, his weight being 80 lb.?

8''. A laborer lifts a stone weighing 6 lb. in a shovel weighing 4.0 lb., the center of gravity of the loaded shovel being 3.0 ft. from the end of the handle. The man's left hand grasps the end of the handle while his right hand acts at a point 2.0 ft. from it. Find (*a*) the force exerted by the left hand, and (*b*) that by the right hand.

9''. The weight on the front wheels of an automobile is 1,200 lb.; that on the rear wheels is 1,000 lb. The distance between the front wheels and the rear wheels is 100 in. What is the distance of the center of gravity of the car from the front wheels?

10''. The center of gravity of an irregular log is 6.0 ft. from one end. The log is

15 ft. long and weighs 150 lb. How much force must be applied at each end to support it?

11″. A tramp carries a parcel weighing 2.0 kgwt. (kilogram-weight) attached to one end of a stick which is 100 cm. long. The stick rests on his shoulder at a point 60 cm. from the parcel, and the other end is supported by his hand. Find (a) the down-force exerted by the hand and (b) the up-force exerted by the shoulder.

12″. A cubical box, 2.0 ft. on each side, weighing 100 lb., rests on a level floor. What horizontal force against the upper edge of the box will cause it to tilt?

13″. A man A and boy B carry a 60-lb. uniform pole 12 ft. long. If the boy supports one end, where must the man hold the pole so that he may carry two-thirds of the load?

CHAPTER IV

WORK, POWER, AND MACHINES

The word work is related to the same Greek root as irksome. It is used in many senses and often means some activity, perhaps unpleasant, for which pay is received. A golf caddy is "working" when he stands idly while the perspiring player tries to hit a golf ball. A watchman works when he sits by a railroad crossing. A schoolboy works at his problem in arithmetic.

In physics it is important that each term shall have but one restricted meaning, and so it is necessary to define work very carefully.

23. What is Work? The following are examples of work as the physicist uses the term. When a laborer carries coal up a flight of stairs, or lifts it up onto a wagon, he does work. Likewise when a team of horses drags a plow across a field, or a locomotive pulls a train along a railway, work is done. In each of these examples a force acts on a moving body, and the amount of work done depends upon two factors, namely, the amount of force exerted and the distance the body advances in the direction of the force.

We define work as **the product of the force exerted and the distance the body moves in the direction of the force.**

The **foot-pound** equals the work done when a body which weighs 1 lb. is raised vertically through a distance of 1 foot.

Example. How much work is required to lift a 100-lb. cask onto a truck which is 4.0 ft. above the pavement?

$$\text{Work} = \text{Force} \times \text{Displacement}$$
$$= 100 \text{ lb.} \times 4.0 \text{ ft.}$$
$$= 400 \text{ ft-lb.}$$

In the metric system, the **kilogram-meter** is often used. It is defined as the work done when a 1-kilogram body is raised vertically through a distance of 1 meter.

The metric unit most used in scientific investigations is the **erg** or dyne-centimeter. It is the amount of work done when a force of 1 dyne acts through a distance of 1 centimeter. This unit is very small, being about equal to the work done when a flea crawls 1 centimeter up a vertical wall. For many purposes the **joule** is preferred. It equals 10,000,000 ergs or dyne-centimeters.

25

$$\text{One joule} = 10,000,000 \text{ ergs}$$
$$= 10,200 \text{ gwt-cm. (approximately)}$$
$$= \tfrac{3}{4} \text{ ft-lb. (approximately)}$$

It should be emphasized that forces may act on bodies without work being done. For instance, a man holds a trunk in a fixed position (Fig. 1). He does no work in supporting the trunk because the body is not raised. This does not appeal to common sense. If the man does no work in supporting the trunk, why does he become tired? An analogy will help to explain the difficulty. Suppose that an automobile is at rest on a hill, with the engine "idling." Then no work is being done in pushing the car up hill, but work is expended in overcoming frictional forces to maintain motion inside the engine.

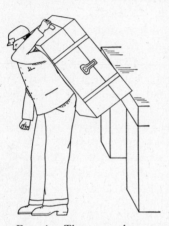

FIG. 1.—The man does no work when he merely supports the box.

In general, **when work is done one body exerts a force against another and the second body moves in the direction of the force acting on it.**

Example. A laborer carries a 40-lb. sack of cement up a ladder 16 ft. long to the roof of a porch 10 ft. above the street. How much work does he do in lifting the cement? The force which he exerts is directed vertically upward, and the vertical distance traversed is 10 ft., hence the work done is 400 ft-lb. Neither the length of the ladder nor its angle of inclination makes any difference.

24. What is Power? The term power, like work, is popularly used in many ways and often it means strong or forceful. In physics, the word is restricted to mean **the time rate of doing work.**

If given sufficient time, a hod carrier can transfer 5 tons of brick from the ground to the roof of a skyscraper. A hoisting engine can do this work more quickly and is said to exert more power.

$$\textbf{Power} = \textbf{Work/Time}$$

The British units of power are the **foot-pound per second** and the **standard horsepower.**

The origin of the horsepower unit was as follows: Before the improvement of the steam engine by Watt in the days of King George III, horses were used to pump water in draining coal mines in Great Britain. When Watt began to sell his engines to the mine owners, they asked how many horses an engine would replace. To answer this question, Watt harnessed strong work horses to a load and found that each of them could work several hours at the average rate of about 550 foot-pounds per second, which is the standard horsepower unit.

One horsepower = 550 ft-lb./sec.

In the metric system, the **watt** is defined as follows:

$$\text{One watt} = 1 \text{ joule/sec.}$$
$$= 10{,}200 \text{ gwt-cm./sec.}$$
$$= \tfrac{3}{4} \text{ ft-lb./sec.}$$

Also:

$$\text{One kilowatt} = 1{,}000 \text{ watts}$$
$$= 4/3 \text{ hp., approximately.}$$

Example 1. A 150-lb. man runs up a stairway, raising himself 16 ft. in 10 sec. What is his power?

The work done is 150 lb. × 16 ft. = 2,400 ft-lb.
The power is 2,400 ft-lb./10 sec. = 240 ft-lb./sec.
$$= 0.436 \text{ hp.}$$
$$= 0.327 \text{ kw.}$$

Example 2. An automobile engine propels a car along a level road at a rate of 30 mi./hr. (44 ft./sec.). Find the power exerted if the opposing frictional force is 40 lb.

$$\text{Power} = 40 \text{ lb.} \times 44 \text{ ft./sec.} = \frac{1{,}760 \text{ ft-lb.}}{\text{sec.}} = 3.2 \text{ hp.}$$
$$= 2.4 \text{ kw.}$$

MACHINES

25. Machines are devices for doing work. Usually they are complicated assemblies of **pulleys, levers, gear wheels, screws,** and **inclined planes.** These elements are called the **simple** machines. They are used to transmit forces, whose **directions** and **magnitudes** they may change. A pulley fixed near the roof of a barn changes a down-pull into an up-pull without appreciably altering the magnitude of the force (Fig. 2). A lever changes a downward push into a larger upward one, altering both the direction of the force and its magnitude.

A machine is a device for doing work which changes either the direction or the magnitude of a force or both.

The Mechanical Advantage of a Machine. If an "input" downward force of 50 lb., acting on one end of a lever, causes an "output" force of 150 lb. at the other end, the lever causes a threefold gain in force, and we say that the mechanical advantage is 3.

The mechanical advantage **(M.A.)** of a machine equals the "output" force exerted by the machine divided by the "input" force exerted on it.

$$M.\ A. = \frac{\text{Output force}}{\text{Input force}}$$

Example. A workman exerts a downward force of 10 lb. on the handle of an automobile jack and the jack exerts an upward force of 700 lb. on the axle of a car. What is the mechanical advantage?

$$M.\ A. = (\text{Output force})/(\text{Input force})$$
$$= \frac{700\ \text{lb.}}{10\ \text{lb.}} = 70$$

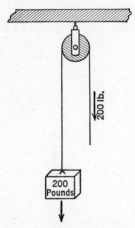

200 lb.

200 Pounds

FIG. 2.—The fixed pulley changes the direction of the force, but not the magnitude.

In many problems it is desirable to find out what the mechanical advantage would be if the friction were zero. In these problems the principle of work is used.

The Principle of Work. When frictional effects are zero or negligibly small, the output work done by a machine equals the input work done on it.

As a very simple illustration of the use of the principle, consider a fixed pulley used to raise a 200-lb. load which is transferred or displaced through a vertical distance of 4 ft. (Fig. 2). In lifting the load, the input force must act through an equal distance.

From the principle of work:

$$\text{Input force} \times \text{Displacement} = \text{Output force} \times \text{Displacement}$$
$$f \times 4.0\ \text{ft.} = 200\ \text{lb.} \times 4.0\ \text{ft.}$$
$$f = 200\ \text{lb.}$$

The frictionless mechanical advantage is therefore 1.

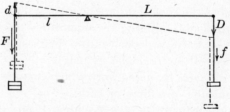

FIG. 3

The lever (Fig. 3) is in equilibrium and the two torques about the fulcrum are equal.

$$F \times l = f \times L$$

and

$$F/f = L/l \tag{1}$$

Let the input force f act downward through a small vertical distance D, while an output force F acts upward through a smaller distance d. The input and output works are equal.

$$F \times d = f \times D$$
$$F/f = D/d \tag{2}$$

From similar triangles:

$$D/d = L/l \tag{3}$$

Hence, if (1) is true, (2) must be also, and the principle of work is derived from the principle of torques.

Presently we shall define energy as the ability to do work, and we shall discuss the law of the conservation of energy which asserts that energy is never created or destroyed. From the energy viewpoint, the principle of work is as follows: If friction is negligible, the energy **input** to a machine equals its energy **output**.

26. The Movable Pulley. The pulley represented in Fig. 4 is not fixed in position but rises as the load is lifted. The mechanical advantage can be estimated readily since the 100-lb. load is supported by two strands of the rope and the pull of each must be 50 lb. If friction is negligible, a force of 50 lb. is sufficient to raise the load, and the mechanical advantage is 2.

The principle of work leads to the same value. Let the two strands supporting the load have a combined length of 30 ft. If all this rope is pulled over the upper pulley, the load will rise 15 ft.

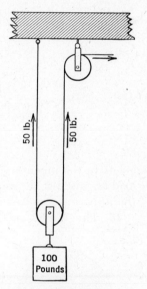

From the principle of work:

$$f \times 30 \text{ ft.} = 100 \text{ lb.} \times 15 \text{ ft.}$$
$$f = 50 \text{ lb.}$$

Therefore, the frictionless mechanical advantage is 2.

This problem illustrates a truth applicable to all machines, namely, that a gain in force is always accompanied by a loss in distance moved. Moreover, if the friction is zero:

Fig. 4.—A movable pulley has a frictionless mechanical advantage of 2.

Frictionless mechanical advantage =

$$\frac{\text{Distance through which input force acts}}{\text{Distance through which output force acts}}$$

27. The Block and Tackle. When two or more pulleys are mounted in blocks as represented in Fig. 5, the arrangement is called a block and tackle. The frictionless mechanical advantage of this machine may be found by counting the number of strands of the single rope supporting the load. In Fig. 5A, the number of strands is four and the required input force is 50 lb. In 5B, there are five strands and the required force is only 40 lb. The use of the principle of work in this illustration

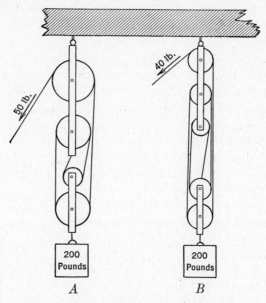

FIG. 5.—Block and tackles.

is left to the ingenuity of the student. (SUGGESTION: Assume that the load is raised 1 ft. and find out how much rope must be pulled over the uppermost pulley.)

28. The Wheel and Axle. In the wheel and axle (Fig. 6), the input force is applied to the wheel, causing a large output force on a rope wound on the axle. If the wheel and axle make one complete revolution, the input force f acts through a distance $2\pi R$ and the output force F through a distance $2\pi r$.

By the principle of work:

$$f \times 2\pi R = F \times 2\pi r$$

and

The frictionless M.A. $= F/f = R/r$ (4)

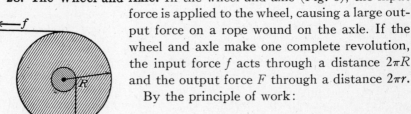

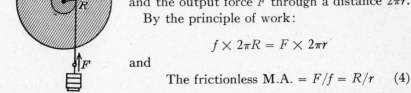

FIG. 6.—A wheel and axle.

In this arrangement the mechanical advantage is larger than unity and a loss of distance moved results. If one so desired, he might apply the input force to a rope wound on the axle; then the mechanical advantage would be less than 1 and the distance moved would be increased.

29. Gears, Chains, and Belts. The wheel and axle are rigidly fastened together and both turn at the same rate. There is another type of machine, closely resembling it, in which two wheels turn at different rates, being interconnected by gears, chains, or belts. The two wheels depicted in Fig. 7A are geared together by cogs. The smaller "drive"

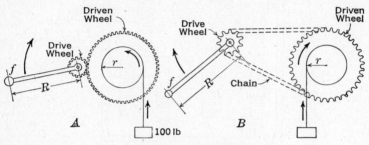

FIG. 7.—Gear wheels.

wheel is turned by means of a crank of length R, and the load is lifted by means of a cord wound onto an axle of radius r. To determine the frictionless mechanical advantage, find the distances through which the output and the input forces act. Suppose that the drive wheel makes N turns for one revolution of the axle. Then the load is lifted through a distance $2\pi r$ while the input force acts through a distance $2\pi RN$. The same procedure may be used when the wheels are interconnected by a chain (Fig. 7B).

With either device:

$$\text{The frictionless M.A.} = 2\pi RN/2\pi r = RN/r$$

30. The Automobile Transmission. The forces required to overcome friction when an automobile travels at uniform speed on a level highway are relatively small, and the speed may be high. In climbing a hill, additional force is required to propel the car. The driver therefore "goes into second gear" so that the rear wheels turn more slowly with reference to the engine. Thus the automobile travels a smaller distance for each revolution of the engine crankshaft and greater forces can be exerted tending to keep it moving. The arrangement of gears to decrease the ratio of the speed of the rear wheels to that of the engine is called the **transmission** (Fig. 8). When the gears are in neutral, the engine turns the cog wheels C, E, H, and R, but the shaft G connected to the rear wheels of the automobile is not driven. To put the car into "low" the gear B is moved toward the engine and is driven by the wheel H, turning the drive shaft at a relatively low speed. In order to shift to "second," B is moved to its first position and D is moved backward so that it is driven by E. In high gear the

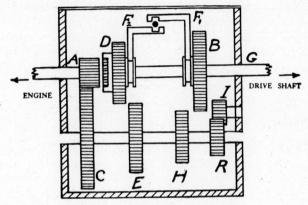

Fig. 8.—Automobile transmission.

wheel D is moved forward so that it is rigidly connected to A, and the engine drives the shaft at full speed. Moving D back to its first "free" position and then shifting B so as to engage I puts the transmission into "reverse."

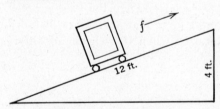

Fig. 9.—An inclined plane.

31. The Inclined Plane. One of the most familiar types of simple machines is the inclined plane. When a heavy cask or an iron safe is loaded onto a truck, less force is required when the object is pushed up a gentle slope than when it is lifted vertically.

The frictionless mechanical advantage of an inclined plane is found by means of the principle of work. A laborer pushes a 300-lb. iron safe from the pavement onto a truck which is 4 ft. above the street level. He uses an inclined plane 12 ft. long (Fig. 9). If there is no friction, he must do the same amount of work as though he lifted the safe directly onto the truck. That is, the required work is 1,200 ft-lb.

The output work = 300 lb. × 4.0 ft. = 1,200 ft-lb.

Since the plane is 12 ft. long:

$$f \times 12 \text{ ft.} = 1{,}200 \text{ ft-lb.}$$
$$f = 100 \text{ lb.}$$

Thus the frictionless mechanical advantage is given by

$$\text{Frictionless M.A.} = \frac{300 \text{ lb.}}{100 \text{ lb.}} = 3.0$$

In general, if the height of the plane is h and its length is l, and f and F are the input and output forces respectively:

The output work $= F \times h$
The input work $\quad = f \times l$
Frictionless M.A. $= F/f = l/h$

32. The Screw. The screw is a modified inclined plane. Wrapping a triangular piece of paper around a cylinder such as a lead pencil gives

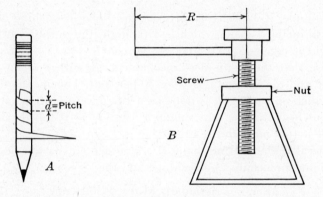

FIG. 10.—(A) Illustrating the principle of the screw. (B) The Jack Screw.

the simplest illustration of the screw (Fig. 10A). A spiral inclined plane is thus formed along which an insect might climb to the top of the pencil. In traveling once around it, the insect would rise the distance between successive ridges. This distance is called the "pitch" of the spiral.

In making a screw such as that of the automobile jack (Fig. 10B), a spiral thread or ridge is formed on a cylindrical rod. This thread fits into a spiral groove in the "nut." When the screw is turned through one complete revolution, the input force f acts along a circle. Its radius R equals the distance from the point where the force is applied to the axis of the screw. During this revolution, the weight W is lifted through a distance equal to the pitch d.

From the principle of work:

$$f \times 2\pi R = W \times d$$

whence

$$\text{Frictionless M.A.} = \frac{2\pi R}{d}$$

33. What is Efficiency? In the problems which we have been considering, it has been assumed that the output and the input works are equal. In actual machines, work must be done in overcoming friction, and hence the output work done by a machine is always less than the input work done on it. Efficiency is defined as the ratio of the useful output work to the input work.

$$\text{Efficiency} = \frac{\textbf{Useful output work}}{\textbf{Input work}}$$

For example, if 1,000 ft-lb. of work are done in pushing a 200-lb. safe up an inclined plane which is 4 ft. high, the output work is 800 ft-lb. and the efficiency is 0.80 or 80 per cent.

Suppose that the frictionless mechanical advantage of an inclined plane is 5 and the efficiency is ½ or 50 per cent. This means that one-half as much output work is done as if there were no friction. Hence the output force will be only one-half as great as if the friction were zero. The actual mechanical advantage is 2.5 instead of 5.

In general the actual mechanical advantage equals the product of the frictionless mechanical advantage and the efficiency.

$$\text{M.A.} = \text{Frictionless M.A.} \times \text{Efficiency}$$

Example. The pitch of the screw of an automobile jack is 0.25 in., and the radius of the circle along which the input force acts is 2.0 ft. What is the actual mechanical advantage if the efficiency is 20 per cent, and how large a force is needed to raise a 500-lb. load?

$$\text{F.M.A.} = \frac{2\pi \times 24 \text{ in.}}{0.25 \text{ in.}} = 600$$

$$\text{M.A.} = 0.20 \times 600 = 120$$

$$\text{The required force} = \frac{500 \text{ lb.}}{120} = 4.2 \text{ lb.}$$

SUMMARY

Work is defined as the product of the applied force and the displacement, the two being parallel.

Commonly used units of work are the foot-pound, the gram-weight-centimeter, the kilogram-weight-meter, the erg, and the joule.

One joule equals 10,000,000 ergs.

Power is rate of doing work.

One horsepower = 550 foot-pounds per second = 746 watts.

One watt = 1 joule per second.

A machine is a device for changing either the magnitude or the direction of a force, or both.

REVIEW QUESTIONS

1. Illustrate several meanings of the word *work*, and define its usage by physicists.

2. State several units in which work is measured.

3. Give an instance in which a force acts on a moving body without doing work.

4. Define "machine," "input force," "mechanical advantage."

5. Discuss the question: "Are machines a blessing or a menace?"

6. State expressions for the frictionless mechanical advantages of (a) the lever, (b) the movable pulley, (c) the inclined plane, (d) the screw.

7. State the principle of work, and illustrate by the inclined plane.

8. What is efficiency, and how does its value affect the actual mechanical advantage of a machine?

9. Why does a road wind around a hill instead of going straight up the slope?

10. Make diagrams of movable pulley systems having frictionless mechanical advantages of 2, 3, and 4.

11. Given a pulley system, one block having one pulley, the other one having two, show that it may have two different mechanical advantages, depending on which block is fastened to the ceiling.

12. Can you design an inclined plane by which an input force of 50 lb. acting through a distance of 20 ft. will raise a weight of 200 lb. to an elevation of 10 ft.?

13. Why is it helpful to use a fixed pulley in raising a flag to the top of a pole?

14. Does the use of a lever increase one's power?

15. Discuss the jack screw as a machine.

16. Can (a) the efficiency and (b) the mechanical advantage of a machine ever be greater than unity?

PROBLEMS

1. A 50-lb. boy sits on a sled which is dragged 40 ft. on a frozen pond. The force of friction is 2.0 lb. (a) How much work is done in pulling the sled? (b) How much work does the boy do?

2. A 150-lb. man carries a 50-lb. bag of cement up a ladder 16 ft. long to an elevation 14.0 ft. above the floor. What is the total work? The useful work?

3. A force of 7.0 kgwt. acts through a distance of 4.0 m. How much work is done?

4. A mule drags a harrow across a field, exerting on it a horizontal force of 100 lb. If the mule travels 3.30 ft./sec., what is its horsepower?

5. How much work is done in pumping water from a lake to fill a cubical tank, 10 ft. on each edge? The water is pumped in at the bottom of the tank which is at the water level. (One cubic foot of water weighs 62.4 lb.) (HINT: How far is the center of gravity of the water in the filled tank above the water level in the lake?)

6. What horsepower is required to fill the tank (Problem 5) in 5.0 min.?

7. An elevator raised 10 passengers, each having a mass of 80 kg., to the top story of a building 300 m. high. (a) How much work was done? (b) If the journey required 100 sec., what was the output power of the motor?

8″. How much work is required to upset a cubical block of ice 1.00 ft. on each side, weighing 56 lb., resting on a level floor? (HINT: How much must the center of gravity be raised?)

9′. An iron pipe is 10 ft. long and weighs 20.0 lb. How much work is required to tilt it from a horizontal position on the floor and stand it up on end?

10′. A man raises a 500-lb. stone by means of a lever 4.40 ft. long, the distance from the fulcrum to the load being 0.40 ft. (a) If the input force acts through a distance of 1 ft., through what distance is the load raised? (b) What is the frictionless M. A. of the lever? (c) What is the required input force?

11′. A farmer raises a bucket of water weighing 30.0 lb. from the bottom of a well. In so doing, he uses a wooden cylinder or axle 8.0 in. in diameter on which the rope is wound. This axle is turned by means of a crank 2.00 ft. long. Find (a) the frictionless M.A., (b) the required input force.

12′. An automobile trailer weighing 2,000 lb. was towed up a hill 5,000 ft. long and 100 ft. high. Neglecting friction (a) how much work was done, and (b) what force, parallel to the roadway, was required?

13′. The pitch of a jack screw is 0.20 in., and the input force acts along a circle of radius 1.00 ft. Find (a) the frictionless M.A. and (b) the input force required to lift a load of 3,140 lb. if the efficiency is 20 per cent.

14″. A man can exert a force of 100 lb. What is the length of the shortest board he can use as an inclined plane to push a safe weighing 300 lb. onto a truck 4.0 ft. above the street? (a) Assume no friction; (b) let the efficiency be 90 per cent.

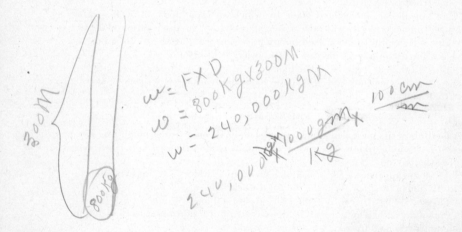

force = mass times acceleration

or F = MA

$$1 gm F = 1 gm \times 980 \frac{cm}{sec^2}$$

$$F = 980 \frac{gm \ cm}{sec^2} = 980 \, dynes$$

CHAPTER V

FRICTION

Whenever one body slides over another, frictional forces oppose the motion. These forces are caused in part by the adhesion of one surface to the other, and in part by the interlocking of the "hills and valleys" of the two surfaces which rub against each other (Fig. 1). The amount of opposing frictional force depends upon the roughness of the surfaces, their natures, and the force pushing one against the other.

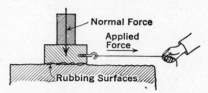

Fig. 1.—Friction opposes the motion of two surfaces which rub against each other.

The harmful effects of friction are threefold. First, it increases the work necessary to operate a machine; second, it causes heat which may do damage; and third, it may cause ex-cessive wear of the rubbing surfaces. For these reasons it is often advantageous to diminish friction. The automobile manufacturer takes great pains in designing his car. He provides rollers and balls for some of the axles and uses different kinds of lubricants in different places. Also, in recent years, he has changed the shape of the body of the car in order to decrease the friction with the air, which becomes important at high speeds.

It should be emphasized, however, that friction is not always harmful and that sometimes we try to increase it. On an icy street, it is difficult to stop a car because of the skidding of the wheels. Cinders are scattered over the surface and chains are attached to the tires in order to increase the friction. In operating machinery, belts could not be driven without it and brakes could not be used. In a frictionless world it would be practically impossible to start an automobile. Neither could nails be used to hold boards in place.

There are several different types of friction, the most familiar being **sliding friction,** which occurs when one solid surface rubs against another, **rolling friction,** and the **internal friction** of liquids and gases.

34. Friction of Solid Surfaces is Independent of Surface Area. Place one wooden block on top of another and drag the two over a table top (Fig. 2A). The force required is about the same as that when

37

the two are connected in "tandem" as in Fig. 2B. In the two cases the total weight is the same, but the area of contact differs.

Friction is independent of surface area, provided that the force pushing one body against the other is not sufficient to cut or otherwise modify the surfaces. When the rubbing surfaces are distorted by the force, this law no longer holds. For example, a sled with narrow runners is harder to drag over soft snow than one with wide runners because the narrow runners cut deeper grooves in the roadway.

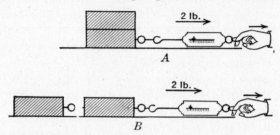

Fig. 2.—Friction is independent of area.

35. Starting Friction is Greater Than Sliding Friction. When a block of wood is dragged over a table top, greater force is required to start the motion than to maintain it, and so we say that **starting** friction is greater than **sliding** friction. One reason for this difference is that when the block is at rest the small hills and valleys of the two surfaces have time to become intermeshed to a greater degree than when it is moving.

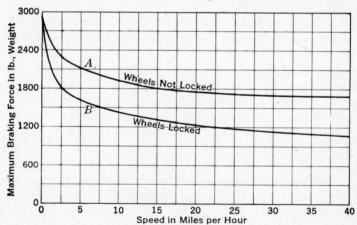

Fig. 3.—Frictional forces of the road surface decrease with speed. *A* shows the maximum braking force on a 3,000-pound car when there is no skidding, *B*, that when all wheels are locked. (After Moyer)

36. Friction and Speed. Laboratory experiments show that the forces required to overcome friction in starting a body are considerably greater than those required to keep it moving. Often it is stated that friction is independent of velocity, but at high speeds there is a marked decrease in friction. When an automobile is traveling slowly, the tires grip the ground with great force, and the car stops with a jolt. At higher speeds the friction between tires and roadway is much smaller.

The maximum braking forces, at different speeds, for a 3,000-lb. car are shown in Fig. 3. The upper curve A shows the retarding force at each speed when the brakes are set as strongly as possible without locking the wheels. At 40 mi./hr., the braking force is only about 60 per cent of that just before the car stops. The lower curve B shows the braking force when all four wheels are locked, and the wheels skid. For this condition the braking force at 40 mi./hr. is less than two-thirds that when the brakes are set as hard as possible, without skidding.

When the wheels of a car begin to skid, the friction is greatly reduced and the problem is to get the wheels turning again. To do this, the expert driver releases the brakes for an instant and then applies them again, but not quite strongly enough to lock the wheels.

37. The Coefficient of Sliding Friction. Suppose that a force of 2 lb. is required to drag a 10-lb. block over a level table top (Fig. 4). If, now,

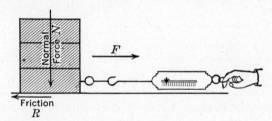

Fig. 4.—The frictional force is proportional to the normal force pushing one surface against the other.

a second, equal block is placed on top of it, the weight is doubled, and a force of 4 lb. will be required to overcome the friction. The addition of a third block will cause the frictional force to increase to 6 lb. Experiments like this show that **the frictional force is directly proportional to the force pushing one surface against the other.** Hence, the ratio of the two forces is constant.

The ratio of the frictional force R **parallel to the surface** to the **normal** force N is called the **coefficient of sliding friction.**

$$\text{Coefficient of friction (K)} = \frac{R}{N} = \frac{\text{Resisting force of friction}}{\text{Force normal to surface}}$$

TABLE I

Coefficients of Sliding Friction

Oak on oak, grains parallel....................	0.4 –0.5
Metal on metal.............................	0.15–0.4
Iron on automobile brake lining...............	0.2 –0.4
Automobile tire on wet road surfaces at 20 mi./hr..	
On clean concrete.........................	0.7 –0.9
On wood, steel, muddy concrete.............	0.2 –0.3

Example 1. A boy and a sled together weigh 80 lb. A horizontal force of 20 lb. is required to drag the loaded sled on a level pavement. What is the coefficient of sliding friction?

The vertical force pushing the sled against the ground is 80 lb., and the friction is 20 lb. Hence the coefficient of sliding friction is

$$K = 20 \text{ lb.}/80 \text{ lb.} = 0.25$$

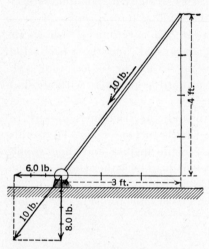

Example 2. A force of 10 lb., parallel to the handle, is required to move a mop at the angle shown in Fig. 5 at uniform speed over a level floor. What is the coefficient of sliding friction? (The weight of the mop itself is negligibly small.)

The applied force may be resolved into a horizontal component of 6.0 lb. which overcomes friction, and a vertical component of 8.0 lb. which pushes the mop against the floor. The ratio of these forces is the coefficient of sliding friction, namely:

Fig. 5.—The frictional force on the mop equals the normal component of the force times the coefficient of friction.

$$K = R/N = 6.0 \text{ lb.}/8.0 \text{ lb.} = 0.75$$

38. Automobile Brakes. In the automobile brake, the amount of friction is controlled by varying the force pushing the brake bands against the brake drum (Fig. 6). When the brake rod is pulled, the two semicircular brake shoes are forced against the inner surface of the drum which is attached to the wheel of the car. The rubbing surfaces of the shoes are covered with a brake lining which is usually made of cotton cord and asbestos, interwoven.

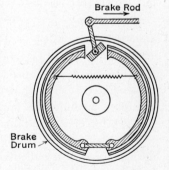

Fig. 6.—Automobile brake.

39. The Automobile Clutch. The engine driveshaft of an automobile is connected to the transmission by means of a "clutch" which may be released so that the engine runs freely. Clutches are of several forms; the simplest, now obsolete, is represented in Fig. 7. In this type, the flywheel of the engine has a depression into which a "cone" fits snugly, being held in place by a strong spring. The surface of the cone is coated with brake-lining

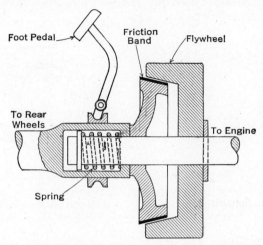

Foot Pedal   Friction Band   Flywheel

To Rear Wheels

To Engine

Spring

FIG. 7.—An old-fashioned automobile clutch.

material, and friction prevents slipping. The flywheel and the cone turn with equal speeds, and power is transmitted to the rear wheels. In order to put the car into "neutral," disconnecting the engine, the clutch pedal is pushed forward, and the cone is released from the flywheel.

40. Rolling Friction. When an automobile travels along a concrete highway, work is done in overcoming rolling friction. This friction arises because the tires and the pavement are deformed where they make contact with each other (Fig. 8). As the wheel rolls along, the various parts of the tire are successively deformed and work must be done in overcoming friction within the tire. It

FIG. 8.—The tire and roadway are deformed at the region of contact with the pavement.

follows that, the greater the air pressure and the smaller the deformation, the less will be the rolling friction. On a hard roadway, one saves gasoline by keeping the tires of his car well inflated; but on a soft road, the pressure should be smaller to prevent sinking into the mud. When a locomotive moves along a railway track, the distortion of wheel and rail is much less than that produced in an automobile tire on a highway, and in consequence, the rolling friction is much smaller, but it can never be zero. Rolling friction is less than sliding friction, and for this reason roller bearings and ball bearings are used on automobile axles and the like. When a wheel turns on an ordinary axle (Fig. 9) there is sliding friction where the two surfaces rub against each other, but when a ball bearing is used the sliding friction is replaced by rolling friction (Fig. 10).

FIG. 9.—A bearing sliding on an axle. (The space between bearing and axle is exaggerated.)

FIG. 10.—A ball bearing. (From Automotive Construction and Operation. John Wiley. 2nd edition, p. 329.)

41. Fluid Friction. The third type of friction is that of moving fluids. Its laws are quite different from those of sliding friction in solids. When water flows in a pipe, the internal friction in the liquid opposes the motion and we say that the fluid is viscous. The viscosities of liquids vary widely, that of molasses, for instance, being much greater than that of water. The viscosities of gases are generally much less than those of liquids.

42. Fluid Friction Increases with Velocity. The first respect in which fluid friction differs from that of solid surfaces is the variation with velocity. In sliding friction the forces diminish with increasing velocity, but in fluid friction they increase. When a fan is moved through the air at low speed, the viscous friction opposing its motion is relatively small; and when the speed increases, the opposing force does also. A bather walking about in a swimming pool does not notice the friction, but if he attempts to run, he encounters a great impeding force. The fact that fluid friction increases with speed is well known to steamship operators. A tramp steamer, traveling at 6 miles per hour, can traverse the Atlantic using about one-tenth as much fuel as it would if it traveled at 18 miles per hour. High speed in sea vessels is expensive because very powerful engines must be used and because a great deal of fuel is required for a journey.

43. Lubrication. When two sliding surfaces are greased or oiled, a thin film of lubricant forms between the two surfaces, forcing them apart so that rubbing of the solid surfaces is prevented and the friction occurs inside the liquid film. The friction forces are nearly independent of the load; they vary as the speed, as the area of contact of the two surfaces, and as the viscosity of the lubricant. Since the friction varies as the viscosity, it is advisable, in choosing a lubricant for an axle or bearing, to use the least viscous oil that is able to keep the two rubbing surfaces separated.

The lubrication of automobile engines is very difficult for they must operate both in hot weather and cold weather. The viscosities of oils decrease with temperatures, and those suitable for winter use are less viscous than summer oils. When an engine is first started in zero weather, the oil is so hard that it behaves like a solid and does not form films in the bearings. The wise motorist allows a cold engine to "idle" at low speed until the oil has warmed a little, and then he starts the car, increasing the load on the engine.

44. Terminal Velocities. The fact that fluid friction increases with speed explains why aviators with parachutes can leap from airplanes with safety. In such descents the aviator reaches the ground with the same velocity, whether he jumps from an elevation of a mile or of 10 miles. Sometimes men leap from airplanes and purposely fall great distances before pulling the release cords of their parachutes. In such an event, the aviator falls faster and faster, with ever-increasing friction, until the opposing force equals his weight, after which the velocity becomes constant at about 100 mi./hr. When the aviator is ready, he pulls the release cord, his parachute opens, and it grips the air. The increased back-pull of friction causes the speed to diminish to a few feet per second, such that the up-pull of friction again equals the weight of the aviator and his parachute.

45. Streamlining. Fluid friction differs from the sliding friction of solid surfaces in that it depends upon the size and shape of the body which is dragged through the fluid. For example, an open umbrella "grips" the air, but when it is closed the friction opposing its motion is much smaller. Move a fan through the air with its surface at right angles to the motion, and the air streaming past it forms eddies and whirlpools. Because of these eddies, the friction is increased and energy is wasted. Wave the fan with its surface parallel to the motion, and the frictional force is diminished. The production of eddies can be greatly reduced by changing the shape of the body which is dragged through the fluid. The best form of body to minimize friction is fish-shaped, like a teardrop. A body of this form experiences only about one-fourteenth as much force as would a disk of equal diameter (Fig. 11).

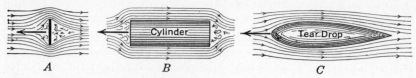

FIG. 11.—The frictional force on the flat disk is about fourteen times that on the teardrop-shaped body.

46. Streamlining of Airplanes and of Automobiles. In the days of the oxcart, speeds of travel were small, and little attention was given

FIG. 12.—The modern car is streamlined.

to the streamlining of vehicles. The coming of the airplane made it important to study the problem. Early airplanes had numerous guy

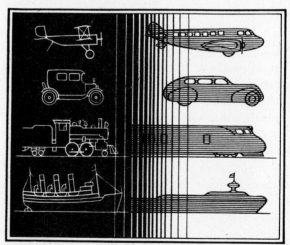

FIG. 13.—Progress in streamlining. (Courtesy of General Motors.)

wires and braces which greatly increased the friction; these have now been eliminated, and the body approximates more closely to the ideal teardrop form. The wheels and supports of the landing gear cause about one-half of the friction drag, and in some large planes the landing gear is drawn up inside the body after the plane leaves the ground.

When an automobile travels at low speeds, the air friction is negligible compared with that of the bearings, roadway, etc. As the speed increases, the air friction becomes much greater, but the other kinds of friction are more nearly constant. The air friction at 30 mi./hr. is about equal to that of the other forms, and at 60 mi./hr. it is about three times as great. In recent attempts to diminish air friction, projections such as lamps and horns have been removed, and in some cars the wheels are shielded. The most important change is to increase the size of the front of the car and to make the rear slope back more gradually, giving a closer approximation to the ideal form of streamlining (Fig. 12). If ever the engine is shifted from the front end to a position over the rear wheels, advantage will be gained because better streamlining will be secured by moving the passenger compartment forward.

SUMMARY

Friction is the resisting force opposing the motion of one body which slides or rolls over the surface of another.

The frictional force of two solid surfaces which are not cut or distorted (a) is greater when the motion starts than when the motion is established, (b) decreases with speed, (c) is independent of the area of contact, (d) is directly proportional to the force pushing one surface against the other.

The coefficient of friction of two surfaces is the ratio of the friction force parallel to the surfaces to the normal force pushing one surface against the other.

Rolling friction is caused by the deformation produced where the wheel or cylinder pushes against the surface on which it rolls. Rolling friction is less than sliding friction.

Fluid friction increases with the viscosity of the fluid and with the velocity. It depends upon the size and shape of the body that moves with respect to the fluid.

When a body falls through a fluid, the velocity becomes constant when the friction equals the weight of the body.

REVIEW QUESTIONS

1. Define friction, and state several facts about the friction of solid surfaces.

2. State instances in which friction is desirable and others where it should be avoided.

3. Distinguish between starting friction and sliding friction.

4. Define "coefficient of friction," and give a numerical example.

5. Make a sketch showing the structure of an automobile brake.

6. Make a sketch showing the structure of some type of automobile clutch, and explain its operation.

7. How does fluid friction differ from that of solid surfaces?

8. Discuss the following. "If the speed were sufficiently small, a steamship could be drawn across a lake by means of a thread."

9. How can the fluid friction opposing the motion of a body be diminished?

10. Why are wide brake bands for automobiles preferable to narrow ones?

11. Discuss the limiting or "terminal" velocity of a falling body. Upon what factors does it depend?

12. When a car coasts down a long, uniform hill (with the clutch disengaged), the speed continues to increase to a relatively high value. If the car is in low gear, however, the speed soon becomes constant at a lower value. Why? (HINT: Is there any fluid friction?)

13. When the wheels of a car begin to skid, why should the brakes be released and then applied again?

14. Why can an automobile, on a concrete pavement, stop in a shorter distance than a streetcar traveling with equal speed?

PROBLEMS

1. A 100-lb. sled is drawn along an icy, level street, the coefficient of friction being 0.030. Find the horizontal force required and the work done in moving the sled 60 ft.

2. If in Problem 1 the speed at which the sled is drawn is 2.0 ft./sec., what is the horsepower?

3'. A football player strengthens his leg muscles by pushing a loaded sled over a field. The total weight is 200 lb., and the coefficient of friction is 0.50. (a) What is the required force? (b) At what horsepower is the "player" working if the speed is 1.10 ft./sec.?

4'. A polishing block weighing 10.0 lb. rests on a level floor. It is pushed by means of a handle making an angle of 30° with the horizontal. If the input force, parallel to the handle, is 10.0 lb., (a) what is the total vertical force pushing the block against the floor; (b) what is the horizontal component of the applied force; (c) what is the frictional force, if the coefficient of starting friction is 0.40; (d) will the block start to move?

5'. Solve the preceding problem if the force is a pull instead of a push.

6''. A wooden block weighing 20.0 lb. rests on an inclined plane whose length is 10.0 ft., height 8.0 ft., and base 6.0 ft. Find (a) the downhill component of the weight and (b) the component normal to the surface. (c) If the coefficient of sliding friction is 0.30, what is the frictional force? (d) Will the block continue to slide downhill if started?

7. When a scow is towed at a rate of 3.00 mi./hr., the pull of the rope is 100 lb. (a) Assuming that the frictional force is proportional to the square of the speed, what is the force required at 6.00 mi./hr.? (b) What is the horsepower required at each speed?

8'. A block weighing 10.0 lb. is pushed against a wall by a normal force of 30 lb. The coefficient of friction being 0.50, find the force required to cause the block to move (a) horizontally, (b) vertically upward, (c) vertically downward.

CHAPTER VI

RECTILINEAR MOTION

Experiment is the interpreter of nature. Experiments never deceive. It is our judgment which sometimes deceives itself because it expects results which experiment refuses. We must consult experiment, varying the circumstances, until we have deduced general rules, for experiment alone can furnish reliable rules.—LEONARDO DA VINCI.

The chief task of the physicist is to discover and to state the general laws of the behavior of the physical world. He needs to determine not only the positions of bodies, but also their motions. In this book, first the linear motions of visible bodies such as baseballs, footballs, and automobiles will be considered, then the rotary motions of grindstones, flywheels, and gyroscopes. Afterwards we shall study the behavior of particles too small to be seen, the molecules and atoms. Following that, in electricity we shall deal with electrons, protons, and other components of atoms. Many of these motions are very involved, and as a preliminary step we shall consider the simplest of all, namely, a body so moving that its particles travel in parallel straight lines. This is called **rectilinear** (that is, straight-line) motion.

The automobile driver is greatly interested in three instruments, the speedometer, the road meter, and the clock. The speedometer tells him how fast he is going, the road meter how far he has gone, and the clock what period of time is required for the journey.

47. Speed and Velocity. Every motorist knows that if he travels 60 mi. in 2 hr., keeping the speedometer reading constant, then his speed is 30 mi./hr. That is:

Speed is the Distance Traveled per Unit of Time.

The terms speed and velocity are often used interchangeably, but, technically speaking, there is an important difference between them. Briefly, it is as follows. To state the speed of a body tells merely its rate of travel, but to specify its velocity the direction of motion must also be stated. A few examples from the football field will make clear the distinction. A football halfback carries the ball 10 ft./sec., and his speed is the same whether he travels south, toward the enemy goal posts, east toward the side lines, or even north toward his own line of defense. In these three instances, the three velocities are quite different, for **velocities are directed quantities.**

The velocity of a point is its speed in a specified direction.

When a body travels at a constant velocity v for a time t, the distance traveled or **displacement** d is given by

$$d = vt$$

Displacement = Velocity × Time

48. What is Acceleration? A motorist pushes down the accelerator pedal of his car, the speedometer needle moves up the scale, and the car is *accelerated*. Later, he shuts off the gas, pushes the brake pedal, and the car is *retarded* or *decelerated*.

49. Acceleration is Change of Velocity per Unit Time. Let v_0 be the initial velocity of a particle, v that after a time t, and a the average acceleration. Then:

$$a = (v - v_0)/t \tag{1}$$

An advertisement for a well-known automobile states that the engine can cause a "pick-up" or "acceleration" from 3 mi./hr. to 27 mi./hr. in 8 sec. This is a change of velocity of 24 mi./hr. in 8 sec., or (3 mi./hr.)/sec. Notice that time is mentioned twice, once in specifying the **change of velocity** and again in stating the **time** in which that change occurred.

Example. The velocity of a car increases from 5.0 ft./sec. to 20 ft./sec. in 10.0 sec. What is the average acceleration?

$$a = \frac{20 \text{ ft./sec.} - 5.0 \text{ ft./sec.}}{10.0 \text{ sec.}}$$
$$= 1.50 \text{ (ft./sec.)/sec.}$$

This is often written 1.50 ft./sec.[2]

50. Distances Traveled with Uniform Acceleration. Suppose that an automobile starts from rest and coasts down a slope (Fig. 1). Let the record be as represented in Table I.

TABLE I

Time, sec.	Speedometer Reading, ft./sec.	Total Distance Traveled, ft.
0	0	0
1	3.2	1.6
2	6.4	6.4
3	9.6	14.4
4	12.8	25.6
5	16.0	40.0

The first question to be answered is: "What was the acceleration?" In each successive second the velocity increased by the same amount, namely, 3.2 ft./sec. Therefore the acceleration was 3.2 ft./sec.²

Next we inquire how the total distance traveled varies with the time, and we note that in 2 sec. the car traveled 4 times as far as in 1 sec., and in 3 sec. it traveled 9 times as far. In other words: **With constant acceleration the distance traveled from the starting point varies as the square of the time.**

Finally let us ascertain how far the car advanced during the third and fourth seconds after starting. To do this we first find the average

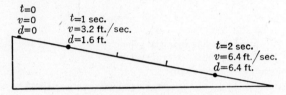

$t=0$
$v=0$
$d=0$

$t=1$ sec.
$v=3.2$ ft./sec.
$d=1.6$ ft.

$t=2$ sec.
$v=6.4$ ft./sec.
$d=6.4$ ft.

Fig. 1.—The car travels 4 times as far in 2 seconds as in 1 second.

velocity during these 2 sec., which was $\frac{1}{2}$ (6.4 ft./sec. + 12.8 ft./sec.) or 9.6 ft./sec. Then the distance traveled is found to be

Average speed × Time = 9.6 ft./sec. × 2.0 sec. = **19.2 ft.**

To derive an equation for the total distance traveled from rest with constant acceleration, notice that the final velocity is $v = at$, and the average velocity $\frac{1}{2} at$. Then the distance traveled d is given by

$$d = \tfrac{1}{2} at \times t = \tfrac{1}{2} at^2 \tag{2}$$

Another convenient equation is derived by combining equations (1) and (2).
From (1):

Since $v_0 = 0$
$$a = (v - v_0)/t = v/t$$
$$t = v/a$$
$$t^2 = v^2/a^2 \tag{3}$$

$$S = V_{av} T$$
$$S = \left(\frac{V_0 + V_F}{2}\right) T$$

From (2):
$$d = \tfrac{1}{2} at^2$$
$$t^2 = 2d/a$$

$$V_F = V_0 + at \tag{4}$$

From (3) and (4):
$$v^2 = 2ad$$
$$v = \sqrt{2ad}$$

$$S =$$

51. Accelerated Motions When the Initial Velocity is Not Zero.
When a body is moving at the beginning of an experiment, the following rules are convenient:

1. Find how far the body would travel if the velocity remained constant ($d = v_0t$).

2. To this distance add the distance which the body would move if it were accelerated from rest ($d = \frac{1}{2} at^2$).

The resulting equation is

$$d = v_0t + \frac{1}{2} at^2 \qquad (5)$$

By similar reasoning, the student can show that

$$v^2 = v_0^2 + 2ad \qquad (6)$$

Example 1. An automobile has an initial velocity of 20.0 ft./sec. and the acceleration is 4.0 ft./sec.^{2} What is the distance traveled in 3.0 sec.?

If v were constant and a were zero:

$$d_1 = v_0t = 20 \text{ ft./sec.} \times 3.0 \text{ sec.} = 60 \text{ ft.}$$

If a were constant and v_0 were zero:

$$d_2 = \frac{1}{2}at^2 = \frac{1}{2}\ 4.0 \text{ ft./sec.}^2 \times (3.0 \text{ sec.})^2 = 18 \text{ ft.}$$
$$d = d_1 + d_2 = 78 \text{ ft.}$$

If the body is decelerated, the second term d_2 should be subtracted.

A study of equation (6) is helpful to automobile drivers, for it shows how the stopping distance for a car varies with its speed. This is especially important for persons driving at night when the clear view ahead is much shorter than in daylight. Assume a good, dry roadway, and that the brakes of your car are in excellent condition. Then your average deceleration in an emergency stop will be about 22 ft./sec.^{2}

In computing the stopping distance, notice that most drivers have reaction times of about $\frac{3}{4}$ sec. That is, this period is required to set the brakes.

Example. What is the stopping distance at 30 mi./hr. (44 ft./sec.), when the deceleration is 22 ft./sec.^{2}? The time required to set the brakes is $\frac{3}{4}$ sec.

(a) The distance traveled before the brakes are set is given by:

$$d_1 = v_0t$$
$$= 44 \text{ ft./sec.} \times \frac{3}{4} \text{ sec.} = 33 \text{ ft.}$$

(b) The distance traveled, afterward:

$$v^2 = v_0^2 + 2ad$$
$$0 = (44 \text{ ft./sec.})^2 - 2 \times 22 \text{ ft./sec.}^2 \times d$$
$$d = 44 \text{ ft.}$$

Total distance = 77 ft.

Keep in mind that a car traveling at 20 mi./hr., having a fairly alert driver, has an imaginary "nose" about 40 ft. long (Fig. 2). At 60 mi./hr., the "nose" lengthens to 240 ft., for that is the approximate stopping distance.

52. Falling Bodies. Drop a feather and a coin at the same instant; the coin reaches the ground long before the feather does. As explained

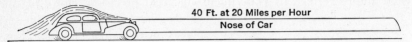

40 Ft. at 20 Miles per Hour

Nose of Car

FIG. 2.—When traveling 20 miles per hour, a car has a "nose" 40 feet long, for that is the stopping distance.

in the previous chapter, this difference in time occurs because the air friction opposing the motion of the feather is relatively greater than that opposing the motion of the coin. The question then arises, would the coin fall faster than the feather if the air friction were zero?

One way to answer this question is to enclose the two in a long glass tube which is then evacuated (Fig. 4). When the two objects are re-

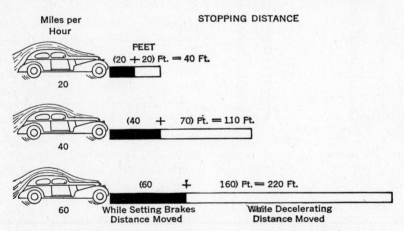

Miles per Hour

STOPPING DISTANCE

FEET

(20 + 20) Ft. = 40 Ft.

20

(40 + 70) Ft. = 110 Ft.

40

(60 + 160) Ft. = 220 Ft.

60 While Setting Brakes While Decelerating
Distance Moved Distance Moved

FIG. 3.—The stopping distances for a car with excellent brakes.

leased, they fall together, both striking the bottom at the same instant.

The laws of falling bodies were first derived by Galileo, Professor of Physics at Pisa in Italy, about three centuries ago. Some of his experiments resemble those with the coasting automobile which we have described. Placing a ball at the top of an inclined plane and releasing it, he noted the distance it traveled in a chosen time, for instance, 3 sec. Then he measured the distance traveled in 6 sec., and found it to be 4 times as great. That is, **the distance varies as the square of the time.** He demonstrated that this law continued to hold when the plane was made steeper, and so he decided that it should apply to freely falling bodies. Finding that small, light balls accelerated just as rapidly as heavy, large ones, he reasoned that **all freely falling bodies have equal accelerations at a given location.** This law has since been amply verified by experiments of great precision. However, the values vary slightly at different places on the earth's surface. Reasons for these variations will be given in the chapter on gravitation.

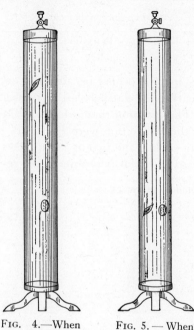

The laws of falling bodies are so well understood nowadays that it is hard to realize that three centuries ago Galileo encountered great opposition in teaching them. At that time, scholars believed that a 2-lb. stone should fall twice as fast as a 1-lb. stone, citing the Greek philosopher Aristotle as their authority. Galileo boldly challenged this view, claiming that his experimental results far outweighed the authority of Aristotle. Amid the wordy disputes that followed, someone suggested a very simple experiment to decide the issue. He proposed that two stones, one large, the other small, be dropped from the Leaning Tower of Pisa to see which would be the first to reach the pavement below. Accordingly, he led them to the tower, climbed to an

FIG. 4.—When the air is at normal pressure, the feather is retarded.

FIG. 5. — When the tube is evacuated, the two reach the bottom simultaneously.

upper gallery, and released the two stones. Both struck the ground at the same instant, and the impact "sounded the death knell of authority in physics." The year in which this experiment was performed is the birth year of modern science. Since then scientists have been less inclined to justify their theories by tradition. This famous experiment marks the beginning of a new epoch in which men are more willing to search out nature's inmost secrets, using experiments as tools of investigation.

SUMMARY

The *velocity* of a body equals the distance it travels in a specified direction per unit time.

Acceleration is the change of velocity of a body per unit time. It may be expressed in feet per second per second or in centimeters per second per second.

The general equations for the rectilinear motion of a particle which has constant acceleration are:

$$a = (v - v_0)/t$$
$$d = v_0 t + \tfrac{1}{2} a t^2$$
$$v^2 = v_0^2 + 2ad$$

[handwritten in margin:] $a = \dfrac{v - v_0}{T}$ $a T = v - v_0$ $T = \dfrac{v - v_0}{a}$

REVIEW QUESTIONS

1. Define *acceleration*, stating units in which it may be expressed.

2. Derive the equation $d = \tfrac{1}{2} a t^2$.

3. State an expression for the velocity v of a body after traveling a distance d from the starting point, the acceleration being a.

4. Using Table I, estimate how far the car would travel during the sixth second. (SUGGESTION: Find the average speed during that second.)

5. If a stone is dropped from a balloon, will its acceleration be greater during the first second or the tenth second? Why?

6. Discuss Galileo's contributions to our knowledge of falling bodies, and state the law which he proved.

7. Fill in the blank spaces in the following table for a freely falling body. Acceleration = 32 ft./sec.²

Time of Fall (from rest)	Speed	Average Speed	Total Distance
0 sec.	....	....	....
¼ sec.	....	....	....
½ sec.	....	....	....
1 sec.	....	....	....
2 sec.	....	....	....
3 sec.	....	....	....

8. How could you compute the acceleration of a car, watching its speedometer?

PROBLEMS

Assume that g, the acceleration of gravity, = 32 ft./sec.² = 980 cm./sec.² Neglect air friction. 1 mi./hr. = 1.47 ft./sec.

1. An automobile has a speed of 60 mi./hr. Reduce this to feet per second.

2. When the brakes were set as strongly as possible, the speed of a car traveling on a straight line changed from 30 mi./hr. (44 ft./sec.) to 3.0 mi./hr. in 1.50 sec.; what was the average deceleration?

3. In knocking out flies, a baseball's speed changed from 0 ft./sec. to 80 ft./sec. in 1/50 sec. What was the average acceleration?

4'. When a batter struck a baseball, its velocity changed from 100 ft./sec. due west to 100 ft./sec. due east. What was the change (*a*) in speed and (*b*) in velocity?

5. A sprinter increased his speed from 0 ft./sec. to 20 ft./sec. in 2.00 sec. What was his acceleration?

6'. A baseball is thrown downward from the top of the Washington Monument the initial velocity being 100 ft./sec. What will the speed be after 3.0 sec.?

7'. A stone is dropped from the top of the Eiffel tower in Paris, which is 300 m. high. After what time will it reach the ground, and what will its speed be?

8'. An oil well is 14,400 ft. deep. How long a time would be required for a stone to fall freely to the bottom of the well?

9. A ball is dropped from an elevation of 256 ft. How soon will it strike the earth?

10'. A ball is dropped from a window. What are the distances traveled during the first, second, third, and fourth seconds?

11'. An automobile accelerated from 20 ft./sec. to 44 ft./sec. in 4.00 sec. Find (*a*) the acceleration and (*b*) the distance traveled in this time interval.

12'. An automobile traveling 60 mi./hr. (about 90 ft./sec.) ran into a stone wall and stopped in 0.10 sec. (*a*) What was the deceleration? (*b*) From what height would it have to fall from rest to acquire the given speed?

13'. A rifle barrel is 2.0 ft. long, and the speed of the rifle bullet fired from it is 2,000 ft./sec. (*a*) What is the average speed of the bullet while being accelerated in the barrel? (*b*) How long does it take for the bullet to travel the length of the barrel? (*c*) What is the average acceleration?

14'. A stone is thrown vertically downward from an airship, the initial velocity being 100 ft./sec. Find the average speed and the distance traveled during the first 3 sec.

15. The initial speed of a car having excellent brakes was 30 mi./hr. (44 ft./sec.). When the brakes were applied it stopped after 2.0 sec. Find the deceleration and the distance moved.

16'. A stone is thrown vertically upward, the initial speed being 96 ft./sec. (*a*) How long does it continue to rise? (*b*) How high does it go?

17'. A stone sliding over a frozen pond had an initial velocity of 50 ft./sec. and stopped after 4.0 sec. What was the average deceleration, and how far did it travel?

18'. An automobile driver traveling 60 mi./hr. (88 ft./sec.) saw a fallen tree on the road 300 ft. ahead. To set the brakes required ¾ sec. Afterward the deceleration was 22 ft./sec.² (*a*) What was his total stopping time? (*b*) How far did he travel before the brakes were applied? (*c*) What was his stopping distance?

19. In 1910, the baseball player LeJeune caught a baseball, dropped from the top of the Washington Monument, which is 550 ft. high. What was the velocity of the baseball when it struck his glove?

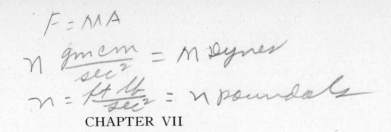

$$F = MA$$
$$n \frac{gm \cdot cm}{sec^2} = n \text{ Dynes}$$
$$n = \frac{ft \cdot lb}{sec^2} = n \text{ poundals}$$

CHAPTER VII

FORCE AND ACCELERATION

53. What is Inertia? An automobile rushes along a highway at a speed of 60 mi./hr. Suddenly a tire bursts and the car crashes into a concrete wall. The passengers tend to keep moving, and they bump against the windshield. A youngster sits at the rear end of a truck. The truck starts forward unexpectedly, and the boy falls off. **Bodies in motion tend to keep moving, and those at rest tend to remain at rest.**

This tendency of bodies to maintain their conditions of rest or of uniform motion is due to **inertia,** a term signifying the laziness of matter or its tendency to oppose any change of velocity.

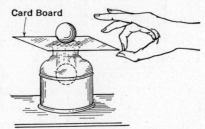

Fig. 1.—The ball falls into the bottle when the card is snapped out.

As an illustration of inertia, place a marble on a card which rests on top of a bottle (Fig. 1). Snap the card suddenly, and the marble falls into the bottle. Its inertia is so great that the sidewise force exerted by the card is insufficient to get it started appreciably before the card is removed. Watch a carpenter as he drives the head of a hammer more firmly onto the handle. He strikes the lower end of the handle against a log (Fig. 2). The head tends to keep moving, and it is forced firmly into place.

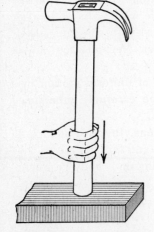

Fig. 2.—The hammer head is driven onto the handle because of inertia.

54. A Brake Tester or Decelerometer. Place a glassful of water on the floor of an automobile and speed the car to a velocity of a few miles per hour. Suddenly jam on the brakes, and water will spill out because of its inertia. The greater the deceleration, the more water will escape; hence we can judge the effectiveness of the

55

brakes from the amount of water that spills over. The decelerometer or brake tester depicted in Fig. 3 works on the same principle. It consists of a U-shaped glass tube containing mercury, and it is mounted on the car with the end R toward the engine. In making a test, the car is brought to a sudden stop by setting the brakes as hard as possible. During the deceleration, mercury, because of its inertia, spills over into

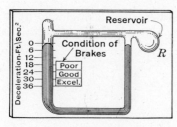

FIG. 3.—A brake-tester or "decelerometer" is used to determine the effectiveness of the brakes of a car.

the trap R. If the brakes are in excellent condition, the deceleration will be large and a great deal of liquid will be displaced. The scale measures the amount of mercury left behind, and it may be marked off to show the deceleration.

55. When No Force Acts on a Moving Body.

Imagine a stone sliding on the surface of a frozen pond, its velocity gradually decreasing. We know that friction exerts a backward force causing the deceleration, and we are aware that ashes sprinkled on the surface would increase the friction and cause the stone to stop in a shorter time. Suppose, on the contrary, that the ice could be treated in some way so as to decrease the friction. Then the stone would move farther before stopping. Finally, if the opposing force were reduced to zero, would not the stone continue to travel onward with constant speed? The answer to this question is given in Sir Isaac Newton's first law of motion, which is as follows:

Every body persists in its state of rest or of uniform motion in a straight line unless it is acted upon by some external, unbalanced force.

56. Unbalanced Forces Produce Accelerations.

Practice at kicking a football, and you will find that, the harder you kick it, the greater will be its acceleration. In fact, **the force acting on a body is proportional to the acceleration which is produced.**

When one holds out a 1-lb. block of wood, the earth-pull on it is balanced by the up-push of one's hand, and the block remains at rest. Release it, and the unbalanced force of the earth's attraction produces an acceleration of approximately 32 ft./sec.² Next mount the block on wheels and pull it along a table top, exerting a force equal to the weight of the block. Then the acceleration will again be 32 ft./sec.² In this way the following table can be verified:

Weight of Body Accelerated W (lb.)	Force Acting F (lb.)	Acceleration Experienced by Body
1	1	32 ft./sec.^{2}
1	½	16 ft./sec.^{2}
1	¼	8 ft./sec.^{2}

That is:

$$\frac{\text{The force acting}}{\text{Weight of body}} = \frac{\text{Acceleration of the body}}{\text{Acceleration of gravity}}$$
$$F/W = a/g$$

In this equation the forces and the accelerations may be expressed in any desired units.

Example 1. What force will cause an acceleration of 4.0 ft./sec.^{2} in an automobile weighing 3,200 lb.?

$$\frac{F}{3,200 \text{ lb.}} = \frac{4.0 \text{ ft./sec.}^2}{32 \text{ ft./sec.}^2} = \frac{1}{8}$$
$$F = 400 \text{ lb.}$$

Example 2. A 5.0-gram five-cent piece sliding on a level table decelerates 98 cm./sec.^{2} What is the force of friction?

$$\frac{F}{5.0 \text{ gwt.}} = \frac{98 \text{ cm./sec.}^2}{980 \text{ cm./sec.}^2} = 1/10$$
$$F = 0.50 \text{ gwt.}$$

57. Force, Mass, and Acceleration. The equation $F/W = a/g$ may be put into the form $F = W/g \times a$, which expresses the fact that the force acting on a body is proportional to the acceleration produced and also to the quantity (W/g). This quantity equals the weight of the body divided by the acceleration of gravity at that place. First weigh a body at sea level and divide the weight by the value of g. Then carry it to the top of a mountain and weigh it again, using the same spring balance. The pull of the earth will decrease a little, but g will diminish **in the same proportion**, and the ratio W/g will be unchanged. It is, in fact, the **mass** of the body. Hence we may write either

$$F = W/g \times a$$

or

$$F = M \times a$$
Force = Mass × Acceleration

This relationship is expressed by Newton's second law of motion, one form of which is as follows:

The force required to accelerate a body is proportional to the product of the mass of the body and the acceleration produced.

58. The Gravitational System of Force Units. In the gravitational system of force units, we have defined unit force as the pull of the earth on a pound-mass or a gram-mass at a point where the acceleration of gravity has a prescribed value (32 ft./sec.² or 980/cm./sec.²). The question arises: What is the unit of mass in this system? In other words, what is the mass of the body which will receive unit acceleration when acted upon by a force of 1 lb.?

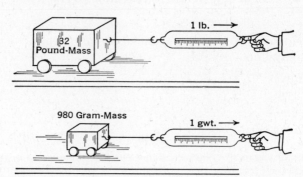

Fig. 4.—A force of one pound-weight imparts an acceleration of 1 ft./sec.² to a 32-pound body. A gram-weight imparts an acceleration of 1 cm./sec.² to a 980-gram body.

One pound-weight causes an acceleration of 32 ft./sec.² in a mass of 1 pound; hence it would cause unit acceleration in a mass of 32 pounds. This is the **gravitational unit of mass.** Sometimes it is called a **slug.**

One slug = 32 pounds (approximately)

= 32.1740 pounds (exactly)

Similarly, in the metric system, the gravitational unit of mass is 980 grams, approximately (Fig. 4).

The gravitational system is advantageous in that the force units, the gram-weight and the pound-weight, are widely used in daily life. It is disadvantageous in that the units are defined in terms of the earth-pull on a pound-mass or a gram-mass at some specified position on the earth's surface. Moreover, the units of mass (32 pounds or 980 grams) are not commonly used.

59. An Absolute Force Unit, the Dyne. The **dyne** is defined as that force which produces in 1 gram-mass an acceleration of 1 cm./sec.² It is called an absolute unit or, better, an absolute C.G.S. (centimeter, gram, second) unit because it is defined in terms of the three fundamental units. Since a force of 1 gwt. causes an acceleration of approximately 980 cm./sec.^{2} in 1 gram-mass, it follows that

$$980 \text{ dynes} = 1 \text{ gwt. approximately}$$

Example 3. Solve Example (2), p. 57 using the dyne as the unit of force and the gram as the unit of mass.

$F = ma$

$F = 5.0 \text{ grams} \times 98 \text{ cm./sec.}^2 = 490 \text{ dynes.}$

The advantage of the dyne is that it is independent of location, whereas the weight of a pound-mass or a gram-mass is variable. Its disadvantage is that it is not used in commercial transactions and also that it is inconveniently small.

The following table will help to explain the relationship between the force units.

TABLE I

	Unit of Force	Unit of Mass	Unit of Acceleration
Gravitational System	1 lb. 1 gwt.	32 pounds = 1 slug 980 grams	1 ft./sec.^{2} 1 cm./sec.^{2}
Absolute C.G.S. System	1 dyne	1 gram	1 cm./sec.^{2}

60. The "Force Twins," Action and Reaction. Experience leads to the belief that, whenever one body exerts a force on another, the second body exerts an equal and opposite force on the first one. In other words, forces always appear as pairs or "twins." The force which acts **on** the body is called the **action**, and that exerted **by** the body is the **reaction**. Hit a golf ball with a club, and the forward, action force accelerating the ball will be equal and opposite to the reaction force tending to slow down the club. Strike your fist against a wall, and during the impact there are two forces, one your action, the other the reaction of the wall. Fire a bullet from a rifle, and the

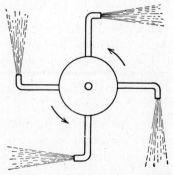

FIG. 5.—The reaction force causes the sprinkler to revolve.

forward force accelerating the bullet will be equal to the backward force causing the gun to recoil. The rotary lawn sprinkler (Fig. 5) provides another excellent illustration of action and reaction. The water, rushing out of the curved nozzles, is accelerated, and the forward force on the liquid is equal to the backward reaction force which causes the rotary motion of the sprinkler. When a diver jumps from a canoe, two forces are exerted: one pushes him away; the other causes the canoe to move backward. Lastly, imagine a 200-lb. man standing on a spring scale in an elevator at rest (Fig. 6). The spring scale exerts an upward force of 200 lb. on the man, and he exerts an equal downward force on it. The two forces are unaltered when the elevator travels at uniform speed. Suppose, however, that the elevator is accelerated upward 3.2 ft./sec.² Then the spring scale must exert an *added* force of 20 lb. to accelerate the man. What will be the reaction force? The answer is 220 lb., that is, the man's weight, 200 lb., plus 20 lb. which is the force with which the mass opposes the acceleration. Thus, action and reaction are always equal and opposite.

Fig. 6.—The up-push of the scale always equals the down-push of the man.

The fact that forces are paired is expressed in Newton's third law:

When one body exerts a force on a second body, the second body exerts a force equal in magnitude but opposite in direction on the first body. Action and reaction are equal and opposite. They are always experienced by different bodies.

SUMMARY

The inertia of a body manifests itself in the tendency to keep moving or to remain at rest.

The acceleration produced by a force F in a body of weight W is given by

$$F/W = a/g$$

Newton's laws of motion are as follows:

1. Every body persists in its state of rest or of uniform motion in a straight line unless it is acted upon by some external, unbalanced force.

2. The force required to accelerate a body is proportional to the product of the *mass* of the body and the *acceleration produced.*

3. When one body exerts a force on another, the second body ex-

erts on the first body a force, equal in magnitude but opposite in direction: action and reaction are equal and opposite.

The pound-weight is the amount of force that produces in a body of 1 pound-mass an acceleration of 32 ft./sec.^{2}, and the gram-weight produces in a body of 1 gram-mass an acceleration of 980 cm./sec.^{2}

The dyne is that force which produces in 1 gram-mass an acceleration of exactly 1 cm./sec.^{2}

$$980 \text{ dynes} = 1 \text{ gwt. (approximately)}$$

REVIEW QUESTIONS

1. What is inertia?

2. How can you compare the masses of two balls without weighing them?

3. State Newton's laws of motion, and give illustrations of each.

4. Why cannot a man in a canoe make it move forward by pushing against one end?

5. If a boy stands on a frictionless, frozen pond, how can he get off?

6. Would a pound of feathers require a smaller force to produce a given acceleration than a pound of gold? (Neglect air friction.)

7. A man stands on a spring scale on the floor of an elevator; what would be the reading of the scale if the supporting cables should break and the elevator cage should fall freely?

8. Could you throw a ball if you were on the surface of a frozen pond, assuming that the friction were zero?

9. Could a rocket accelerate itself in a vacuum?

10. Since the pull of gravity on a 2-lb. ball is twice as great as that on a 1-lb. ball, why are the two accelerated equally when falling freely?

11. A monkey clings to one end of a rope passing over a pulley, and a mirror and weight are attached to the other end of the rope (Fig. 7). Assuming the system to be frictionless and in equilibrium, what happens to the mirror (*a*) if the monkey climbs up the rope, (*b*) if he climbs down, (*c*) if he releases the rope? Can he get away from his image seen in the mirror?

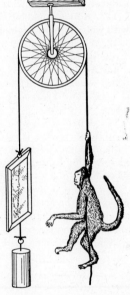

FIG. 7.—Can the monkey get away from his image, seen in the mirror?

PROBLEMS

(Assume that 1 gwt. = 980 dynes; 1 mi./hr. = 1.47 ft./sec.)

1. A boy and sled together weigh 100 lb. If an unbalanced horizontal force of 10 lb. acts on them, what will be the acceleration (friction neglected)?

2'. In the preceding problem, what will be the acceleration if the coefficient of friction is 0.050?

3'. An automobile weighing 3,200 lb. can accelerate from 3.0 mi./hr. to 27 mi./hr. in 8.0 sec. What is the accelerating force?

4. How great an acceleration will a force of 20 lb. give to a body which weighs 100 lb.?

5. How great an acceleration will a force of 1.00 gwt. cause in a body weighing 10 gwt.?

6. What force is required to impart an acceleration of 32 ft./sec.² to a body which weighs 100 lb.?

7′. A baseball weighing 5/16 lb. having a speed of 100 ft./ sec. is stopped by a catcher's mitt in 1/100 sec. Find (a) the average deceleration; (b) the force exerted on the ball by the glove.

8′. (a) What force is required to drag a block which weighs 1,000 gwt., at uniform velocity, along a horizontal table top, if the coefficient of friction is 1/10? (b) What would be the required force if the acceleration were 98 cm./sec.²?

9″. A 5-cent piece weighing 5.0 gwt. slides along a table top. The initial velocity is 200 cm./sec., and the coin travels 50 cm. before stopping, being uniformly decelerated. Find (a) the deceleration; (b) the frictional force; and (c) the coefficient of sliding friction.

10. A man weighing 150 lb. stands close to the rear wall of a streetcar. If the car suddenly accelerates 3.2 ft./sec.², with what force will the man push against the wall?

11″. A rope would be broken by a force of 120 lb. What is the smallest acceleration with which a man weighing 160 lb. can slide down the rope without breaking it?

12. A rifle bullet weighing 10.0 gwt. acquires a velocity of 400 m./sec. in traversing a rifle barrel 50 cm. long. Find (a) the acceleration; and (b) the accelerating force.

13. An automobile weighing 3,200 lb. is towed on a level street by means of a rope which would break if the pull were greater than 100 lb. If the coefficient of friction is 1/100, how great an acceleration can be given to the car without breaking the rope?

14′. A ball which weighs 1.00 lb. falls through the air with a vertical acceleration of 30 ft./sec.² What is the frictional force acting on it?

15. A man who weighs 200 lb. stands in an elevator. What force does the floor exert on him (a) when the elevator rises at constant speed; (b) when it has an upward acceleration of 8.0 ft./sec.²?

16″. A boy and sled weighing 100 lb. coast down a hill at constant velocity, the angle with the horizontal being 30.0°. What are the (a) downhill component of the weight; (b) the friction opposing the motion; (c) the component of the weight normal to the road; (d) the coefficient of friction? Make a diagram of the forces acting on the system. Is their sum zero?

$$F = MA$$
$$F = \frac{MV^2}{R}$$

CHAPTER VIII

CURVILINEAR MOTION

In the preceding chapter accelerations of bodies traveling along straight lines were studied. Now we shall consider the accelerations of bodies moving in curved paths. Familiar examples are the motions of projectiles such as baseballs and footballs.

In preparation for these studies, it should .be emphasized that velocities, like forces, are directed or "vector" quantities. A man rows a boat causing a velocity of 3 mi./hr. and the river carries him southward with a velocity of 4 mi./hr. His velocity with respect to the earth is the resultant of the velocity of the river and that due to his rowing. Suppose, first, that the boat is pointed downstream. The resultant velocity will be the sum of the velocity of the river and that produced by the effort of the man. This sum is 7 mi./hr., directed south. Next, let the boat be pointed upstream, and the resultant will be the difference between the two, 1 mi./hr., directed south. Lastly, if the boat is headed eastward, the resultant velocity—5 mi./hr.—is found by the parallelogram method (Fig. 1).

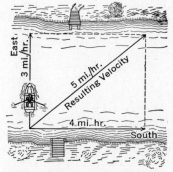

FIG. 1.—The velocity of the river, and that due to the man's rowing, cause a resultant velocity found by the parallelogram rule.

61. The Path of a Projectile. A baseball, thrown horizontally, falls just as fast as if it were dropped from rest. The reader can verify this fact for himself by throwing a stone horizontally from a window and dropping a second one at the same instant. The two stones will strike the level street simultaneously. In a particular test, suppose that two stones are released from an elevation of 64 ft. and that the second one has a horizontal velocity of 10 ft./sec. (Fig. 2). Then each stone will strike after 2 sec., and the second stone will hit at B, 20 ft. from the wall. Repeat the experiment, this time throwing one body with a velocity of 20 ft./sec., and it will strike at C, 40 ft. from the building. Such experiments prove that the two motions are independent. That is, the stones continue to travel horizontally with constant velocity, and fall with constant vertical acceleration. This behavior is in accord with Newton's laws of motion. Neither stone accelerates hori-

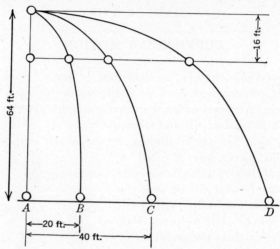

FIG. 2.—A ball dropped from rest and the one thrown horizontally strike the ground at the same instant.

zontally, for no horizontal force acts on it. Both accelerate downward equally because of the earth's attraction.

Example. A bomb is released from an airplane traveling horizontally at an elevation of 6,400 ft., the velocity being 200 ft./sec. (a) How soon will the bomb strike the earth, and (b) how far will it advance horizontally while falling? (Neglect air friction.)

$$6,400 \text{ ft.} = \tfrac{1}{2}at^2 = \tfrac{1}{2} \ 32 \text{ ft./sec.}^2 \ t^2$$
$$t = 20 \text{ sec.}$$

Sidewise displacement $= v_0 t = 200$ ft./sec. $\times$ 20 sec. $= 4,000$ ft.

62. The Velocity of a Projectile. The next problem is to determine the velocity of the projectile at various positions on its path. This can be accomplished by the parallelogram method. At B (Fig. 3), the ball has been falling for 1 sec., hence the vertical component of its velocity BE is 32 ft./sec. The horizontal component of its velocity BF is the same as the initial velocity, namely 40 ft./sec. The resultant of these two vectors is BG, and by measurement the value is found to be 51.4 ft./sec. The reader can apply the same method in finding the velocity when the ball reaches C after falling for 2 sec.

The path of a punted football can be determined by a method closely resembling that for a stone which is projected horizontally. Suppose that the football traveled initially along the line AE (Fig. 4) with a velocity of 70 ft./sec. If the earth did not attract it, the ball would continue to travel in this direction with constant velocity. Actually, the attraction of the earth pulls it down 16 ft. during the first second,

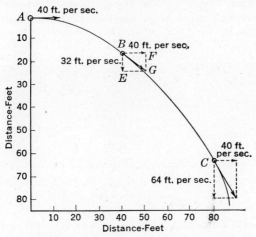

FIG. 3.—Determining the velocity of a projectile.

64 ft. during the first 2 sec., etc. Hence (neglecting air friction), the path is that represented in the figure. It is a parabola.

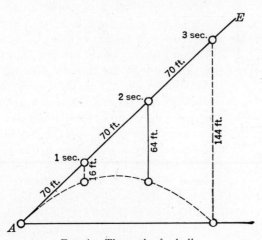

FIG. 4.—The path of a ball.

The paths of projectiles can be illustrated by a stream of water from a garden hose (Fig. 5). Notice that the water jet deviates from the parabolic path on which it would travel if the air friction were zero.

This result of air friction is important in affecting the paths of bullets and shells. During the World War, a German cannon, the "Big Bertha," bombarded Paris from a distance of about 75 miles. During most of its flight, the projectile traveled at elevations greater than 10 miles, where the air was so rarefied that the fluid friction was greatly diminished.

FIG. 5.—If the air friction were zero, a stream of water from a hose would describe a parabolic curve.

63. Centripetal Forces. A very important type of motion is that of a body which travels in a circular path at constant speed. In this case the force acting on the body is constant in magnitude but it is always directed toward the center of the arc. Hence it is called a **centripetal** force (Latin *centrum*, the center, + *petere*, to seek).

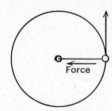

FIG. 6.—The centripetal force pulls the ball toward the center of a circle on which it moves.

As an automobile goes around a curve, a passenger tends to move forward in a straight line in accord with Newton's first law, hence if no sidewise force acted on him, he would fall out of the car. In fact, the side wall pushes against him and, as it were, forces him around the curve. A stone tied to a cord is whirled in a circle and the cord constantly pulls on the stone, exerting a centripetal force which causes it to move in a curved path. Many other examples of centripetal forces will occur to the reader. When a ball is whirled in a circle by means of a string, a force directed toward the center of the circle must be exerted (Fig. 6). An athlete whirls a 16-lb. ball in a circle. He must exert a centripetal force on it (Fig. 7). When he releases the wire, the ball flies off tangentially. An automobile skids in going around a curve because the friction between the tires and pavement is insufficient to provide the necessary centripetal force. Some washing machines have spinners to remove water from the clothing. The wet clothes are placed in a vertical cylinder with perforated walls. As this cylinder rotates, the water, clinging to the cloth by adhesion, is whirled around in a circular path. As the speed increases, the adhesion is not sufficient to cause circular motion and the water flies off on a tangent.

64. The Cream Separator. One of the most familiar uses of centripetal forces is the separation of cream from milk. To illustrate how this is done, place some mercury and water in a glass bowl which can be revolved rapidly. When the bowl is at rest, the mercury, being the more dense, goes to the bottom; but when the vessel is rotated rapidly, the mercury rises to the outer edge and the water collects nearer

FIG. 7.—An athlete swings a hammer.

to the center. Similarly, if milk is used, the rotation will cause the heavier constituent, the skim milk, to accumulate at the sides while the cream gathers nearer to the center. If the bowl revolves with sufficient rapidity, the forces separating the cream from the milk are much greater than the weight of the liquid, and the separation is accomplished in a few seconds.

In the cream separator used in dairies, the revolving system consists of a number of funnel-shaped disks which rotate many hundred times per minute (Fig. 8). The liquid enters near the top of the assembly, travels down through the vertical tube, and then rises through the inverted funnels. The skim milk, being relatively more dense, travels outward. It goes to the edges of the funnels, then moves upward, and escapes as shown in the drawing. The cream moves inward and upward, escaping at the upper opening.

65. Centripetal and Centrifugal Forces. The expression "centrifugal force" (Latin *centrum*, the center, + *fugere*, to flee) is used more frequently than centripetal force, and it is important that we understand the difference between them. Remember that when an automobile goes around a curve an inward force acts on the passenger, pushing him toward the center of the circle, and this is the centripetal force. The

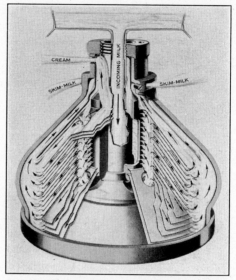

FIG. 8.—A cream separator.

opposite force which he exerts on the side of the car is the centrifugal force.

The centripetal force is the action force exerted on the body which travels on the circle, and the centrifugal force is a reaction force exerted by that body. It acts on some other body.

In accord with Newton's third law, these two forces (action and reaction) are equal in magnitude.

66. Acceleration Can Occur without Change of Speed. Strange as it may seem, when a body moves in a circular path with constant speed, it is accelerated. True, the **magnitude** of the velocity is constant, but its **direction** changes. The following illustration will help to clarify the matter.

Suppose that a cannon ball is dropped from the top of a tower 400 ft. high. If air friction is negligible, the ball reaches the ground after 5 sec. Next, suppose that it is projected horizontally, striking the earth at B (Fig. 9). If in a third trial the initial horizontal velocity is greater, the ball will strike at some more distant point C. Then shoot the cannon ball with a speed of 10 mi./sec. and it will travel along AE and escape from the earth. Finally, let the horizontal velocity be 5 mi./sec. In this trial, the ball, accelerated as before, will be pulled down toward the center of the earth. The speed is carefully chosen so that the path is circular and **parallel to the surface of the earth.** In other words, at D, the ball, though it has been continually falling toward the earth, is still moving horizontally, and, incidentally, is no nearer the center of the earth than it was at A. If air friction were negligible, the ball would

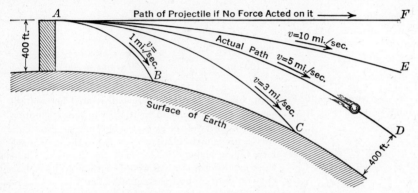

FIG. 9.—A ball thrown horizontally may travel off into space, descend to earth, or move in a circular path as the moon does.

continue to move in a circle as the moon does and the attraction of the earth would constantly cause it to fall just enough to keep it at a constant distance from the curved surface. But why does the speed of the ball not increase during its motion? In dealing with this question, it should be noted that the pull at each instant is at right angles to the line of motion and, therefore, the force has no effect on the forward velocity of the ball so that the speed remains constant. It is possible, then, for a body to move with constant speed on a circular path, the centripetal force changing the direction of the velocity without changing its magnitude.

67. The Formula for Computing Centripetal Forces. Every automobile driver realizes that when a car changes direction the tendency to skid increases with its speed and also with the suddenness of the turn. In general, when a body of weight W and mass $M = W/g$ travels with a velocity v on a curve of radius R, the centripetal force (and the equal and opposite centrifugal force) is given by

$$F = (W/g)(v^2/R) = Mv^2/R$$

Example 1. A man weighing 160 lb. rides in an automobile which makes a sudden turn. He moves along a curve of radius 80 ft., with a speed of 40 ft./sec. What is the centripetal force acting on him?

$$F = \frac{160 \text{ lb.}}{32 \text{ ft./sec.}^2} \times \frac{(40 \text{ ft./sec.})^2}{80 \text{ ft.}} = 100 \text{ lb.}$$

Example 2. An airplane travels with a speed of 300 mi./hr. (440 ft./sec.). What is the radius of the curve along which the airplane moves if the centripetal force on a pilot weighing 160 lb. is 440 lb.?

$$F = \frac{160 \text{ lb.} \ (440 \text{ ft./sec.})^2}{32 \text{ ft./sec.}^2 \times R} = 440 \text{ lb.}$$
$$R = 2,200 \text{ ft.}$$

Example 3. What centripetal force acts when a stone weighing 50 gwt. is whirled in a circle of radius 100 cm., the velocity being 200 cm./sec.?

$$F = \frac{50 \text{ gwt.}}{980 \text{ cm./sec.}^2} \times \frac{(200 \text{ cm./sec.})^2}{100 \text{ cm.}} \qquad \text{or} \qquad \begin{aligned} F &= ma \\ &= 50 \text{ grams} \times 200 \text{ cm./sec.}^2 \end{aligned}$$
$$= 20.4 \text{ gwt.} \qquad\qquad\qquad\qquad\qquad\qquad = 20,000 \text{ dynes}$$

68. Derivation of the Equation. Imagine that a cannon ball is fired horizontally from a point A (Fig. 10), and assume that there is no air friction to slow its motion.

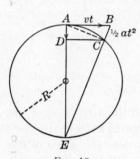

Let the velocity of the projectile be 5 mi./sec., so that it travels along a circular path parallel to the earth's surface, falling about 8 in. for each mile traveled. Under these conditions, the ball would continue to move on a circular path around the equator. Let a time t be required for the journey from A to C, so that the length of the curved path is vt. Suppose that, instead of being projected horizontally, the ball was dropped into a deep mine or well. If so, it would fall to D in the time t, the distance being $\frac{1}{2}at^2$, a being the acceleration of gravity. But this is the same distance that the projectile must fall in traveling from A to C.

FIG. 10   The remainder of our task is mostly geometrical. First notice that if the time of flight is short the curved path is approximately equal to the straight-line distance from A to B. (If AC is 1 mile, the difference in the length of the path is only about 4 in.)

The triangles ADC and ACE are similar. (Both are right angled, and the angle DAC is common.) Hence

$$AD/AC = AC/AE$$
$$AD \times AE = AC^2$$
But
$$AD = \frac{1}{2}at^2, \ AE = 2R, \ AC = vt$$
Hence
$$\frac{1}{2}at^2 \times 2R = v^2t^2$$
$$a = v^2/R$$

The centripetal force required to produce the acceleration $a = v^2/R$ is given by

$$F = Ma = W/g \times v^2/R$$

The student can readily prove that this equation applies generally to any body that travels at uniform speed on any circular path.

69. Banking of Curves. A bicycle rider, going around a sharp curve, leans inward to provide the necessary centripetal force to push him sidewise toward the center of the circle on which he moves. The forces acting on such a rider are represented in Fig. 11A. In the force diagram (Fig. 11B), AB represents his weight, AC is the upward push of the bicycle, and AD the resultant of these two forces. This resultant is the horizontal, centripetal force required to push the rider sidewise as he goes around the curve. The sharper the turn and the greater the speed, the greater must be the angle of tilt of the bicycle. When the cyclist rounds a curve the wheels are likely to skid. To prevent this, it is desirable that the roadway be "banked" as shown in the figure,

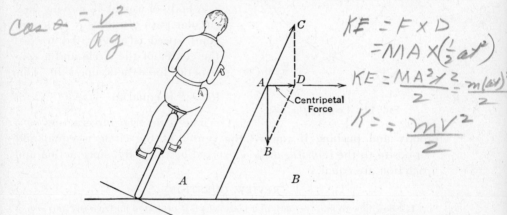

$$\cos \alpha = \frac{v^2}{Rg}$$

$$KE = F \times D$$
$$= MA \times (\tfrac{1}{2}at^2)$$
$$KE = \frac{MA^2t^2}{2} = \frac{m(at)^2}{2}$$
$$K = \frac{mv^2}{2}$$

FIG. 11.—A rider leans inward to provide the necessary centripetal force to push him toward the center of the circle.

the tilt of the street being made equal to that of the bicycle. Railway tracks are usually tilted at curves, the outer rail being higher than the inner one, and automobile highways are banked. Unfortunately, the best angle of banking depends upon the speed. A curve which is safe for cars traveling at 40 mi./hr. may be dangerous for those traveling at 60 mi./hr.

70. Centripetal and Centrifugal Forces in Airplane Travel. Because of the high speeds of travel, centripetal forces are more important in airplanes than in other vehicles. Pilots must be careful not to change direction suddenly, lest damage be done to the airplanes themselves or to the passengers. When an aviator "loops the loop," the force on the pilot must overcome gravity and also supply the needed centripetal force. At A (Fig. 12), the required upward external force is the vector sum of the two. At B the force to overcome gravity is upward, the centripetal force is sidewise, and the total required force may be found by the parallelogram method. The most interesting position is at C where gravity supplies part of the centripetal force and the push of the seat on the pilot is the difference between the weight and the required centripetal force.

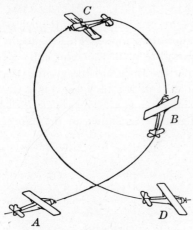

FIG. 12.—Looping the loop.

SUMMARY

If a ball is thrown horizontally and a second ball is dropped at the same instant, the two will fall equal vertical distances in equal times.

A body of weight W moving on a circular path of radius R with constant speed is accelerated toward the center of the circle and a centripetal force acts upon it. This force F is equal to $\dfrac{W}{g} \times \dfrac{v^2}{R}$.

The *centripetal* force acting *on* a body and pushing it toward the center of the circle is equal and opposite to the *centrifugal* force exerted *by* the body, since action and reaction are equal.

REVIEW QUESTIONS

1. Show how to find the path of a body which is projected horizontally and also of one projected at some acute angle with the horizontal.

2. A train moves with a constant velocity of 88 ft./sec.; a picture hanging against the front wall of a car 4.0 ft. above the floor falls from its support. Where will it strike the floor?

3. Discuss the meaning of "centripetal" force, and state the factors on which it depends. Also show the difference between it and "centrifugal" force.

4. Upon what factors does the desirable angle of tilt of a roadway depend?

5. Wrap a handkerchief tightly around a closed jack knife, and throw the knife causing it to spin like a top as it moves through the air. The blade will open. Explain.

6. Explain why water escapes from the wet clothing in a "spinner" or centrifugal dryer.

7. When an automobile went around a curve, the force exerted by a rider broke one of the windows. Was this force centripetal or centrifugal?

PROBLEMS

(Neglect air friction. Use $g = 32$ ft./sec.^{2} = 980 cm./sec.^{2})

1. A rifle is aimed horizontally at the bull's-eye of a target 1,000 ft. away, and the velocity of the bullet when it leaves the muzzle of the gun is 1,000 ft./sec. How far below the bull's-eye will the bullet strike?

2. A baseball thrown horizontally from a window at an elevation of 64 ft. strikes the level street at a distance of 100 ft. from the building. With what velocity was it thrown?

$d = VT$

$d = V\cos\theta \cdot V\sin\theta$

3'. Make sketches showing the paths of a golf ball with an initial velocity of 100 ft./sec. projected from a cliff (a) horizontally and (b) at an angle of 30° with the horizon.

4''. In Problem 3b, how long will it take the golf ball to reach its greatest elevation? How high will it rise, and how far will it travel horizontally before returning to the (level) surface of the earth?

5'. An airplane travels horizontally with a speed of 68 mi./hr. (100 ft./sec.) at an elevation of 10,000 ft. If it drops a bomb, (a) how soon will the bomb strike the earth; (b) how far will the airplane travel while the bomb is falling?

6'. A ball was thrown vertically upward at an initial velocity of 96 ft./sec. Find (a) the speed and velocity after 6.0 sec.; (b) the change of speed and velocity during the 6.0 sec.

7''. A ball is thrown upward at an angle of 30° with the horizon, the initial speed being 64 ft./sec. (a) Using the parallelogram method, find the direction and magnitude of the velocity after 1.00 sec. (b) What was the change of velocity? (c) What was the change of speed?

8. A ball weighing 100 gwt. is whirled on a horizontal circle of radius 98 cm., the speed being 980 cm./sec. What is the centripetal force acting on the ball?

9. A stone weighing 0.10 lb. is whirled in a horizontal circle of radius 2.0 ft., the speed being 32.0 ft./sec. What is the centripetal force acting on the stone?

10'. The rotator of a cream separator has a radius of 3.0 in. (a) Find the speed of milk particles when whirled on a circle of this radius, making 100 revolutions per second. (b) Also find the centripetal force on a pound of the milk.

11. An athlete whirls a "hammer" weighing 16 lb. on a horizontal circle of radius 4.0 ft., and its speed is 20 ft./sec. What is the horizontal component of the pull of the wire on the ball?

12'. A ball weighing 490 gwt. is whirled in a horizontal circle the radius of which is 36 cm. With what maximum speed can it travel if the breaking strength of the cord is 5,000 gwt.?

13'. An airplane dives toward the earth at a speed of 340 mi./hr. (500 ft./sec.). Then the machine "levels off" to a horizontal direction. The radius of the curve on which it travels is 1,000 ft. What centripetal force acts on the pilot, his weight being 160 lb.?

14''. If the earth revolved fast enough, the apparent weight of a 100-lb. body at the equator would be zero. (a) What would be the speed of the body? (Assume $R = 20,000,000$ ft.) (b) If the earth rotated at this speed, how long would a day be?

15''. A drum major whirls his baton at constant speed in a vertical circle of radius 2.0 ft. The ball on the end of the baton weighs 1.00 lb., and its speed is 10 ft./sec. Find the force exerted on the ball by the stick (a) when the ball is at its greatest elevation, and (b) when at its lowest elevation.

16''. A roadway is 30 ft. wide. An automobile weighing 3,200 lb. goes around a curve of radius 500 ft., with a speed of 60 ft./sec. (41 mi./hr.). (a) What is the centripetal force on the car? (b) Approximately how much should the outer edge of the road be elevated above the inner edge so that there may be no tendency to skid?

17''. If the curved roadway described in the preceding problem were level, at what maximum speed could the car travel (a) in dry weather when the coefficient of friction of the tires on the roadway was 0.40, and (b) in icy weather when the coefficient was 0.10?

18''. A boy weighing 96 lb. sits on a "joy wheel," or horizontal rotating platform, at a distance of 5.0 ft. from the axis of rotation. If the coefficient of friction is 1/10, (a) what is the greatest sidewise force available to prevent his sliding? (b) At what maximum speed can he move without sliding?

CHAPTER IX

ENERGY, IMPULSE, AND MOMENTUM

The word energy is comparatively young, having been used for less than a century; but work is one of the oldest words in the language. The two are closely related, for the energy of a body or system means its **capacity for doing work.** "Energy" is derived from the Greek expressions, *en* = in, and *ergos* = work. Many illustrations of energy are familiar. A rapidly moving hammer strikes a nail and forces it into a board. An old-fashioned clock is wound, and the falling weight does work in turning the wheels of the clock. Gasoline supplies energy to propel an automobile, and the waters of Niagara yield energy to run the streetcars of Buffalo.

The relationship between work and energy is like that between money and a bank account. A bank account may be increased or decreased by depositing or withdrawing money; and the energy of a body may be altered either by doing work on it or by causing it to do work. In either case the change equals the amount of work done, and it may be expressed in work units.

TABLE I

UNITS OF WORK AND ENERGY

Foot-pound
Erg or dyne-centimeter
        Joule = 10,000,000 ergs
            = 10,200 gram-weight-centimeters = $\frac{3}{4}$ foot-pound
    Kilowatt-hour = 3,600,000 joules = 2 ton-miles
  Horsepower-hour = 2,000,000 foot-pounds

71. Kinetic Energy. The energy of a body due to its motion is called **kinetic energy.** For example, a rapidly moving sledge hammer strikes a nail and forces it into a plank. In so doing, the hammer does work as it slows down, losing all its kinetic energy. A cannon ball traveling at a rate of $\frac{1}{2}$ mi./sec. has considerable kinetic energy and can do work in demolishing a wall. The kinetic energy of a speeding automobile enables it to ascend a hill after the power is shut off, or to break off a fence post in a collision.

Kinetic energy is energy due to motion.

The kinetic energy of a body of weight W, mass W/g, and velocity v is given by

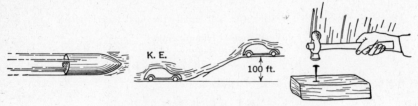

FIG. 1.—Kinetic energy is energy of motion.

$$\text{K.E.} = \tfrac{1}{2}(W/g)v^2 = \tfrac{1}{2}Mv^2$$

According to this equation, doubling the velocity of a body quadruples its kinetic energy. When the velocity of an automobile is doubled, the time required for a given force to stop it is doubled and also the average velocity during the deceleration. Inasmuch as both factors are doubled, the distance traveled is quadrupled. Thus the work required to stop the car is 4 times as great, and it has 4 times as much kinetic energy.

Example 1. A baseball weighing 5/16 lb. has a velocity of 96 ft./sec. What is its kinetic energy?

$$\text{K.E.} = \tfrac{1}{2}\frac{5/16\ \text{lb.}}{32\ \text{ft./sec.}^2} \times (96\ \text{ft./sec.})^2$$
$$= 45\ \text{ft-lb.}$$

Example 2. A rifle bullet weighing 10.0 gwt. has a velocity of 1 km./sec. (100,000 cm./sec.). What is its kinetic energy?

$$\text{K.E.} = \tfrac{1}{2}\frac{10.0\ \text{gwt.}}{980\ \text{cm./sec.}^2} \times (10^5\ \text{cm./sec.})^2 \quad \text{or}$$
$$= 51,000,000\ \text{gwt-cm.}$$
$$= 5,000\ \text{joules}$$
$$= 50 \times 10^9\ \text{ergs}$$
$$= 3,750\ \text{ft-lb.}$$

$$\text{K.E.} = \tfrac{1}{2}\ mv^2$$
$$= \tfrac{1}{2}\ 10.0\ \text{grams}\ (10^5\ \text{cm./sec.})^2$$
$$= 50 \times 10^9\ \text{ergs}$$

Example 3. An automobile weighs 3,200 lb., and its velocity is 40 ft./sec. (27 mi./hr.). What is its kinetic energy?

$$\text{K.E.} = \tfrac{1}{2}\frac{3,200\ \text{lb.}}{32\ \text{ft./sec.}^2} \times (40\ \text{ft./sec.})^2$$
$$= 80,000\ \text{ft-lb.}$$

72. Derivation of the Formula for Kinetic Energy. A player throws a baseball of weight W, causing an acceleration a. Then, from Newton's second law of motion, the average accelerating force F on the ball is given by

$$F = (W/g)a \tag{1}$$

This average force is exerted on the ball during a time t, and the distance d through which the force acts is given by

$$d = \tfrac{1}{2}at^2$$

The work done in accelerating the ball equals the final kinetic energy, that is:

$$\text{Work done} = \text{Kinetic energy}$$
$$F \times d = \text{K.E.}$$
$$(W/g)a \times \tfrac{1}{2}at^2 = \tfrac{1}{2}(W/g)(at)^2 = \text{K.E.}$$

But at equals the final velocity v. Hence

$$\text{K.E.} = \tfrac{1}{2}(W/g)v^2$$

73. Potential Energy. Many bodies have energy though they are not moving. For example, when water is pumped to a tank on the

Fig. 2.—Examples of potential energy.

roof of a building, work is done in lifting it against gravity and energy is stored, which can do work in turning a water wheel. An archer draws back the bowstring and imparts energy to the bow. When the string is released, work is done in speeding the arrow and the potential energy becomes kinetic energy. A gallon of gasoline contains sufficient energy to lift a car to the top of a mountain. These are examples of potential energy.

Energy which is due to motion is termed kinetic, and all other forms are classified as potential.

Throw a baseball vertically upward. At first all its energy is kinetic. As it rises, losing kinetic energy, its potential energy increases. At the highest point of its path, the ball is at rest for an instant, and its energy is all potential. Then it speeds downward, and strikes the earth. It can be proved that, neglecting air friction, the ball would return to the point from which it was thrown with the same speed and the same energy that it had initially. Moreover, **the energy, kinetic and potential taken together, would be the same at every point on the path.**

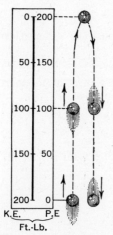

FIG. 3. — The total energy of the ball remains constant.

But what happens when the ball strikes the ground? Is there not a destruction of energy? Later, it will be shown that the impact of the ball caused its molecules and those of the ground to oscillate or vibrate more violently. That is, the energy was transformed into molecular energy or **heat**. When the brakes of a car are applied, the kinetic energy of the car diminishes. Heat is produced by friction, and the brake bands become hot. The final amount of energy is the same as the original; energy has been transformed, but not destroyed.

It is our firm belief, justified by numerous experiments, that **energy can be transformed but it is never created or destroyed.**

This is the principle of the **conservation of energy.** It exemplifies the idea that in physics, at least, we cannot get something for nothing.

The principle of work, introduced in the chapter on machines, was a special case of the conservation of energy. Now it may be stated more completely, as follows:

The energy input to a machine equals the energy output plus that used in overcoming friction.

Another example of the conservation of energy is afforded by a youngster in a swing. His energy, at the highest elevation, is entirely potential, and at the lowest point it is kinetic. If there were no friction, the swing would continue to oscillate indefinitely; but actually when the youngster ceases to exert himself, "the old cat dies," and the swing comes to rest. The work done in overcoming friction appears as heat, and no energy is destroyed.

The principle of the conservation of energy is useful in solving problems.

Example 1. An archer pulls back a bowstring 1.00 ft. and then discharges an arrow that weighs 1/20 lb. The velocity of the arrow when released is 128 ft./sec. What was the average force exerted on it by the bowstring?

$$K.E. = \frac{1}{2}\frac{1/20 \text{ lb.}}{32 \text{ ft./sec.}^2} \times (128 \text{ ft./sec.})^2$$
$$= 12.8 \text{ ft-lb.}$$
$$F \times d = 12.8 \text{ ft-lb.}$$
$$F \times 1.00 \text{ ft.} = 12.8 \text{ ft-lb.}$$
$$F = 12.8 \text{ lb.}$$

Example 2. From what elevation must a 3,200-lb. automobile fall in order to acquire a velocity of 60 mi./hr. (about 90 ft./sec.)?

$$K.E. = \frac{1}{2}\frac{3,200 \text{ lb.}}{32 \text{ ft./sec.}^2} (90 \text{ ft./sec.})^2$$
$$= 405,000 \text{ ft-lb.}$$
$$3,200 \text{ lb.} \times d = 405,000 \text{ ft-lb.}$$
$$d = 126.5 \text{ ft.}$$

74. The Importance of the Law of the Conservation of Energy. The law that energy is indestructible is extremely important in physics. Lengths of bodies may change, their speeds and velocities may alter,

20 MI./HR.
HEIGHT 13.4 FEET

40 MI./HR.
HEIGHT 53.5 FEET

60 MI./HR.
HEIGHT 120.3 FEET

Fig. 4.—Distances of fall for an automobile to acquire different speeds.

"time marches on," but energy, like Tennyson's brook, "goes on forever." Energy of the sun has been coming to the earth during the ages. Part of it was captured and stored in the carbon of growing plants. These plants, preserved in fossil form as coal, yield heat energy for our furnaces.

75. Matter as a Form of Energy. There is a second very important law which states that matter, like energy, is indestructible. This law is true under ordinary circumstances, but there is evidence that the masses of bodies are greater at very high velocities than when they are at rest. That is, when the energy of a body is increased, its mass also increases. For this reason, matter is often regarded as a form of energy. In a later chapter, evidence will be presented showing that the energy of the stars is stored as matter and that they become less massive as the years go by. Probably there is sufficient energy condensed in a pound of hydrogen, of nitrogen, or of any substance, to heat a residence for many years. Thus far, no means have been devised to set free this energy in paying quantities.

76. What is an Impulse? When a boy pushes a sled on a frozen pond, the increase in velocity depends upon the magnitude of the accelerating force F, and also upon the time t that the force acts. A force (in excess of friction) of 10 lb. acting on a body for 1 sec. produces just as great a change of velocity as does a force of 1 lb. acting for 10 sec.

The product of a force and the time that it acts on a body, called the **impulse**, may be expressed in pound-weight-seconds or in gram-weight-seconds.

An impulse is the product of a force and the time that it acts in accelerating a body.

$$\text{Impulse} = \text{Force} \times \text{Time}$$

Impulse and Momentum. The momentum of a body is sometimes called the quantity of its motion, but it is better to use a defining equation.

$$\text{Momentum} = \text{Mass} \times \text{Velocity}$$
$$= W/g \times v = Mv$$

Notice that, whenever the velocity of a body increases, both the kinetic energy and the momentum become greater. The momentum is proportional to the velocity of the body; the kinetic energy to the square of the velocity. Thus, doubling the velocity of a body **doubles** the momentum but it **quadruples** the kinetic energy.

When a force F acts on a body for a time t, changing its velocity from v_1 to v_2, the change of momentum is given by

$$Ft = (W/g)(v_2 - v_1) = Mv_2 - Mv_1$$

In other words, **the impulse equals the change of momentum produced**.

A forward force causes an increase in momentum; a backward or retarding force, a decrease.

77. Derivation of the Momentum Equation. An unbalanced force F acts for a time t on a body of weight W, causing an acceleration a and changing the velocity from v_1 to v_2.

$$F = (W/g)a$$
$$Ft = (W/g)at$$
$$at = (v_2 - v_1)$$
$$Ft = (W/g)(v_2 - v_1) = Mv_2 - Mv_1$$

Impulse = Change of momentum

Example 1. In kicking a football, the average applied force was 20 lb. and it acted for 0.10 sec. What was the impulse?

$$F \times t = 20 \text{ lb.} \times 0.10 \text{ sec.}$$
$$2.0 \text{ lb-sec.}$$

Example 2. A car weighing 3,200 lb. has a velocity of 20 ft./sec. (*a*) How much momentum has it? (*b*) How long will be required to stop it if the braking force is 800 lb.?

(*a*)
$$(W/g)v = \frac{3,200 \text{ lb.}}{32 \text{ ft./sec.}^2} \times 20 \text{ ft./sec.}$$
$$= 2,000 \text{ lb-sec.}$$
$$F \times t = 800 \text{ lb.} \times t = 2,000 \text{ lb-sec.}$$
$$t = 2.50 \text{ sec.}$$

78. The Conservation of Momentum. A third important law of conservation states that **momentum is indestructible.** To illustrate its

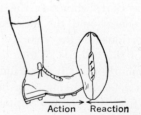

Action → Reaction

Fig. 5A.—The momentum lost by the golf club is gained by the ball. (Courtesy of Prof. H. L. Edgerton.)
Fig. 5B.—The momentum lost by the foot equals that gained by the ball.

meaning, suppose that an automobile bumps into another one which is at rest. The forward action force on the second car increases its velocity, and the backward, reaction force on the first car slows its motion. Therefore, after the collision, the momentum of one car has increased and that of the other has diminished. Further, the gain of momentum of one car is equal to the loss of momentum of the other. Hence no momentum is lost in the collision. Similarly when a golf club strikes a ball or a football player kicks a ball, the loss of momentum of the club equals the gain of momentum of the ball (Fig. 5).

Example. A ball weighing 1 lb. having a velocity of 10 ft./sec. strikes a 9-lb. clay ball which is at rest. If the first ball embeds itself in the second, what is their velocity after the impact?

Momentum before impact = (1 lb./32 ft./sec.^{2}) × 10 ft./sec.

Momentum after impact = 10 lb./(32 ft./sec.^{2})v ∴ v = 1 ft./sec.

SUMMARY

The energy of a body or system is its capacity for doing work.

The kinetic energy of a body of weight W and mass W/g, moving with a velocity v, is given by

$$\text{K.E.} = \tfrac{1}{2}(W/g)v^2 = \tfrac{1}{2}Mv^2$$

All kinds of energy due to motion are classified as kinetic, and those not due to motion are potential.

The principle of the conservation of energy asserts that energy is neither created nor destroyed.

The impulse of a force is the product of the force and the time that it acts on a body.

The momentum of a body of weight W and velocity v is given by $(W/g)v = Mv$.

The change of momentum of a body equals the impulse producing the change.

$$Ft = (W/g)(v_2 - v_1) = Mv_2 - Mv_1$$

Whenever one body gains momentum, some other body loses an equal amount. **Momentum is never created or destroyed.**

REVIEW QUESTIONS

1. Distinguish between *work* and *energy*; *potential energy* and *kinetic energy*. Give several examples.

2. A block weighing 100 lb. hangs at an elevation of 6.0 ft. above the top of a table which is 2.0 ft. high. What is the potential energy of the block before and after the table is removed? Is potential energy absolute or relative?

3. Discuss the law of the conservation of energy, using several illustrations not given in the text.

4. Prove that K.E. = $\tfrac{1}{2}(W/g)v^2 = \tfrac{1}{2}Mv^2$.

5. Define impulse and momentum, stating units in which each can be expressed. State the law of the conservation of momentum. How does it apply when an automobile runs into a wall and stops suddenly? Is momentum destroyed?

6. A clay ball weighing 1 lb. moving north at a velocity of 32 ft./sec. strikes an equal ball moving south with equal speed. What was the momentum of each before the impact? What was the sum of the momentums? (Remember that one velocity was negative.) Also find the total energy of motion before and after the impact.

7. What was the second body which lost or gained momentum in each of the following:

(*a*) A bullet fired from a rifle.
(*b*) An automobile accelerated forward on a highway.
(*c*) A baseball struck by a bat.

8. Discuss the law of the conservation of momentum as regards Newton's third law of motion.

9. A shell explodes in mid-air. How is its momentum affected?

potential E. = wt H

PROBLEMS

1. A tank 4.0 ft. high contains 2,000 pounds of water when full. It rests on a platform at the water level of a lake. How much potential energy has it?

2′. A 5-oz. baseball is thrown vertically upward with an initial velocity of 100 ft./sec. (*a*) How much kinetic energy has it? (*b*) From energy considerations find how high it will rise?

3′. A car weighing 2,000 lb. traveling 20 mi./hr. (30 ft./sec.) can be stopped by good brakes in 20 ft. (*a*) What is the corresponding stopping distance at 40 mi./hr.? (*b*) What is the force tending to stop the car?

4″. A block weighing 2.0 lb. slides down an inclined plane 12 ft. long and 9.0 ft. high. With what speed will it reach the bottom (*a*) if the friction is negligible, and (*b*) if half the energy is required to overcome friction?

5′. A car weighing 3,200 lb. has a velocity of 61 mi./hr. (90 ft./sec.). (*a*) What is its kinetic energy? (*b*) From how high a cliff would it fall from rest in order to acquire this kinetic energy?

6′. An automobile weighing 2,000 lb. coasts from rest down a hill which is 64 ft. high. If the friction were zero, with what speed would it reach the bottom?

7′. A 5-oz. baseball dropped from the top of the Washington Monument (550 ft. high) was caught by Babe Ruth as it reached the ground. If his catcher's mitt moved downward 2.0 ft. in stopping the ball, how much force was exerted on the ball?

8. A hammerhead weighing 1.00 kgwt. having a velocity of 200 cm./sec. struck a spike and drove it 2.0 cm. into a block of wood. What was the force exerted on the spike?

9′. An automobile weighing 3,200 lb. has a speed of 62 mi./hr. (90 ft./sec.). (*a*) What is its momentum? (*b*) What force will stop it in 5.0 sec. and in 100 sec.?

√10′. A bullet weighing 1.96 gwt. has a velocity of 1,000 m./sec. (*a*) What is its momentum? (*b*) What force will stop it in 0.010 sec.?

11′. An arrow weighing 0.080 lb. was discharged from a bow with a speed of 40 ft./sec. (*a*) How much momentum did it have? (*b*) If the accelerating force acted on the arrow for 0.010 sec., what was its average value?

12′. A bullet weighing 0.032 lb. traveling northward 2,000 ft./sec. struck a bear weighing 800 lb. traveling southward 10.0 ft./sec. Find the momentum of each before the collision, remembering that the momentum of the bear was negative. Did he "stop in his tracks"?

13′. A bullet weighing 0.032 lb. is discharged from a rifle with a muzzle velocity of 2,000 ft./sec. The gun weighs 16 lb. (a) With what velocity will it recoil? (b) What force will stop it in 0.25 sec.?

14′. An empty railway car weighs 32,000 lb., and its speed is 3.0 ft./sec. What is the momentum of the empty car, and what will be the speed after 1,600 lb. of coal are dumped into it?

CHAPTER X

ROTARY MOTION

We have been considering motions on straight or curved paths when the moving bodies do not rotate, and we have learned the relationships between forces, masses, and accelerations. We now turn to the study of rotary motion in which a body spins or turns about a certain line or axis. We shall find that in this type of motion there are quantities closely analogous to those of linear motion. For instance, it has been pointed out that a moving body tends to remain in motion unless acted upon by some external **force**. Similarly, a rotating body tends to continue spinning, with constant angular velocity, unless acted upon by some external **torque**. Push on the handle of a grindstone, exerting a torque, and the stone will begin to turn (Fig. 1). Release

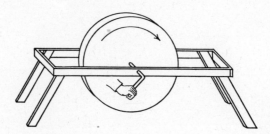

FIG. 1.—A torque changes the angular velocity of the grindstone.

the handle, and the rate of spin will gradually decrease because of the friction of the bearings. If the frictional torques could be reduced to zero, the stone would continue spinning with constant angular velocity. The earth rotating on its axis provides a good illustration of the tendency of a body to keep spinning. Its rate of rotation is so constant that it provides an excellent timepiece, which has marked off the days for thousands of centuries.

Newton's first law of motion as applied to rotating bodies is as follows:

Every rotating body persists in its state of uniform rotation about a certain axis unless acted upon by some external torque.

84

79. Rotational Inertia. In linear motion, the inertia of a body depends only upon its mass (W/g); but in rotary motion, the inertia of spin depends upon another factor. Consider the flywheel of a gasoline engine (Fig. 2). Its purpose is to maintain the motion during the intervals between explosions. To this end the wheel should have large rotational inertia (or moment of inertia). How is this accomplished? First, the mass W/g of the flywheel is large; and second, most of the metal is located in the rim, as far from the axis as is conveniently possible. Imagine a thin hoop of metal of weight W, mass W/g, and radius R, mounted like a flywheel on an axle through its center. Its rotational inertia I is given by

$$I = \frac{W}{g} \times R^2 = MR^2$$

Thus if the ring weighs 64 lb. and its radius is 2 ft., the rotational inertia is given by

$$I = \frac{64 \text{ lb.}}{32 \text{ ft./sec.}^2} \times 4 \text{ ft.}^2 = 8 \text{ lb-ft-sec.}^2$$

FIG. 2.—The rotational inertia of the flywheel makes the rotational velocity more uniform.

A uniform disk, such as a grindstone, has a smaller rotational inertia

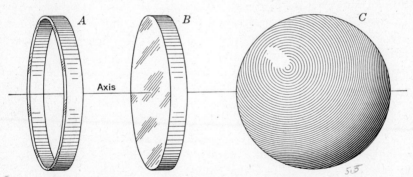

FIG. 3.—The ring has more rotational inertia than the disk or the sphere of equal mass and radius.

than a ring of equal weight and radius because its substance is located between the rim and the axis. Its rotational inertia is one-half that of the ring. A uniform sphere, rotating like the earth, on a line through its center, has a rotational inertia two-fifths as great (Fig. 3).

ang. Dist = $W_{av} T$

80. Angular Momentum. The momentum relationships for rotary motion are similar to those for linear motion. By definition the angular momentum of a rotating body is the product of its rotational inertia I and its angular velocity ω (omega). In accord with Newton's first law of motion.

When no external torque acts on a body, its angular momentum is constant.

Several interesting demonstrations are explainable by the constancy of angular momentum. Attach a ball to one end of a cord which passes through a hollow tube or pipe, and whirl the ball in a circle. Pull the cord suddenly through the tube so as to decrease the radius of the circle on which it travels. Then the angular velocity will increase, so that the ball revolves faster. Drawing the ball in closer to the axis diminishes its rotational inertia. The angular velocity increases sufficiently to keep the angular momentum constant.

In a second demonstration, let a student stand on a stool which can rotate with little friction and let a bystander give him a push to set him into rotation. Then the student can control his rate of spin by raising or lowering his arms. When he raises them, the rotational inertia of the system increases and the spin velocity decreases. Lowering them again increases the spin velocity.

A diver jumps from a springboard into a pool and gives himself a certain amount of angular momentum. As he moves through the air, he can double up or straighten out, controlling his angular velocity through alteration of his rotational inertia, so as to strike the water either head first or feet first at will.

81. The Gyroscope. A gyroscope is a massive wheel so mounted that its axle can tilt up and down or sidewise. Its behavior is quite peculiar, but can be explained in terms of the principles which have been presented in this book. To see how it acts and why, suppose that a solid wooden wheel, mounted on an axle, has several holes bored through it parallel to the axle, and let a ball be placed in each hole (Fig. 4). Hold the axle pointing north, and spin the wheel clockwise so that each ball travels in a circular path. Suddenly turn the axle to an east-west position, and the ball at A will continue its eastward velocity, and will move out from the hole. Similarly, the ball at C will travel west, and will leave its receptacle. This behavior is in accord with Newton's first law of motion. A little thinking will make clear that all the balls in the upper half of the wheel will fall out and travel east, while those in the lower half will travel west. Moreover, not only the balls but every particle in the upper half of the wheel had an eastward component of velocity at the moment when the axle was shifted, and every particle in the lower half had a westward component. Hence the entire wheel tends to tilt.

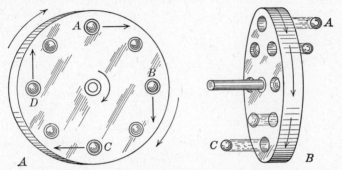

FIG. 4.—The wooden wheel tends to tilt when its axle is turned 90°.

The bicycle wheel (Fig. 5) is mounted so that it can revolve around three axes, namely, AB, CD, and the vertical axis Y. The end B of the axle points north, and the wheel spins clockwise. Suddenly turn the system so that the end B points east. Then the upper half of the wheel will move eastward, the lower half westward, and the wheel tilts on the axis CD. Thus an attempt to rotate the system about the Y axis causes it to tilt on the axis CD. This effect is called precession.

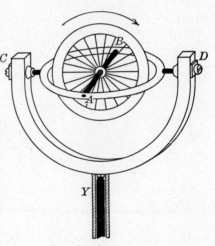

FIG. 5.—A gyroscope.

Hang a small weight at the end A of the axle of the gyroscope. If the wheel is at rest, the loaded end will move downward; but if spinning, the result is quite different. Instead of tilting, the gyroscope revolves on the vertical axis Y and the end A swings around in a horizontal circle. Thus an attempt to turn the system on the axis CD causes it to revolve on the vertical axis Y. This is another example of precession.

An airplane with a single propeller tends to "nose down" or "nose up" whenever it changes direction. This is a gyroscopic effect like those just described. Suppose that the airplane is traveling northward and that the four-bladed propeller is rotating clockwise as viewed by the pilot (Fig. 6). At a certain instant the top blade of the propeller is traveling east, the lower one west. If, at that instant, the plane

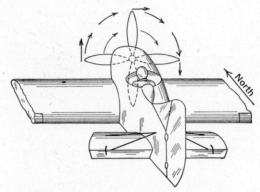

FIG. 6.—The airplane will "nose-dive" when it heads east.

suddenly heads eastward, the upper blade will tend to continue its motion east, the lower one west, and the plane will nose dive. If the plane heads west, it will tend to nose up.

82. The Gyrocompass. Gyroscopic compasses are always employed in submarines and often on other vessels. They are especially useful

FIG. 7.—Gyroscopic horizon indicator.

in aeronautics. The gyroscope wheel, kept spinning by an electric motor or by compressed air, has a large angular momentum, and its axle continues to point in the same direction, regardless of the tilting or turning of the airplane. Hence it acts like a compass needle (Fig. 7).

Gyroscopes are also used in the automatic piloting of airplanes. Suppose that the airplane flies northward and that the gyroscope spins clockwise on an axis parallel to the motion. If the airplane deviates to the right, the forward end of the axle of the gyroscope tilts downward, for example, closing an electric circuit which operates levers to bring the airplane back to its course.

83. Angular Velocities and Displacements. The angular velocity of a rotating body may be expressed in degrees per second or in revolutions per second. However, in dealing with rotary motion it is customary to use the radian per second. Draw a circle and mark off on its circumference an arc AB equal in length to the radius (Fig. 8). Then the angle θ is 1 radian.

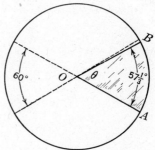

FIG. 8.—A radian is an angle the arc distance of which equals the radius.

A radian is an angle whose arc is equal to the radius.

The length of the circumference of the circle is 2π times the distance AB. Hence 2π radians equal $360°$ and

One radian = $360°/2\pi$ = $57.3°$ (approximately).

Thus an angular velocity of 1 rev./sec. equals 2π radians/sec.

84. Torques and Angular Accelerations. In linear motion, as we have seen, the force to cause an acceleration is given by

Force = Mass × Acceleration

Similarly, in rotary motion, the torque to cause an angular acceleration is given by

Torque = Rotational inertia × Angular acceleration

Example. A grindstone weighs 64 lb. Its radius is 2.0 ft. (a) What is its rotational inertia? (b) What angular acceleration will be imparted to it if a force of 8.0 lb. is exerted on a rope wound around its rim? (Neglect friction.)

$$I = \tfrac{1}{2} \times W/g \times R^2 = \tfrac{1}{2}\ 64\ \text{lb./32 ft./sec.}^2 \times (2\ \text{ft.})^2 = 4.0\ \text{lb-ft-sec.}^2$$

$$A = \frac{\text{Torque}}{\text{Rotational inertia}} = 16\ \text{lb-ft./4.0 lb-ft-sec.}^2 = 4.0\ \text{radians/sec.}^2$$

85. The Kinetic Energy of a Rotating Body. Every particle of a rotating flywheel has kinetic energy. The kinetic energy of the entire wheel depends upon its rotational inertia and its angular velocity. It is given by:

$$K.E. = \tfrac{1}{2}I\omega^2$$

Example 1. A flywheel weighs 320 lb. and revolves at a rate of 3.2 rev./sec. Its radius is 2.0 ft. Find (a) its rotational inertia, assuming that all the mass is located in the rim; (b) its angular velocity; and (c) its kinetic energy.

(a) $$I = (W/g)R^2 = \frac{320 \text{ lb.}}{32 \text{ ft./sec.}^2} \times 4.0 \text{ ft.}^2$$
$$= 40 \text{ lb-ft-sec.}^2$$

(b) $$\omega = 3.2 \times 2\pi \text{ rad./sec.}$$
$$= 20 \text{ rad./sec.}$$

(c) $$\text{K.E.} = \tfrac{1}{2}\ 40 \text{ lb-ft-sec.}^2 \times 400 \text{ rad.}^2/\text{sec.}^2$$
$$= 8{,}000 \text{ ft-lb.}$$

Example 2. If this wheel were to slip off its axle, how high a hill could it climb?

$$\text{Available energy} = 8{,}000 \text{ ft-lb.}$$
$$= 320 \text{ lb.} \times d$$
$$d = 25 \text{ ft. (measured vertically)}$$

86. Derivation of the Kinetic Energy Formula. Assume that all the metal of a flywheel is concentrated in a narrow rim of radius R. Let its weight be W, and its angular velocity ω. Let the flywheel make one revolution in a time t so that its angular velocity is

$$\omega = \frac{2\pi}{t} \tag{1}$$

During one revolution, each particle in the rim travels a distance $2\pi R$, and its velocity is therefore

$$v = \frac{2\pi R}{t} \tag{2}$$

From (1) and (2)

$$v = R\omega \tag{3}$$

The kinetic energy of the wheel is

$$\text{K.E.} = \tfrac{1}{2}(W/g)v^2$$
$$= \tfrac{1}{2}(W/g)R^2\omega^2$$
$$= \tfrac{1}{2}I\omega^2$$

87. A Puzzle Regarding Kinetic Energy. A metal block and a cylinder of equal mass "run a race" starting from rest at the top of an inclined plane. The block slides and the cylinder rolls. Neglecting friction, which will win?

The first point to note is that the two have equal potential energies at the top of the hill and they therefore must have equal kinetic energies at the bottom. Secondly, part of the cylinder's energy at the bottom is rotational, and hence part only is translational. Therefore, the cylinder has a smaller final translational velocity than that of the block. It requires more time for the journey, and it loses the race.

88. Resemblances between Linear and Rotational Units. In studying rotary motions, it is helpful to keep in mind the close resemblances between its units and those of linear motion as shown in Table I.

TABLE I

CORRESPONDING UNITS IN LINEAR AND ROTATIONAL MOTION

Linear Motion		Angular Motion	
	Units		Units
Distance d	ft.	Angle θ	rad.
Velocity v	ft./sec.	Angular velocity ω	rad./sec.
Acceleration a	ft./sec.^{2}	Angular acceleration A	rad./sec.^{2}
Mass m	lb./(ft./sec.^{2})	Rotational inertia I	lb-ft-sec.^{2}
Force f	lb.	Torque	lb-ft.
Momentum mv	lb-sec.	Angular momentum $I\omega$	

SUMMARY

A radian is an angle such that the arc distance is equal to the radius; $360° = 2\pi$ radians; 1 radian = $57.3°$.

The laws of rotary motion are analogous to those of linear motion. If no unbalanced external torque acts on a spinning body, its angular velocity and its angular momentum are constant.

The rotational inertia I of a ring of mass $m = W/g$ and radius R, rotating like a flywheel on an axis through its center, is given by $I = mR^2 = (W/g)R^2$; that of a uniform circular disk by $I = \frac{1}{2}mR^2 = \frac{1}{2}(W/g)R^2$; and that of a sphere by $I = 2/5mR^2 = 2/5(W/g)R^2$. Torque = $I \times$ Angular acceleration. Angular momentum = $I\omega$. K.E. = $\frac{1}{2}I\omega^2$.

REVIEW QUESTIONS

1. In rotary motion, what quantities are analogous to velocity, mass, and force?
2. What is a radian?
3. Show how the angular velocity of a body may be changed.
4. State Newton's first and second laws of motion for rotating bodies.
5. State expressions for the moment of inertia of (a) a circular ring of mass $m = W/g$ and radius R, and (b) a uniform circular disk. (Assume that each rotates like a flywheel on an axis through its center.)
6. Explain why the angular velocity of a circus performer increases when he "doubles up" his body in mid-air.
7. An airplane is traveling eastward. Its propeller rotates clockwise as viewed by the pilot. If it turns toward the south, does it tend to "nose dive" or to tilt upward? Why?
8. How can you compute the kinetic energy of a rotating body?
9. Why does a disk rolling down a hill accelerate more slowly than if it were sliding without friction?

PROBLEMS

1. (a) What is the average angular velocity of the second hand of a clock? (b) If the hand is 10.0 cm. long, what is the average speed of the tip?
2. A grindstone weighs 96 lb. and its radius is 1.00 ft. (a) What is its rotational inertia? (b) When it makes 1 rev./sec., what is its angular velocity?

3. A 5-cent piece is 2.0 cm. in diameter. It rolls along a level table making 6.0 rev./sec. Find (a) its angular velocity and (b) its linear velocity.

4. A rope wound on the rim of the grindstone described in Problem 2 exerts a pull of 2.0 lb. Find (a) the torque, (b) the angular acceleration, and (c) the angle of rotation during the first second after starting.

5. An automobile wheel weighs 64 lb. Assuming that it is equivalent to a ring of equal weight, 1.00 ft. in radius, find its rotational inertia.

6. A boy's hoop weighs 0.64 lb., and its radius is 1.00 ft. It rolls along a pavement, making 1.00 rev./sec. Find (a) its rotational inertia, (b) its angular velocity, and (c) its rotational kinetic energy.

7′. The flywheel and other moving parts of an automobile engine have rotational inertia equal to that of a ring weighing 32 lb. and having a radius of 0.50 ft. (a) What is the rotational inertia of the system? (b) What is its kinetic energy when it makes 1,800 rev./min.? (c) What average horsepower is required to bring it to this speed in 5.0 sec.?

8. A lawn roller weighs 96 lb., and its radius is 1.20 ft. (a) Assuming that all its substance is located in the rim, what is its rotational inertia? When it rotates once per second, what are (b) its angular momentum and (c) its rotational kinetic energy?

9″. Two boys each weighing 62 lb. sit on opposite ends of a plank at points 4.0 ft. from the axis of rotation. A third boy pushes against the plank, exerting a horizontal force of 10 lb. at a point 2.0 ft. from the axis. (a) Find the rotational inertia of the system, neglecting the weight of the plank. (b) What is the angular acceleration?

REFERENCES

H. Crabtree, "Spinning Tops and Gyroscopic Motion."
J. Perry, "Spinning Tops."

$$F = MA \qquad I = \frac{1}{2} M r^2 \ (\text{for a cyl.})$$

$$I_r = M r^2 =$$

$$T = F \times r$$

$$T = MA \times r$$

$$\frac{a}{r} = \alpha$$

$$\therefore a = \alpha r$$

$$T = M \alpha r \times r$$

$$T = M r^2 \alpha$$

$$T = I \alpha$$

CHAPTER XI

GRAVITATION

I know not what the world may think, but to myself it seems that I have been but a child playing on the seashore; now finding some pebbles rather more polished, and now some shell rather more variegated than another, while the immense ocean of truth extended itself, unexplored, before me.—SIR ISAAC NEWTON (when eighty years old).

It is hard to comprehend the difficulties of the ancient peoples in devising ways and means to support the planets and the stars. The Hebrews and Babylonians thought of the earth as an enormous, square raft floating on a great lake. Above this earth was a great arched dome or firmament supported by massive pillars. On this dome the stars were fixed like lanterns, and in it were windows through which the rain might fall.

In the primitive theory just described, no attempt was made to explain the motions of the planets and the stars. Later the Greeks developed a mythology in which the sun was pictured as the god Phoebus driving a flaming chariot across the sky. During the night, he was supposed to make a circuitous journey around the edge of the flat earth, returning to the starting point at daybreak. Gradually the view developed that the earth was a globe and that the sun was mounted on the surface of a gigantic, crystal sphere which revolved around the earth once every 24 hours. Other concentric spheres, revolving with different periods, were provided to carry the moon, the planets, and the "fixed" stars. The last were thought of as mounted on the outermost sphere of all (Fig. 1).

This theory was satisfying because it made the earth the center of creation, and, as everyone knew, man was the lord of the earth. Then, too, the picture of invisible whirling spheres appealed to poetic fancy. People believed that they emitted a heavenly music that could be heard by persons of fine feeling. Little wonder that many believed in the crystal spheres long after they were outmoded among scientists. The poet Milton frequently refers to them in "Paradise Lost."

The theory that the stars revolved around the earth was highly developed by the Greek scholar Ptolemy who lived at Alexandria, Egypt, in the third century A.D. In order to explain irregularities in the motions of the planets, he assumed that some of them traveled in oval rather than circular paths. Among the more difficult problems was that of explaining the reversed motions. For example, Jupiter,

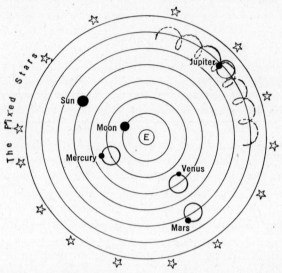

FIG. 1.—Ptolemy thought that the earth was the center of the solar system.

the largest planet of all, makes a complete journey and returns to its initial position with reference to the "fixed" stars in about 12 years. However, it does not progress uniformly from east to west, but peri-

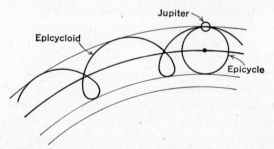

FIG. 2.—The planet Jupiter, mounted on a smaller sphere, was supposed to move on a spiral path.

odically reverses and travels eastward for a few months. To explain this motion, Ptolemy assumed that Jupiter and the other planets traveled on "epicyclic" paths (Fig. 2). This path is like that traced out by the tire valve of a car wheel as the car travels along a highway.

By assuming oval orbits and epicycles, Ptolemy explained the motions of the heavenly bodies so cleverly that his theory survived for 13 centuries.

89. Copernicus. A few years after Columbus discovered America, a young Polish monk, Copernicus, began to doubt the value of Ptolemy's theory. He proposed a new one in which the earth was removed from its central position and the sun took its place (Fig. 3). The great advantage claimed for the theory was that it provided a simpler explanation of the motions of the heavenly bodies. Copernicus urged that the complicated epicycle motion was not real, but was due to the to-and-fro motion of the earth as it traveled around the sun. To understand

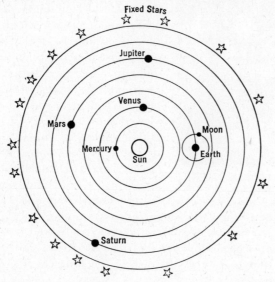

Fig. 3.—Copernicus taught that the sun was the center of the solar system.

how this can be, hold a pencil on the line of sight between your eye and a distant building and wag your head sidewise. Then the pencil will seem to move to-and-fro, oppositely, with reference to the more distant building. In the same manner, as one looks past Jupiter at the more distant fixed stars, and is carried sidewise because of the motion of the earth around the sun, Jupiter seems to move in the opposite direction.

When Copernicus began to advocate his new doctrine, he discovered that the scholars of his day were well satisfied with the good old theory of Ptolemy. It was a comfortable view of the universe, since it made the earth the center of creation, the sun a mere lamp to guide man's footsteps. In contrast to this, young Copernicus would have the earth to be a mere grain of sand, revolving as an insignificant planet around a central sun. The young astronomer had no liking for controversy, and he quietly worked on his new theory for thirty-five years. He buried his ideas in a scholarly book, which was brought to him, newly printed, when he was on his deathbed. Thus did Copernicus avoid trouble and a martyr's crown.

90. Galileo and the Telescope. About ten years after Copernicus' death, a Dutch spectacle maker happened to look through two spectacle lenses which were held at a certain distance apart and found that

FIG. 4.—Galileo's friends view the distant horizon.

distant ships seemed larger. Thus he accidentally invented the telescope and was awarded a small prize for the achievement. When Galileo heard of this invention, he soon constructed a crude instrument of his own, but he did not stop here. With burning zeal he ground the lenses for larger and better instruments, and with these he viewed the landscape. Then, one memorable night, he raised his telescope to the skies and observed the moon. Great was his astonishment and delight when he saw that it was not a mere lantern but that it had mountains on its surface like those of the earth. Then examining the planet Jupiter, he found that it had four moons which revolved about it with different velocities. Later he discovered the rings of Saturn and dark patches or sun spots moving across the disk of the sun, which showed that it rotated on an axis.

When Galileo considered the new evidences, he realized that it would be very difficult to explain them on the basis of Ptolemy's theory since very complicated systems of spheres within spheres would be required. The task would be much simpler if one assumed that the sun was the center of the system according to the Copernican theory. Advocating the new doctrine, he soon ran into trouble. His books were burned; he was forced to recant and to "detest the error and heresy of the movement of the earth." After several years in prison the old man was released, to spend his latter days blind and friendless. His efforts seemed to have been futile, but new generations accepted his teachings.

91. Tycho Brahe, Kepler, and Newton. While Galileo was peering through his telescopes and, later, was arguing in favor of the Copernican theory, a Danish astronomer named Tycho Brahe (*Ty'ko Bra'hey*) was patiently and skillfully making observations of the positions of the planets. These observations were studied by the mathematician Kepler, who found that the planets did not travel on circular paths as they would if mounted on crystal spheres, but that they moved in ellipses. Kepler's discovery was extremely important, for it meant that the crystal spheres must be abandoned. This fact gave rise to a great difficulty, namely, how to support the heavens. The answer to this question was given by Newton, who was born a few months after Galileo died.

When Newton was twenty-four years old and a student at Cambridge University, he was forced to retire to the country because of the "black death," a plague which ravaged England. During this enforced vacation of more than a year, he made three contributions

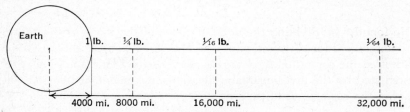

Fig. 5.—The weight of a ball decreases when it is carried farther from the earth's center.

which were very significant. One was a study of the effect of prisms in dispersing a beam of sunlight into rainbow colors; a second, the invention of a kind of mathematics called the calculus; and the third, an explanation of how the attraction of the earth keeps the moon in its orbit. The story is that one day Newton saw an apple fall and, in his own words, he "began to think of gravitation as extending to the orb of the moon." He wondered whether the earth did not attract the moon even as it did the apple, and whether this attraction might not provide the necessary centripetal force to hold the moon in its orbit. If so, it would be easy to explain not merely the motion of the moon around the earth, but also that of the planets around the sun.

In order to test the hypothesis, Newton computed the force with which the earth attracts each pound of the moon's substance, assuming that the attractive forces vary inversely as the square of the distance from the earth's center.

Suppose that a ball having a mass of 1 pound is weighed at the earth's surface using a spring balance (Fig. 5). In this position it is 4,000 miles from the earth's center of gravity. Next, imagine that it is carried 4,000 miles away from the surface, to a position 8,000 miles from the earth's center. By thus doubling the distance of the ball from the center, Newton predicted that the pull of the earth would be diminished to one-fourth of its previous value. That is, even though the mass of the ball was constant, the attraction of the earth would decrease to ¼ lb. At a distance of 16,000 miles from the earth's center, twice as great as before, the attraction should be 1/16 lb. Now the distance to the moon is about 60 times the earth's radius; hence if the inverse square law is true, each pound-mass of the moon's substance should be attracted by the earth with a force of 1/3,600 lb.

Newton next computed the amount of centripetal force required to keep each pound-mass of the moon's substance moving in its (nearly) circular path, using the equation:

$$F = \frac{W}{g}\frac{v^2}{R} = \frac{Mv^2}{R} \tag{j}$$

He found v by dividing the circumference of the moon's orbit by the time required for a "round trip" (27.5 days). When the correct values are used the computed force agrees closely with 1/3,600 lb., the value predicted by the inverse square law. This agreement justifies our belief in the correctness of the inverse square law.

Unfortunately, in Newton's day the accepted value of the earth's radius was in error by several per cent, and he thought the diameter to be somewhat less than 8,000 miles. The two results did not agree, so the twenty-four-year-old student did not publish his work, but shoved his computations into a drawer in his desk. Twenty years later, a new determination of the earth's radius was made, and when the corrected value was used, excellent agreement was achieved. Thus the mystery of the motion of the planets was solved at last, and Ptolemy's crystal spheres were no longer needed.

Newton's universal law of gravitation, which was tested in this manner, is as follows:

Every particle in the universe attracts every other particle with a force directly proportional to the product of their masses and inversely as the square of the distance between them.

92. The Gravitational Attraction of Small Bodies Can Be Measured. Place two small metal balls, each having a mass of 1 gram, with their centers 1 cm. apart. Then each attracts the other with a force of about sixty-eight trillionths of a gram-weight. The measurement of the gravitational attractions of such small bodies is very difficult. The method of Jolly is one of the simplest and the easiest to understand. A spherical vessel containing 5 kg. of mercury was attached to one pan of a sensitive balance, and it was counterpoised by suitable bodies in the other pan (Fig. 6). Next a lead sphere of mass 5,775 kg. (more than 5 tons) was placed below the flask of mercury, their centers being 56.86 cm. apart. The attraction of the lead for the mercury pulled the pan down slightly, and a small mass (0.589 mg.) placed in the other pan was found to be sufficient to raise the mercury to its initial position.

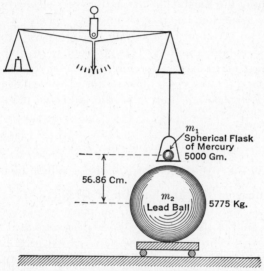

m_1
Spherical Flask
of Mercury
5000 Gm.

56.86 Cm.

m_2
Lead Ball   5775 Kg.

FIG. 6.—The Jolly apparatus, for measuring the attraction between a lead sphere and a flask of mercury.

The equation for the attraction of two balls of masses m_1 and m_2 respectively, when their centers are a distance d apart, in accord with Newton's law of gravitation, is

$$F = Gm_1m_2/d^2 \qquad (1)$$

G being the **gravitational constant**, numerically equal to the attraction between unit masses which are unit distance apart. Its value is 6.664×10^{-8} dyne-cm.^{2}/gram^2. (The forces are given in dynes, hence the masses are in grams.)

From the Jolly experiment:

$$
\begin{aligned}
F &= 0.000589 \text{ gram} \times 980 \text{ cm./sec.}^2 \\
&= 0.577 \text{ dyne} \\
m_1 &= 5,000 \text{ grams} \\
m_2 &= 5,775,000 \text{ grams} \\
d &= 56.86 \text{ cm.}
\end{aligned}
$$

whence

$$G = 6.47 \times 10^{-8} \text{ dyne-cm.}^2/\text{gram}^2$$

More accurate determinations by other methods yield the value accepted today, namely:

$$G = 6.664 \times 10^{-8} \text{ dyne-cm.}^2/\text{gram}^2$$

93. Weighing the Earth. The attraction of two spheres of unit mass, 1 cm. apart, being known, that of any two spheres at a known distance apart can be found by equation (1). Moreover, the mass of the earth itself can be computed. The problem is to find how massive the earth must be to exert a force of 1 gwt. or 980 dynes on a body of 1 gram-mass at its surface. The radius of the earth is about 4,000 miles, or 637,000,000 cm. Let X be the unknown mass of the earth. Then

$$980 \text{ dynes} = 6.664 \times 10^{-8} \text{ dyne-cm.}^2/\text{gram}^2 \times \frac{1.00 \text{ gram} \times X}{(6.37 \times 10^8 \text{ cm.})^2}$$

$$X = 59.7 \times 10^{26} \text{ grams} = 5,970 \text{ billion billion metric tons}$$

94. Variations of the Acceleration of Gravity. The acceleration of gravity varies about ½ per cent from place to place on the earth's surface. The pull of the earth on a body decreases as it moves farther from the earth's center. Hence the acceleration of gravity is smaller at Denver, Colorado (elevation 5,460 feet), than at New York City (Table I).

TABLE I

VALUES OF THE ACCELERATION OF GRAVITY

Place	Elevation	ft./sec.²	cm./sec.²
North Pole	0	32.26	983.2
Equator	0	32.09	978.0
Chicago	600 ft.	32.16	980.2
Denver, Colo.	5,460 ft.	32.12	979.6
New Orleans	0	32.13	979.3
New York City	0	32.16	980.2
Pittsburgh	535 ft.	32.16	980.1
San Francisco	350 ft.	32.15	979.9

The acceleration of gravity at sea level is smaller at the equator than at the poles for two reasons: first, the distance to the earth's center is about 12½ miles greater than at the poles, for the earth is not a perfect sphere; second, a body at the equator travels in a great circle and it is always "falling" toward the earth's center. Being accelerated downward, it seems to weigh less than if it were at rest. The apparent decrease in weight is exactly like that experienced by a passenger when an elevator is accelerated downward. The amount of the decrease depends upon the velocity of the body. If the earth rotated 18 times as fast as it does, the apparent weight of bodies at the equator would be zero.

95. Oil Prospecting by Gravity Measurements. Scientific research has brought great improvements in methods of locating oil. Fifty years ago wells were dug in hit-or-miss fashion, and few were more than 500 ft. deep. Then geologists found that the oil was imprisoned under vaulted domes of rock, and they began to locate these domes by the outcroppings visible at the earth's surface. Guided by expert advice, the oil companies could afford to drill wells 1,000 ft. deep. Today, these domes are located at depths of a mile or more by several physical methods, among them by the increase in the weight of a body caused by the attraction of the dense rock.

The gravimeter is essentially a very delicate spring balance with a small body attached to it. It is so sensitive that one can detect a change in the force acting on the small body of 1 part in 10,000,000. (One of a man's hairs weighs about 1/1,000,000 of his total weight!) In locating a rock formation, this gravimeter, enclosed in an evacuated box, kept at a constant temperature, is moved to various positions in the region surveyed, and the changes of the weight of the small body attached to the spring are noted. The dome of rock, deep underground, acts like the lead ball used to determine the gravitational constant. That is, it causes a slight increase in the weight of the body which is observed in the region near the dome. Then complicated mathematical methods are employed to determine the shape of the formation and its depth below the surface. Afterward a test well is drilled, which may cost several hundred thousand dollars.

96. Doing the High Jump on the Moon, Sun, and Planets. The variations of gravity at different places on the earth's surface are so small that they are neglected in ordinary affairs; but if one could go to the moon, his weight would be about one-sixth that on the earth. A bantam athlete weighing 100 lb. here would weigh only 15 lb. on the moon, and he could do a high jump of 36 ft. On the sun he would weigh more than a ton; on the planet Jupiter, a paltry 260 lb. If our bantam athlete should visit the smallest asteroid (or small planet) yet discovered, he would be able to jump over a skyscraper with the greatest of ease!

97. The Tides. Everyone who lives by the seashore is familiar with tides which rise every 12½ hours, and knows that the rise of the water is caused chiefly by the attraction of the moon. Few people can explain why there are two tides. It is easy to understand why the water should pile up on the side of the earth which is nearer to the moon, but why should there also be an accumulation on the opposite side? An analogy will be helpful. Tie two water-soaked sponges together by a long cord and toss them into the air in such a manner that they revolve about their common center of gravity. Then the water tends to accumulate at the outer edge of each sponge and to fly off tangentially (Fig. 7A). Now let us think of the earth and the moon, the latter of which revolves, not about the center of the earth, as many suppose, but around their common center of gravity (Fig. 7B). If there were any water on the moon, it would tend to accumulate at the outer edge. Water on the earth tends to heap up at B for the same reason. The explanation of the two tides on the earth is quite different. Water gathers at A because of the moon's attraction, and at B because of the centrifugal effect.

FIG. 7.—A. Water flies off tangentially from the two sponges. B. The tide at A is caused by the moon's attraction. That at B is due to a centrifugal effect.

From this explanation it would seem that the tides should be highest at a given location when the moon is directly overhead (or somewhat more than 12 hours later). In fact, high tide always occurs when the moon is near the horizon. The reason is that the friction of the rotating earth tends to hold the tides back so that they always occur several hours later than we should expect.

98. Are the Days Becoming Longer? Push a block of wood against the rim of the spinning grindstone, and the friction slows down the stone and eventually stops it. In a similar manner, the tides cause friction against the surface of the earth and tend to decelerate its motion. Hence probably the days are growing longer. The effect is very small, only a few hundredths of a second per century, but it is to be expected that the earth will slow down till finally one side will always face the moon. The moon, having a smaller rotational inertia and smaller initial kinetic energy than the earth, has long since lost most of its rotational motion and we always see the same face.

The moon has no oceans or lakes on its surface, so the question arises, how can there be tidal action? The reason is that the moon is not rigid but its surface bulges on the side nearer to the earth and on the opposite side. Tides also occur inside the earth. The Washington Monument, for example, rises and falls with this tide more than 1 ft.

99. Tides Due to the Sun. The sun, like the moon, exerts gravitational attractions on the earth. The tides which it produces are less pronounced than those caused by the moon. The resultant tides are abnormally high when the sun and moon both "pull together" along the same straight line, and they are unusually low when the two pull at right angles to each other.

SUMMARY

According to Ptolemy's theory, the earth was a sphere around which the sun, the moon, the "fixed" stars, and the planets revolved. To explain observed irregularities of motion, each planet was supposed to move on an "epicycle" path.

Copernicus urged that the sun, rather than the earth, was the center of the solar system, because this assumption gave a simpler and better explanation of the apparent motions of the planets.

Galileo's observations with the telescope brought new facts which could not be explained by Ptolemy's theory, but could be by that of Copernicus.

Kepler showed that the planets move around the sun in elliptical paths.

Newton demonstrated that, if gravitational attraction varies inversely with the square of the distance between two bodies, the earth's attraction for the moon provides the centripetal force necessary to hold the moon in its orbit.

The attraction F for each other of two small spheres of masses m_1 and m_2, their centers being at a distance d apart, is given by

$$F = \frac{Gm_1m_2}{d^2}$$

The mass of the earth may be found by computing the mass of a sphere which will attract a 1-gram body with a force of 980 dynes, the distance between the centers of the two bodies being equal to the radius of the earth.

The tides are caused principally by the attraction of the moon. The friction of the tides tends to slow down the earth's rotation and to lengthen the day.

REVIEW QUESTIONS

1. Discuss the beliefs of the Hebrews and Babylonians regarding the structure of the heavens.

2. Describe Ptolemy's teaching, and show in what respects it was an improvement over that which preceded it.

3. Contrast the views of Copernicus with those of Ptolemy. Why were the new doctrines unpopular?

4. Describe the contributions of Tycho Brahe and of Kepler, showing how they tended to discredit the theory of Ptolemy.

5. How did Newton prove the universal law of gravitation?

6. Why can the moon move with uniform average speed though it is attracted by the earth?

7. Describe Jolly's method for measuring the gravitational attractions of relatively small bodies.

8. How can the earth be "weighed"?

9. (a) How can you determine the centripetal force exerted by the sun on the earth? (b) From this value, how can you determine the mass of the sun?

10. How much would a gram of matter weigh at the center of the earth?

11. Explain why there are two tides every 24.5 hours instead of but one.

12. Distinguish carefully between mass and weight. How can you compare the masses of two bodies without weighing them?

PROBLEMS

1. How much would a 150-lb. man weigh if he could rise to an elevation 4,000 miles above the earth's surface?

2″. If the mass of the moon is 1/80 that of the earth, and its radius is ¼ as great, (a) how much would a 150-lb. man weigh on the moon; (b) how high could this man jump if he could jump 6 ft. on the earth's surface?

3′. How much would a 160-lb. man weigh at an elevation of (a) 4,000 miles, and (b) 12,000 miles above the earth's surface?

4. Two lead spheres, each having a mass of 1 megagram (10^6 grams), are located so that their centers are 100 cm. apart. (a) Find the force of attraction. (b) How far would one of the balls travel from rest in 1,000 sec. if subject to this force?

CHAPTER XII

ATOMS AND MOLECULES

Let us remember, please, that the search for the constitution of the world is one of the greatest and noblest problems presented by nature.—GALILEO.

Thus far we have dealt with the motions and energies of bodies large enough to be seen—with baseballs, cannon balls, and automobiles. We have considered some of the fundamental laws of physics, such as the conservation of energy and of momentum. From now on, we shall move into the realm of the invisible, dealing with particles too small to be glimpsed even through the most powerful microscope.

The question as to whether or not matter is built up of ultimate particles called atoms has troubled thinkers since the days when Grecian civilization reached its highest peak. Democritus (400 B.C.) wrote as follows:

"Atoms are infinite in number and infinitely varied in form. They strike together and their lateral motions and whirlings are the beginnings of worlds.

"The varieties of all things depend upon the varieties of their atoms in number, size, and aggregation."

In some ways, these views are in striking accord with our present beliefs. Many scholars have urged that there is nothing new under the sun, and that modern science merely rediscovers old truth. However, it should be noticed that the Greeks loved to theorize but did not like to experiment. They had dozens of rival theories. Today we forget the others and remember Democritus' ideas because they happen to correspond with ours. They had little or no experimental justification and were of no practical utility.

For twenty-three hundred years after Democritus, the view that matter is composed of particles remained a mere speculative hypothesis, advocated by some and opposed by others. Then in the early part of the nineteenth century came the birthday of modern chemistry. Dalton, Avogadro, and others secured experimental evidence strongly favoring the atomic theory. This evidence accumulated throughout the century, and today no scientist of repute doubts that atoms are real. This faith is justified because the atomic theory enables us to interrelate multitudes of experimental facts that can be explained in no other way. It affords a beautiful unity which delights the imagination. Small wonder, then, that research workers no longer try to disprove the existence of atoms.

100. What Is an Atom? The word *atom* is derived from a Greek expression meaning *uncut*. The term is well chosen, for atoms are very stable bodies which cannot be broken up by the hottest furnace, nor by any means ordinarily used by chemists.

An atom is a particle indivisible in chemical changes.

Cut a silver dime into two equal halves and again divide one of these pieces, and so on. Imagine that you could continue the sectioning process eighty times. Then you would have a silver atom which can be disrupted only by very violent means. Similar experiments with other substances would lead to the conclusion that there are only 92 different species of atoms. The smallest of these is hydrogen, and atomic weights are expressed in terms of hydrogen as unit (or, more exactly, as 1.0078). Typical values are as follows: hydrogen, 1.0078; helium, 4.001; oxygen, 16.000; uranium (the most massive), 238.

The 92 different kinds of atoms combine into hundreds of thousands of different kinds of **molecules**. Divide a grain of sodium chloride (table salt) into two equal parts and repeat the dividing process just as you did with the dime, and eventually you would have the smallest identifiable particle of salt, that is, the sodium chloride molecule. If this is broken up, chlorine and sodium result, which have properties quite different from those of sodium chloride.

A molecule is the smallest particle of a substance.

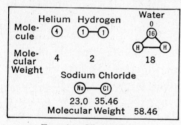

FIG. 1.—Molecules.

The molecules of some substances, such as helium, consist of single atoms; others, such as sodium chloride, have two atoms; and still others are built up of three, four, and even thousands of atoms (Fig. 1).

A substance such as helium or hydrogen, whose atoms are all the same kind, is called an **element**. One whose molecules are composed of different kinds of atoms is a **compound**.

101. The Sizes of Atoms and Molecules. Although atoms and molecules are so small that we can never hope to see one even through the most powerful microscope, yet their diameters may be estimated by indirect methods. The values are so minute as to strain the imagination. The distance between the centers of the neighboring molecules in a glass of water is about one hundred-millionth of a centimeter. To aid in comprehending this magnitude, suppose that the glass of water were magnified until it became as large as the moon. Then one of its molecules would be about as big as a baseball. Again, suppose that a glassful of water were emptied into the Atlantic and that sufficient time were allowed so that this water became equally dispersed through all the oceans. If a second glassful of water were dipped up, how many of the selfsame molecules would be recovered? The answer is about two thousand. The student can show that probably there are several thousand of the identical water molecules in his body which were once in the body of an Egyptian Pharaoh or of Julius Caesar.

102. The Three States of Matter. Matter can exist in three different states: the solid, the liquid, and the gaseous. Gases expand indefinitely and have neither fixed volume nor shape. Turn the valve of a gas stove, and soon the odor of the gas is detected in all parts of a closed room. Open a door into a hall, and after a short period the odor will be noticed there also. This convection and diffusion lead to the belief that the molecules of a gas are not tightly joined together, but, like a swarm of flies, they are relatively free to travel, darting about on zigzag paths, making impacts with one another and with the walls of the enclosure. These motions of the molecules will presently be discussed more fully.

FIG. 2.—Is paraffin solid or liquid?

Liquids have definite volumes but indefinite shapes. Ten gallons of gasoline occupy the same volume whether they be contained in a cylindrical tank or a rectangular one. Since a liquid conforms itself to the shape of the container, it is not rigid.

In solids the molecules are tightly locked together so that a solid body has a definite size and shape. A rubber ball can be distorted by squeezing; but when the distorting forces are removed, it springs back to its original configuration.

Some substances have the properties of both solids and liquids. A lump of pitch is brittle and rigid so that it breaks into small pieces when it is struck by a hammer; yet, if it is placed in a cup and is left there for several weeks, it gradually conforms itself to the shape of the container like a liquid. A paraffin candle, mounted in a candlestick, gradually bends over, and has to be replaced after a few weeks or months (Fig. 2). A piece of glass tubing supported horizontally at its ends gradually sags near the middle. Substances that have no definite, permanent shape are not true solids, and are regarded as extremely viscous liquids. They are said to be "amorphous" (structureless) because their molecules are not arranged in definite patterns.

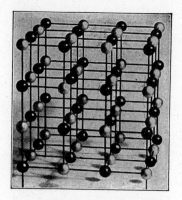

FIG. 3.—The crystalline effect of common salt.

103. Crystal Structure. True solids are said to be **crystalline**, and most of their molecules are regularly arranged like bricks built into a wall. Ordinary table salt is a familiar example. When a specimen is examined with a magnifying glass, the individual grains are seen to be cubical. Sometimes, in salt mines, cubical crystals are found which are several inches on each side. In each salt crystal, whether large or small, the atoms are arranged in regular order at the corners of tiny cubes as shown in Fig. 3. The chlorine atoms are represented by black spheres and the sodium atoms by white ones. The atoms in a piece of mica are arranged in parallel layers so that it can be split into thin sheets.

104. Why is Diamond Harder Than Graphite? Diamond is pure carbon, and it is one of the hardest substances known. Graphite, also pure carbon, is a greasy material so soft that it can be smeared over a surface like paint. The carbon atoms in graphite are arranged in parallel planes which are a considerable distance apart. The attractive forces between adjacent planes are relatively small, like those between the sheets of paper in a book. The layers slip readily, hence the "greasiness" of graphite. The atoms in a

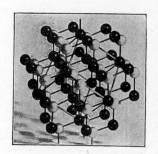

FIG. 4.—The structure of diamond.

diamond are arranged in pyramid fashion. They are closer together than in graphite, and they interlock so that the substance is very hard (Fig. 4).

Rock Salt   Mica   Diamond   Quartz

FIG. 5.—Crystals.

Natural diamonds were made millions of years ago in nature's laboratory. It is supposed that carbon at very high temperatures was subjected to tremendous pressures which compressed it, and the atoms remained interlocked when the material was cooled.

105. Controlling the Sizes of Crystals. A mass of melted copper cooled very slowly, without jarring, may form a huge, single crystal, with all the atoms in an orderly array. Cool it suddenly, or jar it while solidifying, and a jumble of microscopic crystals is produced. When a housewife freezes ice cream in a refrigerator and does not stir the liquid, fairly large ice crystals form so that the mixture is gritty. Occasional stirring prevents the formation of large crystals.

A few years ago a traveler in the Arctic noticed that, when fish were frozen very rapidly in weather below zero, their flavor was better than when they were frozen more slowly, and he introduced the quick-freezing method to the refrigeration industry. The reason that quick freezing is preferable is that large ice crystals do not form, hence the cell walls of the tissue are not ruptured, and the flavor is unchanged.

The mechanical properties of large single crystals are different from those of disorderly mixtures. Thus a copper rod as thick as a lead pencil, when in the "single crystal" state, can be bent with the fingers of one hand. This bending causes the adjacent crystal layers to slip past one another and it disorganizes the system so that a hammer and anvil are needed to straighten the rod again, for it is as rigid as ordinary copper.

106. The Tempering of Steel. The properties of alloys or mixtures of metals and the like are often very different from those of the components. One of the most familiar examples is steel, which is formed by the addition of a little carbon to molten iron. The two constituents combine, producing a compound which solidifies into small crystals which, scattered through the iron, make it harder. The hardness of the steel can be varied by changing the rate at which it is cooled. If a red-hot bar of the metal is allowed to cool slowly, the carbon dissolves and is dispersed evenly through the metal, having a slight hardening effect. When the bar is chilled very quickly, by plunging it into cold water, large crystals of the compound are formed, which give a very hard metal.

SUMMARY

The molecules of a substance are particles that cannot be divided without changing the substance.

Molecules are composed of atoms which cannot be divided by ordinary chemical methods.

Gases have neither definite shapes nor volumes; liquids have definite volumes but not definite shapes, and solids have both definite shapes and volumes.

In amorphous substances the molecules are arranged at random, but in crystalline substances they are arranged in patterns which are repeated throughout each single crystal.

REVIEW QUESTIONS

1. In what ways did the atomic theories of the Greeks differ from those in vogue today?

2. Since no one has ever seen an atom, can you justify our belief that they exist?

3. Distinguish between "atom" and "molecule," and illustrate the difference.

4. Distinguish between solids, liquids, and gases.

5. Is glass a solid or a liquid? Explain.

6. What is a single crystal?

7. Explain why the diamond is harder than graphite.

8. How can the sizes of the single crystals in a solid be controlled?

9. Why is steel that is chilled rapidly harder than if it were cooled slowly?

REFERENCES

LOEB and ADAMS, "Development of Physical Thought."
EDDINGTON, "The Nature of the Physical World."

CHAPTER XIII

MOLECULAR FORCES IN LIQUIDS

Adhesion and Cohesion. Dip a moderately clean glass rod into a vessel of water and then remove it. Some of the water will cling to the glass in small drops. This experiment shows that the attractive forces between the water molecules and those of the glass are greater than those between adjacent water molecules. If the glass rod is dipped into a vessel of clean mercury and then is removed, none of the liquid clings to the glass. Here the interattraction of the mercury molecules for one another, that is, their **cohesion**, is greater than the **adhesion** of the mercury molecules to the glass.

The attractive force between molecules of the same kind is called cohesion, and that between unlike molecules is called adhesion.

107. Surface Films on Liquids. A little mercury spilled on a table top will form numerous globules of different sizes (Fig. 1). The smaller droplets are nearly spherical, and the larger ones are flattened. The cause of this flattening is the pull of gravity on the mercury. If

FIG. 1.—Mercury globules are held together by cohesion.

gravity did not act, each droplet would be a perfect sphere. This tendency to form spherical droplets manifests itself in all liquids. Small gunshot are made by pouring molten lead through a sieve at the top of a tower. As the liquid falls through the air, it breaks up into spherical drops which solidify before they strike a pool of water at the bottom of the tower.

Touch the surface of a mercury globule with a needle. A dimple is formed at the point of contact which disappears when the needle is removed. The drop behaves like an inflated rubber balloon, as though it were enveloped in an elastic membrane or surface film. Elastic films like this appear at the surfaces of all liquids. A needle or safety razor blade can float on a water surface, being supported

FIG. 2.—A razor blade, upheld by a surface film.

by the film (Fig. 2). The needle or blade quickly sinks to the bottom when the film is ruptured. Some insects can walk freely on the sur-

111

faces of water pools, a slight depression or dimple being made where each foot pushes against the water surface.

108. Soap Films. A bit of soap dissolved in water will cause frothing bubbles to appear at the surface. Each soap molecule is known to be a long chainlike structure with three hydrogen atoms at one end and

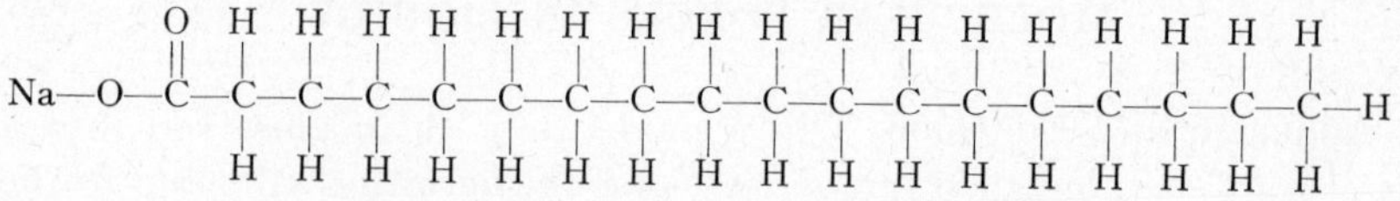

$$\underset{\text{H}\;\;\text{H}\;\;\text{H}\;\;\text{H}\;\;\text{H}\;\;\text{H}\;\;\text{H}\;\;\text{H}\;\;\text{H}\;\;\text{H}\;\;\text{H}\;\;\text{H}\;\;\text{H}\;\;\text{H}\;\;\text{H}}{\overset{\text{O}\;\;\text{H}\;\;\text{H}\;\;\text{H}\;\;\text{H}\;\;\text{H}\;\;\text{H}\;\;\text{H}\;\;\text{H}\;\;\text{H}\;\;\text{H}\;\;\text{H}\;\;\text{H}\;\;\text{H}\;\;\text{H}\;\;\text{H}}{\text{Na—O—C—C—C—C—C—C—C—C—C—C—C—C—C—C—C—C—H}}}$$

Fig. 3.—A typical soap molecule—sodium stearate.
Sodium = Na, Oxygen = O, Hydrogen = H

with a sodium atom at the other (Fig. 3). The hydrogen atoms are relatively inert, having little attraction for water. The sodium is much more active. Its atoms root themselves in the water surface, and the long molecules stand out from it like the bristles of a brush.

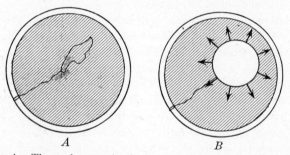

A   *B*

Fig. 4.—The surface tension is the same in all parts of the film.

Soap films can be readily produced by dipping a small hoop or ring into a soap solution and then removing it (Fig. 4A). The film thus formed consists of different parts, the soap solution inside, and the two surface films in which the soap molecules stand out at right angles to the ring. If a loop of thread is placed on this soap film and the film is ruptured inside the loop, the film pulling on the thread draws it out into a uniform circle, and behaves like an elastic sheet of stretched rubber (Fig. 4B). The fact that the loop is uniformly curved shows that the tension of the film is the same in different parts of the surface.

Further evidence that the pull of a film is equal in opposite directions can be secured by floating a toothpick or a match on a water surface. The floating object remains at rest, because the pull of the film on one side is balanced by that on the other. Drop a little alcohol on the water at one side of the toothpick. Then the film on that side is weakened, and it yields so that the toothpick is pulled away.

109. Measuring the Size of an Oil Molecule. When oil is poured onto a water surface, it spreads out into a film. Under certain conditions, the molecules are neatly arranged side by side, covering the surface in a single layer. The length of an individual oil molecule can be found in the following example. Suppose that 1 mm.³ of oil is spread out over the water covering an area of 1,000,000 mm.², forming a layer one molecule thick. Then the thickness of the film—the length of an oil molecule—must have been 1/1,000,000 mm.

110. Oil on Troubled Waters. Sometimes stormy waves at sea are quieted by pouring oil on the water. This effect was noticed in colonial times by Benjamin Franklin, who was on a naval expedition against a French fort in Canada. One evening he observed that, when greasy kitchen refuse was thrown overboard, the waves were quieted to a remarkable degree. Franklin made a study of the phenomenon and he enjoyed mystifying his friends by stilling the waves. He used to carry a cane with a small bottle of oil concealed in it. Once at a garden party at the Prime Minister's estate in England the guests were discussing miracles, and Franklin blandly remarked that he also was able to quiet the waters. His friends were skeptical, and to demonstrate his ability, he walked to the edge of a nearby pool, the surface of which was ruffled by a breeze, made a few mystic passes with his cane, and the waves were quickly stilled! Then he explained to his friends how the magic was accomplished. The cause of this quieting effect is not understood even today. Perhaps the oil film, being more slippery, decreases the friction of the wind and water surface.

111. The Strength of Surface Films. The strength of a sheet of rubber or of cloth can be specified by stating the force that would be required to rupture a piece of the material of given width, and the strength of surface films is described in the same terms. Suppose that a soap film is formed on a wire frame (Fig. 5), the side AD being movable. It should be emphasized that there are *two* surface films attached to the movable wire, one on the side facing the reader and the other on the opposite side.

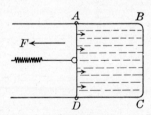

FIG. 5.—Measuring the pull of soap films.

Hence the total width of the two films pulling perpendicularly on the movable wire is $2AD$. The **surface tension** or **force per unit length of film** is given by

$$T = \frac{\text{Force}}{\text{Total length}} = \frac{F}{2AD}$$

Surface tensions are usually expressed in dynes per centimeter. The values for certain liquids are shown in Table I. Notice that the surface tension of water decreases with rising temperature. This is true, also, of all other liquids.

TABLE I

VALUES OF SURFACE TENSIONS

	dynes/cm.	gwt./cm.
Water at 15°C. or 59°F..........	73.5	0.0750
Water at 100°C. or 212°F..........	61.5	0.0628
Methyl alcohol at 15°C............	24.7	0.0252
Mercury at 15°C.................	513.	0.525
Platinum at 2,000°C..............	1,690.	1.73

112. Capillarity. We are familiar with the tendency of water and other liquids to rise in minute pores and tiny openings. Examples of

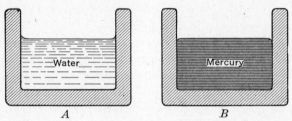

FIG. 6.

this phenomenon are the rise of oil in a lamp wick, the absorption of ink by blotting paper, and the rise of sap in the pores of a tree. This behavior is called capillarity, from the Latin word *capillus*, a hair. It is explained by the relative values of cohesive and adhesive forces.

Pour some water into a clean tumbler. The adhesive forces tend to

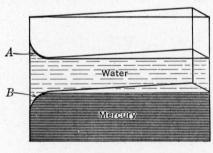

FIG. 7.

pull the water over closer to the glass walls, but cohesion opposes the motion. The adhesion of water to glass is greater than its cohesion, hence the water heaps up beside the glass and some of the molecules travel far up the walls, forming a thin film (Fig. 6A). If mercury is poured into a glass tumbler, the behavior is quite different. The cohesion of mercury molecules is greater than their adhesion to glass, and the mercury tends to draw itself together into a giant globule. Hence it is pulled away from the glass at the upper edge of the liquid (Fig. 6B).

When water and mercury are poured into a wedge-shaped glass vessel (Fig. 7), the water near the narrow corner of the wedge is drawn over toward the glass and rises far above the level surface of the liquid. Water molecules near the corner are within the range of attraction of both glass walls and thus are subject to greater forces than if only one wall were attracting them. The mercury draws away from the narrow corner and, in consequence, the boundary there is lower than in other parts.

Dip a glass tube with a capillary bore into a vessel of water and the liquid will rise in the bore because the adhesion of water to glass is

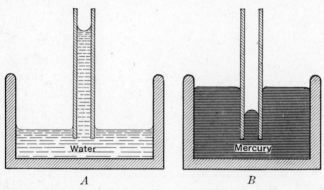

A   *B*

FIG. 8.—(A) The adhesion of the glass draws the water up inside the tube. (B) The cohesion of the mercury draws the mercury down in the tube, away from the glass.

greater than the cohesion of the water (Fig. 8*A*). Dip the tube into mercury, and the downpull of the mercury on the molecules at the surface is so great that the film descends below the level of the surface outside (Fig. 8*B*).

113. Water Rises Higher in Narrow Capillary Tubes Than in Wide Ones. There are numerous examples to show that water and other liquids rise higher in narrow tubes than in wide ones. When the surface of a plowed but uncultivated field is exposed to the sun's radiations, water is brought to the surface through fine, long capillaries, making rapid evaporation possible. However, the farmer who understands what is going on cultivates a plowed field frequently if there is danger from a drought. He substitutes for the long fine capillaries, many short capillaries and loose open spaces, with the result that moisture below the surface is conserved. Concrete pavements are laid on a foundation of cinders in which the openings are very large and water does not rise in them by capillary action. If the pavements were laid on the ground, capillary action would tend to form soft mud, incapable of supporting the weight.

When a board is placed in water, the liquid penetrates the microscopic pores and swells the wood. If the board has been bent, it will tend to straighten out as a garden hose does when water is admitted to it at high pressure. These facts explain the following example of "physical magic."

Break five toothpicks at their midpoints and place them on a metal or crockery plate. Sprinkle a few drops of water on the broken parts of the sticks. As the water enters the capillary pores, the toothpicks will partially straighten so as to form a five-pointed star.

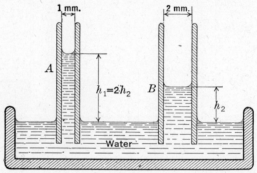

FIG. 9.—The water column in B weighs twice as much as that in A.

114. Why Does Water Rise Higher in the Narrower Tube? Consider the two capillary tubes A and B, the radius of one being twice that of the other (Fig. 9). In each tube a column of water of height h is upheld by a surface film which forms the upper edge of the column. This film is tubular and lies flat against the glass wall. Further, the tubular film in B is twice as large in circumference as that in A, hence it will support twice as heavy a column of water. Why, then, does the water rise higher in the narrow tube? To understand the reason, notice that the cross-sectional area of B is 4 times that of A; therefore the column, though twice as heavy, will be only one-half as high.

The upward force on a column of water of radius R is $2\pi RT$, T being the surface tension (Fig. 10). The volume of the water thus supported is $\pi R^2 h$. Its weight is $\pi R^2 hd$, where d is the weight-density or weight per unit volume. Hence

$$2\pi RT = \pi R^2 hd$$

and

$$h = \frac{2T}{Rd}$$

(When liquid surfaces are depressed in tubes, for instance, mercury in glass, the pull of the film no longer is parallel to the wall of the tube. Therefore, T is replaced by its downward component, parallel to the wall.)

SUMMARY

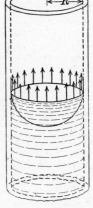

Cohesion is the attraction of molecules of the same kind for one another, and adhesion is that of molecules of different kinds. Cohesive forces tend to draw bodies of liquid into spherical drops. These attractive forces are manifest at the surfaces only of the liquids, which behave as though they were surrounded by elastic films.

The surface tensions of liquids are often expressed in dynes per centimeter.

Capillarity is defined as the tendency of a liquid to rise in capillary tubes or, in certain liquids, to be depressed. It is explained by the difference between the cohesive forces of the liquid and the adhesive forces exerted by the material of which the capillary tubes are made.

FIG. 10.—The total up-pull of the film is $2\pi RT$.

The formula for the rise of a liquid of surface tension T in a tube of radius R is $h = 2T/Rd$, d being the weight per unit volume of the liquid.

REVIEW QUESTIONS

1. Distinguish between adhesion and cohesion. Explain why water adheres to a paint brush but mercury does not.

2. Mercury spilled on the clean surface of a glass plate gathers into droplets, but water does not. If the surface is greasy, however, the water also forms droplets. Explain.

3. Two toothpicks, floating on a water surface, are parallel to each other and a small distance apart. A hot needle is touched at the water surface between them, and the two fly apart. Explain.

4. How can you show that a soap film is equally strong at different parts of its surface?

5. How can you measure the surface tension of a liquid? In what units is it usually expressed?

6. Explain the cause of capillarity. Why does a liquid rise higher in a narrow capillary tube than in a wide one?

7. State several examples of capillarity in addition to those given in the text.

8. In dry farming, why should the soil be cultivated frequently?

9. (a) If a glass rod is coated with paraffin or with oil, water will not cling to it. Explain. (b) All the fat and grease is removed from absorbent cotton and it will soak up much more water than untreated cotton. Why?

10. Why does the end of a glass rod become rounded when it is heated in a Bunsen flame?

11. A glass plate lifted from a water surface comes off wet. When it is lifted from a mercury surface none of the liquid clings to it. Greater force is required in the second case. Explain.

12. Several fog particles merge to form a single particle. Is the total energy of the surfaces increased or diminished in this process?

PROBLEMS

1. What is the force that the surface film exerts on one side of a toothpick 4.0 cm. long floating on water at 59°F.?

2. (a) What is the radius of the bore of a capillary in which water at 59°F. rises to elevations of (1) 1.00 mm., (2) 1.00 cm., (3) 1.00 m.? (b) From these results, do you think that surface tension is sufficient to raise the sap to the top of a forest tree?

3. The distance around the outer edge of a certain plate of artificial teeth is 20.0 cm. If the surface tension of the saliva is 70 dynes/cm., find the force exerted by the film tending to keep the plate in place.

4. A U-shaped platinum wire is dipped into water at 59°F. and then is removed. The width of the U is 2.0 cm. What force is required to break the two surface films formed in the U?

5″. A hemispherical water bubble of radius 1.00 cm. is formed on the surface of a pool. If the surface tension is 75 dynes/cm., find the force tending to prevent the bubble from escaping.

6″. (a) From the data of Problem 5, what is the force per unit area of water surface inside the bubble? (b) Would the pressure inside the hemispherical bubble increase or diminish if the radius became larger?

7′. A soap film, surface tension = 30.0 dynes/cm., is formed on a "hair pin" like that represented on page 113. If the cross piece is 7.0 cm. long, find (a) the force opposing outward motion of the cross piece, (b) the work done in pulling it out 5.0 cm., (c) the resulting increase in area of the film, (d) the increase in energy per square centimeter of new film surface.

8′. A toothpick 4.0 cm. long floats on water, the water film on one side having a surface tension of 50 dynes/cm., while on the other side camphor reduces the surface tension to 40 dynes/cm. Find the resultant force on the toothpick.

CHAPTER XIV

MOLECULAR FORCES IN SOLIDS

The Small Ranges of Molecular Forces. Break a crayon into two pieces, and a considerable force is required to overcome the cohesions of the chalk molecules. Afterward, push the broken pieces together again. They will not adhere because the two irregular surfaces are not sufficiently close for the adjacent molecules to attract one another. Two pieces of ordinary plate glass placed in contact with each other do not adhere. But if surfaces of the plates are unusually flat and free from microscopic hills and valleys, they cling together and are separated with difficulty. The ranges of intermolecular attractions are only a few hundred-thousandths of an inch, and if molecules are much farther apart than this they do not attract one another appreciably.

115. Glues and Cements. Place two plates of ordinary glass in contact, with a little water filling the narrow spaces between them. Then the forces holding the plates together are much greater than if there were no water. The reason for this increase of force is that the water molecules adjacent to each surface adhere strongly to the glass while water molecules adjacent to one another cohere, and so the water acts as a cement holding the plates together. The adhesion helps to hold a plate of artificial teeth to the roof of the mouth. The saliva fills up the small open spaces between the vulcanite and the roof of the mouth, and intermolecular attractions hold the two together. When two boards are glued, the liquid fills up the openings between them, and when it dries the two are gripped and adhere tightly. Similarly, in soldering two copper wires, an alloy of tin and lead is melted, and the liquid, because of molecular attractions, flows into the spaces between the metal surfaces. Later, when it solidifies, it binds them tightly. A blacksmith heats two pieces of iron red hot so that the metal softens. He places them in contact with each other and pounds them with a hammer, forcing the molecules into a closer union so that their attractions bind them securely. Gold foil laid on a plate of glass or of metal is so flexible that it is easily pushed into intimate contact with the plate, and molecular attractions hold the gold in position without the use of a cement. Cavities in teeth are filled by pounding gold foil into the opening, using a small hammer or mallet to strike

119

a thin rod which pushes the gold against the wall of the tooth so that it is gripped by adhesive forces. The block of metal thus formed is stronger than cast gold.

116. Properties of Materials. When engineers design a great viaduct or an improved automobile, or when a farmer makes plans for a new barn, or a dentist fashions a bridge of gold to span the gap where

a tooth has been extracted, they are much concerned with the cohesive properties of the materials. One way to compare these properties is to stretch wires made of the materials and to determine the relative elongations produced by given forces. The term **stretching stress** is defined as the **pulling force per unit of cross-sectional area.**

For example, a wire 0.1 in.^{2} in cross-sectional area supports a load of 1,000 lb. and the stretching stress is 10,000 lb./in.^{2}

$$\text{Stretching stress} = \frac{\text{Applied force}}{\text{Cross-sectional area}}$$

Stretching strain is another useful expression. It measures the amount of deformation which is produced in a body. When a wire 1,000 cm. long is stretched 0.1 cm., the stretching strain is 1 part in 10,000 or 0.01 per cent.

Stretching strain is the elongation per unit length.

What is elasticity? Stretch a piece of chewing gum or taffy. Then release it, and it will not contract. Stretch a rubber band, and it snaps back to its original length. The rubber is more elastic than the chewing gum.

Elasticity is the property of a body which tends to restore its original dimensions when the deforming stress is removed.

FIG. 1.—Measuring the elongation of a wire.

The elastic properties of the metal in a wire can be studied by using simple apparatus. Attach one end of the wire to a rigid support and the other to a weight carrier. Let one end of a lever be fastened to the wire at a point near its lower end (Fig. 1). The motion of the free end of the lever can be used to measure the elongation of the wire. When several equal weights are added, one at a time, the successive elongations are equal, and when all the weights are removed, the pointer C returns to its original position. However, if the load is increased sufficiently, the successive elongations become greater

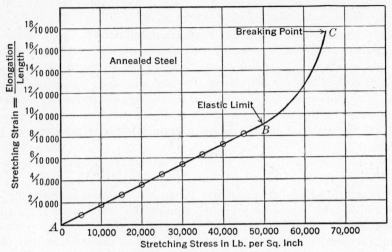

FIG. 2.—Stress and strain in a wire.

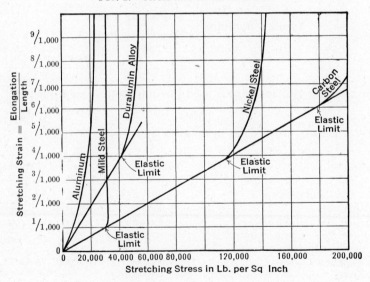

FIG. 3.—Stresses and strains in several metals (Courtesy of A. Karpov).

and we say that the **elastic limit** has been exceeded. If the load is increased sufficiently, the wire begins to stretch like a piece of chewing gum and eventually it breaks.

The results of such an experiment are shown in Fig. 2. From this graph it is clear that, until the stress reached 50,000 lb./in.^{2}, the elongations were directly proportional to the loads. After this elastic limit was exceeded, the elongations began to increase and the wire broke when the stress reached 66,000 lb./in.^{2}

117. Hooke's Law—Strain is Proportional to Stress. In the experiment just considered, the strain was proportional to the stress until the elastic limit was reached. That is, when the amount of stretching force was doubled, the elongation was also doubled. This is a special case of an important law, first stated by the English physicist, Hooke, nearly three centuries ago:

Until the elastic limit is reached, strain is directly proportional to stress.

(His original statement in Latin was admirably concise: *Ut tensio, sic vis.* "As the stretching, so is the force.")

Young's Modulus of Elasticity. When an engineer is designing a suspension bridge, he must know the amount that each wire will stretch when subjected to a given load. He uses an elastic constant called **Young's modulus** which is defined as **the ratio of the stretching stress to the strain which it produces.**

$$\text{Young's modulus} = \frac{\text{Stretching stress}}{\text{Stretching strain}}$$

$$= \frac{\text{Force/Area}}{\text{Elongation/Length}}$$

Let us see how this formula is used in computing elongations.

TABLE I

VALUES OF YOUNG'S MODULUS

Substance	Young's Modulus, lb./in.^{2}	Stress at Elastic Limit, lb./in.^{2}	Breaking Stress, lb./in.^{2}
Aluminum, rolled.................	10,000,000	25,000	29,000
Aluminum alloy (nickel 20%)........	9,400,000	23,000	60,000
Gold..............................			25,000
Gold alloy (10% copper)............			65,000
Iron, wrought.....................	26–29,000,000	21–26,000	42–52,000
Lead, rolled......................	2–2,400,000		3,000
Phosphor bronze...................		60,000	80,000
Steel, annealed...................	29,000,000	40,000	75,000

Example. In a sales room demonstration, a 3,000-lb. automobile was suspended by a single wire, which was one of the spokes ordinarily used in the wheels of a car. Find the elongation produced by the load if the spoke was 10 in. long and 1/25 in.^{2} in cross section. Young's modulus = 30,000,000 lb./in.^{2}

Let the elongation be X

$$\text{Stress} = \frac{3,000 \text{ lb.}}{1/25 \text{ in.}^2} = 75,000 \text{ lb./in.}^2$$

$$\text{Strain} = X/10 \text{ in.}$$

$$\frac{\text{Stress}}{\text{Strain}} = \frac{3,000 \text{ lb.}/1/25 \text{ in.}^2}{X/10 \text{ in.}} = 30 \times 10^6 \text{ lb./in.}^2$$

$$X = 0.025 \text{ in.}$$

118. The Different Kinds of Strain. Not only can bodies be stretched, but they can be compressed, bent, and twisted. In all these deformations elastic forces may arise, which tend to restore the body to its original size and shape. Besides stretching strain, the deformations just described involve two other kinds, **volume** strain and **shearing** strain.

Suppose that a rubber ball is placed in a liquid confined in a vessel and that the hydrostatic pressure is increased, causing the ball to contract. Then the change of stress is the increase in pressure and the volume strain is the fractional change in volume that is produced. The ratio (volume stress)/(volume strain) is called the coefficient of volume elasticity.

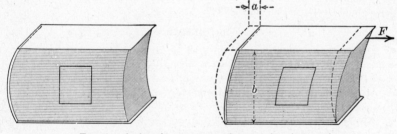

FIG. 4.—A shearing stress produces a shearing strain.

As an illustration of a shearing strain, suppose that a horizontal force F acts on the upper cover of a large dictionary and that the cover is pulled sidewise through a distance a (Fig. 4). Then the shearing strain is defined as the ratio of the displacement a to the thickness b. The shearing stress is the ratio of the force F to the area A of the cover. The ratio (shearing stress)/(shearing strain) is the coefficient of rigidity. In shearing strain the volume of the body is not altered.

SUMMARY

Intermolecular forces are negligibly small at distances greater than a few hundred-thousandths of an inch.

Glues and cements fill up the hills and valleys between objects and bind them together.

The *stretching stress* at a point in a body is defined as the applied force per unit area; the *stretching strain* is the elongation of a body per unit length.

Elasticity is the tendency of a body to resume its original shape or size after it is deformed or distorted.

Hooke's Law.—Strain in a body is proportional to the stretching stress until the elastic limit is reached. Afterward the ratio of strain to stress increases. At the *breaking stress* the wire ruptures.

Young's modulus for a substance is the ratio of the stretching stress to the stretching strain.

REVIEW QUESTIONS

1. Give evidence showing that the ranges of intermolecular forces are very small.

2. Explain the action of glues, cements, and solders, and also welding and the malleting of gold into a cavity in a tooth.

3. Define stretching stress, stretching strain.

4. Define elasticity, giving examples of slightly elastic substances not listed in this chapter.

5. Define elastic limit, breaking stress, and Young's modulus.

6. Which has the greater Young's modulus, steel or rubber?

7. From Fig. 3, which material would be preferable for the spiral spring of a spring balance, mild steel or nickel steel? Why?

PROBLEMS

1. A rubber band 2.00 ft. long and 0.10 in.² in cross section is stretched 1.0 in. by a force of 6.0 lb. What are (a) the stretching stress and (b) the stretching strain?

2′. A wire 1,000 in. long and 1/100 in.² in cross section is stretched 4.0 in. by a force of 2,000 lb. What are (a) the stretching stress, (b) the stretching strain, and (c) Young's modulus?

3′. A wire 100 cm. long and 2.0 mm.² in cross section is stretched 1.0 mm. by a force of 1,000 gwt. What are (a) the stretching stress, (b) the stretching strain, and (c) Young's modulus of the material?

4′. A force of 10 lb. is required to break a piece of cord. How much is required for a cord made of the same material which is (a) twice as long, (b) twice as large in diameter and the same length?

5. How much will an annealed steel rod 100 ft. long and 0.040 in.² in cross section be stretched by a force of 1,000 lb.?

6. How large a load can be supported by the rod of Problem 5 (a) without permanently deforming it, and (b) without breaking it?

7″. From Fig. 3, estimate Young's modulus for (a) carbon steel, and (b) duralumen alloy.

8. A manila rope, 0.40 in. in diameter, is broken by a force of 628 lb. What is the breaking stress?

9′. One end of a wire made of annealed steel is tied to a beam and the other end is tied to a wire made of aluminum-nickel alloy (20 per cent nickel). The two have the same length and diameter. A weight attached to the free end of the aluminum-nickel wire produces in it an elongation of 4.0 mm. How much was the steel wire stretched?

10′. What maximum loads could be supported by wires, each 1/100 in.² in cross section, made of the following: (a) rolled aluminum, (b) gold, (c) gold alloy (10 per cent copper), (d) annealed steel?

11″. An unabridged dictionary is 6 in. thick, and the area of each page is 0.5 ft.² A force of 2.0 lb. parallel to the cover displaces it sidewise 0.60 in. What are (a) the shearing stress, (b) the shearing strain, and (c) the shear or rigidity modulus?

density is $\frac{mass}{unit\ Volume} = \frac{gm}{cm^3}$

$\frac{1 gm}{cm^3} = \frac{1 gm}{L}$

CHAPTER XV

PRESSURES IN LIQUIDS AT REST

Force and Pressure. The word pressure is often used interchangeably with force, but in physics, pressure always means **force per unit area.** For example, in Fig. 1*A* the 2-lb. block resting on a table top is sup-

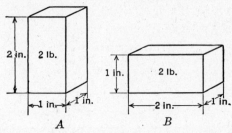

FIG. 1.

ported by a surface 1 in.² in area, so that the average pressure at the surface is 2 lb./in.² In 1*B*, the supporting surface has an area of 2 in.²,

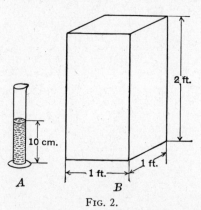

FIG. 2.

and the average pressure is 1 lb./in.² In each position the force exerted against the table top is 2 lb.

119. The Pressure at a Point in a Liquid. The cylindrical glass vessel shown in Fig. 2*A* is 4.0 cm.² in cross section. It is filled with water to a depth of 10 cm. What is the pressure at the bottom caused by the weight of the liquid?

The bottom of the vessel must support the weight of the liquid. The cross-sectional area of the column is 4.0 cm.², its volume is 40 cm.³, and the down-force is 40 gwt. Hence, the pressure at the bottom is 40 gwt./4.0 cm.² = 10 gwt./cm.²

Fig. 2*B* represents a box 1 ft. square and 2 ft. high which is completely filled with water. The 2 ft.³ of water weigh 124.8 lb. so that the pressure at the bottom is 124.8 lb./ft.²

126

density of mercy

Spe. gravity is a ratio $= \dfrac{d_{en}}{d_{H_2O}}$

These illustrations show that, the deeper the water, the greater is the force against the bottom of the vessel and the greater is the pressure. In order to estimate the pressure at a point in a liquid, it is helpful to imagine that a small horizontal diaphragm is supported there. In Fig. 3 the area of the diaphragm A is 4 cm.², and it is 10 cm. below the surface of the water. The volume of liquid above the diaphragm is 40 cm.³, its weight is 40 gwt., and the pressure at the diaphragm is 10 gwt. cm.²

The application of the following simple rule enables one to find the pressure at any point in a liquid.

Imagine a horizontal surface of unit area placed at the point. Find the weight of the column of liquid above this surface. This is numerically equal to the force per unit area, or the pressure caused by the liquid.

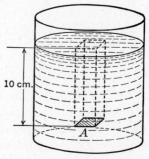

FIG. 3.—To find the pressure at a point in a liquid.

Example. What is the pressure at a point 20 cm. below the surface of a vessel of water?

If a horizontal plate 1 cm.² in cross section were placed at this point, the weight of the water column above it would be 20 gwt. Hence, the pressure is 20 gwt./cm.²

In computing the pressure produced by a column of liquid, it is helpful to use the **weight-density** of the liquid. This term means the **weight per unit volume** of a substance. For example, the weight-density of water is 1 gwt./cm.³, or 62.4 lb./ft.³ (Table I).

The student can prove that a column of liquid of weight-density d and height h produces a pressure p given by*

$$p = hd.$$

TABLE I

WEIGHT-DENSITIES OF LIQUIDS AND SOLIDS

A. Liquids	Gwt./cm.³ or grams/cm.³	Lb./ft.³
Alcohol, ethyl, at 20°C......	0.79	49.4
Water at 4.00°C...........	1.000	62.6
Water at 20°C. (68°F.).....	0.998	62.5
Gasoline (15°C.)..........	0.66–0.69	41.0–43
Milk....................	1.028–1.034	64.0–64.5
Sea water (15°C.).........	1.03	64
Mercury (0°C.)..........	13.6	850
Chloroform (18°C.)........	1.48	92.3

* The two quantities weight-density and mass-density are often confused. One term means the weight per unit volume; the other, the mass per unit volume. In the metric system, the two are numerically equal. Using mass-density, $p = hdg$.

TABLE I (*Continued*)

B. Solids at 20°C.	Gwt./cm.³ or grams/cm.³	Lb./ft.³
Balsa wood...............	0.12	7.5
Oak.....................	0.6–0.9	37–56
Aluminum................	2.7	169
Copper..................	8.30–8.95	5.8–558
Gold, cast...............	19.3	1200
Ice (0°C.)...............	0.92	58
Iron, wrought............	7.8–7.9	487–493
Lead....................	11.3	708
Platinum................	21.37	1334
Silver, cast..............	10.47–.53	650–657
Zinc, cast...............	7.04–7.16	440–447

120. Weight-Density and Specific Gravity. The specific gravity of a substance is often spoken of instead of its weight-density. By this is meant the ratio of the density of the substance to that of water. For example, the weight-density of cork is 0.50 gwt./cm.³ or in the British units 31.2 lb./ft.³, which is one-half that of water; and therefore its specific gravity is 0.50. **In the metric system, the density and the specific gravity of a substance are numerically the same.** For this reason computations of pressures in liquids are more convenient in the metric system than in the British system.

Pressures are often expressed in terms of the heights of the columns of water or of mercury which would produce them. A column of water 100 cm. high and 1 cm.² in cross section weighs 100 gwt. and the pressure it produces is 100 gwt./cm.² (Table II).

TABLE II

PRESSURES PRODUCED BY LIQUID COLUMNS

1 cm.-of-water = 1 gwt./cm.² =   980 dynes/cm.²
1 cm.-of-mercury = 13.6 gwt./cm.² = 13,300 dynes/cm.²
1 ft.-of-water = 62.4 lb./ft.² = 0.433 lb./in.²

In finding the pressure due to a column of fluid it is convenient first to find what pressure a column of water of the same depth would produce and then to multiply this value by the specific gravity of the fluid.

Example 1. An oil well 1,000 ft. deep is filled with petroleum of specific gravity 8/10. What is the pressure at the bottom due to the liquid?

If the liquid were water, the pressure would be 62,400 lb./ft.² Actually, it is 8/10 × 62,400 lb./ft.² = 49,920 lb./ft.²

121. Pressure Independent of Direction. Place a block of wood on a level table. The forces are directed downward. Pour sand into a deep box, and there are also sidewise forces pushing against the walls. If a hole is made in one side of the box, some of the sand escapes. Similarly, when a liquid is poured into a vessel, forces act on the sides of the container as well as on the bottom. Since the liquid has no rigidity, the

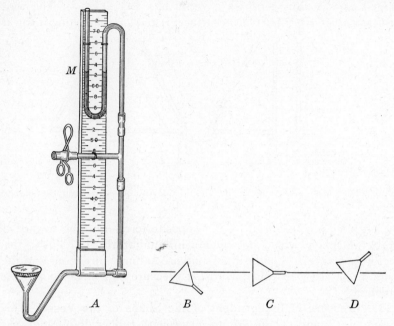

FIG. 4.—A device for measuring pressures in liquids.

forces are transmitted equally in all directions, and the push against unit area of the wall surface is equal to that against a horizontal surface of unit area at the same depth.

The forces caused by the pressure of a liquid can be studied by means of the apparatus shown in Fig. 4A. A rubber diaphragm closes the opening in a glass funnel which is connected to a U-shaped tube containing water or oil. If the rubber diaphragm is pushed inward, the confined air is compressed and the liquid rises in the U-tube. Hence the difference of liquid levels measures the force pushing against the diaphragm. If this funnel is submerged in water, the diaphragm is pushed inward because of the pressure, and the liquid in the tube rises more and more as the pressure increases with depth. Tip the

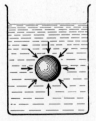

FIG. 5.—Forces acting on a submerged ball.

funnel sidewise as in B. The elevation at M remains the same, showing that the force on the diaphragm is just as great as before. Furthermore, the reading does not change when the funnel is tilted at other angles, showing that the force against the diaphragm is independent of the direction. Consider a small sphere which remains submerged at a certain depth in a vessel of water (Fig. 5). The water pushes against every part of its surface. If the forces pushing it toward

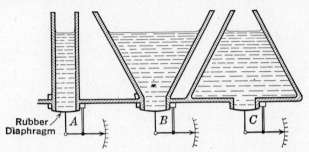

Rubber Diaphragm   A   B   C

FIG. 6.—The pressure at a point in a liquid does not depend upon the shape of the vessel.

the left were not balanced by the opposite forces pushing toward the right, the sphere would not remain in equilibrium. Evidently, then, the forces acting at a point in a liquid are in many directions and their resultant is zero. In other words, **a pressure can have no specified direction.**

122. Pressure is Independent of the Shape of the Vessel. Three vessels, A, B, and C (Fig. 6), are fitted with rubber diaphragms each attached to a pivoted lever. When water is poured into the vessel the force caused by the weight of the water pushes the diaphragm downward and moves the lever. The position of the pointer measures the force against the rubber and hence the pressure at the bottom of the vessel. If all the vessels are filled to the same depth, the pressures are equal, and so it is proved that the pressure in a liquid does not depend upon the shape of the vessel. In B, for example, the diaphragm supports the weight of the water that is vertically above it. The remainder of the liquid is upheld by the sloping walls of the container.

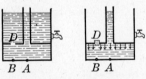

FIG. 7.—In estimating the pressure at a point in a liquid, measure the vertical distance to a free surface.

The vessel depicted in Fig. 7 has a horizontal partition in which a vertical tube is mounted, and there is an opening at D in the partition. The pressure due to the liquid is the same at A and B, since these points are at the same depth. Close the opening D by means of a stopper, and then drain away the water from the upper part of the vessel, keeping the liquid in the narrow tube at the same level. The pressure at A is unchanged, for it is at the same distance from the surface of the liquid. The pressure at B is also the same, though the column of liquid above it is shorter. Part of the pressure at B is caused by the weight of the water above it. The remainder is due to the down force exerted by the partition.

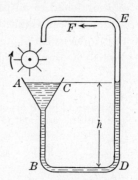

FIG. 8.—A perpetual-motion machine that won't work.

In estimating the pressure due to the weight of a liquid, always measure the vertical distance to a free surface.

123. A Perpetual-motion Machine. Devices like that shown in Fig. 8 have often been suggested as perpetual-motion machines to create energy. The hope is that, since the water in the funnel weighs more than that in the vertical tube, the liquid may be forced upward in the narrow tube and continue to flow, turning the water wheel and doing useful work.

It is easy to see why this arrangement will not function. If the water should rise to E, the pressure at the bottom of the column ED would be greater than that at B and the water would flow toward B. This illustrates the old saying that water seeks its own level.

124. Transmission of Pressures, Pascal's Principle. Place a cubical vessel, 10 cm. on each edge, on a level table and connect a tube to it as depicted in Fig. 9. Fill the vessel and the tube with water to the level B which is 10 cm. above the top of the box. The pressure at C, caused by the liquid, is 10 gwt./cm.^{2} Since all parts of the top of the box are at the same level, the water pressure there is everywhere the same, and a force of 10 gwt. acts upward on each square centimeter of the surface. Pour water into the tube, raising the level 1 cm. The pressure at the level of C is now 11 gwt./cm.^{2}, and a force of 11 gwt. acts upward on each square centimeter of the top of box. Therefore the increase of pressure is transmitted equally to various parts of the liquid at the level of C. The reader can show that the same increase in pressure is caused at the bottom of the box, or, in fact, at any point in the liquid. This is one proof of a general law or principle stated by Pascal nearly three centuries ago, namely:

Any change of pressure in an enclosed fluid at rest is transmitted undiminished to all parts of the fluid.

125. Forces Caused by Pressures. Pressure is force per unit area. The force exerted against a surface may be found by taking the product of the area and the average pressure.

Force = Pressure × Area

Example 1. In the arrangement shown in Fig. 9, find (*a*) the upward force against the top of the box, and (*b*) the downward force against the bottom.

(*a*) The pressure at the level C is 10 gwt./cm.^{2}

Hence
$$F_1 = P_1 \times A = 10 \text{ gwt./cm.}^2 \times 100 \text{ cm.}^2$$
$$= 1,000 \text{ gwt.}$$

(*b*) Similarly
$$F_2 = P_2 \times A = 20 \text{ gwt./cm.}^2 \times 100 \text{ cm.}^2$$
$$= 2,000 \text{ gwt.}$$

Example 2. Find the outward force against one side of the box.

The pressure at the top of the box is 10 gwt./cm.^{2}, and that at the bottom is 20 gwt./cm.^{2} The average pressure is 15 gwt./cm.^{2}, hence the outward force is 1,500 gwt.

126. The Hydraulic Press. Pascal's principle is frequently applied in machines which are used to exert great forces. Assume that in

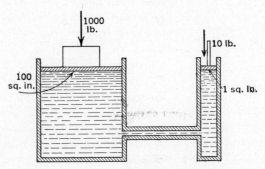

Fig. 10.—A small input force on the small piston causes a large output force on the large one.

Fig. 10 a force of 10 lb. acts on the small piston which has an area of 1 in.^{2} This force causes a pressure of 10 lb./in.^{2} In accord with Pascal's principle, the increase of pressure is transmitted to all parts of the liquid so that a force of 10 lb. acts on each square inch of the larger piston. Its area is 100 in.^{2}; hence, the total upward force acting on it is

1,000 lb. As in all machines, **the gain in mechanical advantage is accompanied by a loss in distance moved.** The smaller piston descends 100 in. for each inch that the larger one rises.

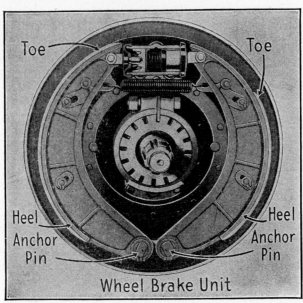

FIG. 11.—Hydraulic brake system. (From Automotive Operation, Wright & Smith, J. Wiley & Sons.)

127. The Hydraulic Brake. Most automobiles have brakes which are actuated by pistons in cylinders (Fig. 11). When the driver pushes the brake pedal (Fig. 12), the piston moves inward in the cylinder, increasing the pressure of the confined liquid. This cylinder is connected to four others, the pistons of which act against the brake shoes. One advantage of hydraulic brakes is that the forces on all the brake bands are equal. A disadvantage is that if a communicating tube breaks or if the liquid leaks out, all four brakes fail.

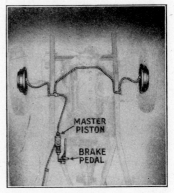

FIG. 12.

128. Buoyancy. A bather, walking into deeper water, notices that, as more of his body is submerged and more water is displaced, his apparent weight decreases until, finally, he floats with only his face above the surface. This up-push of a fluid is called buoyancy.

When a ship is empty it floats high in the water, and as it is loaded it sinks deeper. In each condition, the buoyancy is equal to the weight of the vessel and contents, so that the buoyancy increases with the amount of fluid displaced.

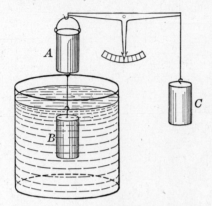

129. Archimedes' Principle. The relationship between buoyancy and the amount of fluid displaced may be determined by the following experiment.

Suspend a cylinder and a bucket of equal volume from the arm of a balance and balance the load by means of appropriate weights (Fig. 13). Submerge the cylinder in a vessel of water, and the left arm will tip upward because of the buoyancy of the liquid. Fill the bucket with

FIG. 13.—The up-push on the submerged cylinder B is equal to the down-pull of the water in the bucket A.

water, and equilibrium will be restored. Since the cylinder and bucket have equal volumes, and the weight of the water in A equals the buoyancy, it follows that the buoyancy equals the weight of the liquid displaced by the cylinder. Similar experiments can be performed with mercury or other liquids.

The law of buoyancy, called Archimedes' principle, is as follows:

A body wholly or partly submerged in a fluid is buoyed up by a force equal to the weight of the displaced fluid.

130. Another Proof of Archimedes' Principle. Submerge a rectangular block of wood of the dimensions shown in Fig. 14 in water so that its upper surface is 6 cm. below that of the water. At A the pressure is 6 gwt./cm.² and the downward force on the block is 600 gwt. At B the pressure is 26 gwt./cm.² and the upward force on the block

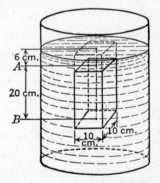

FIG. 14.—The up-push of the water against the bottom of the block is greater than the down-push on the top.

is 2,600 gwt. The resultant upward force or buoyancy, 2,000 gwt., equals the weight of the water displaced by the block. Note that the push on each side of the block is balanced by an equal push against the opposite face.

131. Determining Densities by Archimedes' Principle. The weight-density of a regularly shaped body such as a sphere or a cylinder may be readily determined. The body is weighed, and the volume is found from its geometrical dimensions. The volume of an irregular body such as a piece of coal cannot be found from its dimensions, and indirect methods are employed. One of these, devised by Archimedes about 250 B.C. came about as follows. Hiero, ruler of Syracuse, had given gold to an artisan to use in making a crown. When the crown was completed, Hiero suspected that it was alloyed with silver, so he asked his friend Archimedes how to test the purity of the metal. While the scientist was puzzling over the problem, he went to the public baths one day and noticed that, as he stepped into a tub filled to the brim with water, some of the liquid spilled over. It occurred to him that he could find the volume of Hiero's crown by submerging it in a vessel filled with water and noting the volume that was displaced. The philosopher was so eager to try the experiment, the story goes, that he rushed through the street unclad shouting *"Eureka!"* ("I have found it!")

Often the volume of a body is found by the method just described, but usually the apparent loss of weight on submersion is measured and then the volume, using Archimedes' principle. If a block of stone weighs 100 gwt. in air and 80 gwt. in water, the buoyancy is 20 gwt., which, by Archimedes' principle, equals the weight of the displaced water. But 20 grams of water have a volume of 20 cm.^{3} Hence

$$\text{Weight-density} = \frac{\text{Weight}}{\text{Volume}}$$
$$= \frac{100 \text{ gwt.}}{20 \text{ cm.}^3}$$
$$= \frac{5.0 \text{ gwt.}}{\text{cm.}^3}$$

In general

$$\text{Volume} = \frac{\text{Buoyancy}}{\text{Weight-density of liquid}}$$

Example 1. A piece of marble weighs 130 gwt. in air and 82 gwt. in water. What is its weight-density?

The apparent loss of weight in water = 48 gwt., which is the weight of the displaced water.

Volume = Weight/Weight-density =
       48 gwt./(1 gwt./cm.^{3}) = 48 cm.^{3}
Weight-density = Weight/Volume =
       130 gwt./48 cm.^{3} = 2.71 gwt./cm.^{3}

Example 2. A ball weighs 200 gwt. in air, 180 gwt. in water, and 185 gwt. in gasoline. Find the weight-density of the gasoline.

$$\text{Volume} = \frac{\text{Buoyancy}}{\text{Weight-density of liquid}}$$

$$= \frac{20 \text{ gwt.}}{1.00 \text{ gwt./cm.}^3} = 20 \text{ cm.}^3$$

$$\text{Weight-density of gasoline} = \frac{\text{Buoyancy}}{\text{Volume}}$$

$$= \frac{15 \text{ gwt.}}{20 \text{ cm.}^3} = 0.75 \frac{\text{gwt.}}{\text{cm.}^3}$$

Computations are more laborious when the British system is used because the weight-density of water is not unity.

Example 3. A brick weighs 8.0 lb. in air and 6.72 lb. in water. The buoyancy is 1.28 lb. What is its volume?

$$\text{Volume} = \text{Buoyancy/Weight-density of water} = \frac{1.28 \text{ lb.}}{62.4 \text{ lb./ft.}^3} = 0.020 \text{ ft.}^3$$

Blocks of aluminum, iron, lead, gold, and tungsten, all having unit volume, are placed in a vessel of mercury. The gold and tungsten sink to the bottom because they are denser than mercury and displace less than their weights of the liquid. Each of the other blocks floats at such a depth that it displaces its own weight of mercury (Fig. 15).

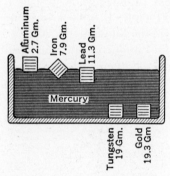

132. Hydrometers. When an ordinary automobile storage battery is fully charged, the density of the acid solution is considerably greater than when it is uncharged. For this reason, the density of the acid in a battery indicates the degree of charge. A hydrometer is used to measure the density of the acid. It has

FIG. 15.—Each floating block displaces mercury equal in weight to that of the block. The weight of the liquid displaced by the blocks of gold and of tungsten are less than the weights of the blocks.

many other industrial applications, such as the determination of densities of milk and of alcoholic beverages. The instrument pictured in Fig. 16 is a weighted glass bulb with a narrow stem. It floats at such a depth as to displace exactly its own weight of the liquid. The smaller the density of the solution, therefore, the greater is the immersion of the bulb. The stem is calibrated to indicate the density of the solution.

FIG. 16.—A hydrometer.

133. Did the Lusitania Sink to the Bottom of the Ocean? Sometimes the statement is made that vessels shipwrecked in mid-ocean do not go to the bottom, but remain in equilibrium somewhere below the surface. To deal with this question, consider how the buoyancy of the water varies with depth. At the deepest part of the Atlantic the water pressure is about 9,000 lb./in.², and at this pressure a cubic foot of solid iron would be slightly compressed, displacing about 0.3 per cent less volume of water than at the surface. The water is also compressed to the same degree approximately. Hence the buoyancy decreases but slightly with depth, and shipwrecked vessels go to the bottom.

SUMMARY

Pressure is defined as force per unit area. Pressures are often expressed in dynes per square centimeter, in gram-weights per square centimeter, in pound-weights per square inch, in centimeters-of-mercury, and in feet-of-water.

The pressure produced by a liquid which is at rest at a point at a depth h below the surface of a liquid equals the weight of a column of the liquid per unit cross section, the height of the column being h.

Weight-density is defined as weight per unit volume of a substance. It is expressed in gram-weights per cubic centimeter or in pound-weights per cubic foot. The specific gravity of a substance is the ratio of its density to that of water.

The pressure at a point in a fluid is independent of direction and of the shape of the containing vessel.

Pascal's principle states that any change of pressure in an enclosed fluid at rest is transmitted equally to all parts of the fluid.

Archimedes' principle states that, when a body is wholly or partly submerged in a fluid, the apparent loss of weight equals the weight of the fluid displaced.

REVIEW QUESTIONS

1. Define pressure, and state units in which it is often expressed.

2. Prove that the pressure at a point in a liquid, caused by its weight, numerically equals the weight of a vertical column of the liquid above a horizontal surface of unit area placed at the point.

3. Define weight-density, and state units in which it may be expressed. What is the difference between weight-density and specific gravity?

4. How can you prove experimentally that the pressure at a point in a liquid is independent of direction? Is pressure a vector (directed) quantity?

5. Prove that the pressure at a point in a liquid does not depend upon the shape of the containing vessel.

6. State and prove Pascal's principle.

7. Is it possible, using a quart of water or less, to burst a metal drum filled with water? Explain.

8. Derive an expression for the frictionless mechanical advantage of a hydraulic press.

9. State Archimedes' principle.

10. Does a ship wrecked in mid-ocean sink to the bottom, or does it remain suspended at some great depth? Justify your opinion.

11. How can you prove Archimedes' principle experimentally and theoretically?

12. How can you determine the density of a solid body and that of a liquid, using Archimedes' principle?

13. Would the pressure produced by a 1-ft. column of mercury be the same on the earth as on the moon? Why?

14. A can full of water is suspended from a spring balance. Will the reading of the balance change (a) if a block of cork is placed in the water, and (b) if a piece of lead is placed in it? Why?

15. To secure a great sensitiveness, should the stem of a hydrometer be narrow or wide? Why?

16. (a) Compare the force required to hold a wooden block barely under the surface of a pool with that required to hold it at a depth of 6 ft.

PROBLEMS

1′. A vertical force of 2.00 lb. pushes a pencil against a table top. If the point of the pencil has an area of 1/100 in.^{2}, find the pressure at the surface.

2. The water level in a certain reservoir is 200 ft. above the level of a faucet in a kitchen. Find the water pressure at the faucet if the water is not flowing.

3′. What is the pressure due to the water, at the deepest part of the Atlantic, depth = 20,000 ft.? Weight-density of sea water = 1.03 times that of fresh water.

4′. The water pressure at the faucet in the basement of an office building is 100 lb./in.^{2} What is the pressure at a faucet on the tenth floor at an elevation 100 ft. above that of the other one?

5′. Three cm.^{3} of ethyl alcohol are dissolved in 7 cm.^{3} of water. Neglecting the small change of total volume resulting, find the density of the solution.

6′. A swimming pool is 20 ft. wide and 40 ft. long. Its depth varies uniformly from 4.0 ft. at one end to 10.0 ft. at the other. Find the total force on the bottom due to the weight of the water.

7′. A vertical valve in the wall of a dam is 500 ft. below the water surface, and is 2 ft.^{2} in cross section. Find the force on it caused by the weight of the water.

8′. Find the pressure at the bottom of a barrel 80 cm. high if filled (a) with water, and (b) with gasoline of weight-density 0.80 gwt./cm.^{3}

9″. A cubical glass vessel 20 cm. high is half-filled with mercury and half with water. Find the pressure at the bottom.

10′. In the apparatus shown in Fig. 9, find the pressure at the center of the box.

11′. The "master" piston of the hydraulic brakes of a certain car is 0.50 in. in diameter, and the pistons attached to the brake shoes are 1.0 in. in diameter. If a force of 20 lb. is exerted against the master piston, what is the force pushing a brake shoe against the drum?

12′. The piston of a hydraulic device for lifting automobiles is 6.0 in. in diameter. The device is driven by water from the city system. What is the necessary water pressure to raise a car if the total load lifted is 3,142 lb.?

13. A boy stands in a swimming pool, submerged up to his neck. He finds that, when he exhales, his apparent weight increases 10 lb. What is the volume of the exhaled air?

14. What is the volume of a 200-lb. man who can barely float in a lake?

15″. The volume of a block of wood is 100 cm.³, and a downward force of 40 gwt. is required to keep it submerged in water. What is its weight-density?

16′. An empty bottle weighs 500 gwt.; when filled with water it weighs 1,500 gwt. How much gasoline of weight-density 0.66 gwt./cm.³ will it hold?

17″. A piece of brass weighs 100 gwt. in air, 92 gwt. in water, and 80 gwt. in a liquid. What is (a) the weight-density of the brass and (b) that of the liquid?

18′. A gold ring weighs 10.00 gwt. in air and 9.40 gwt. in water. (a) What is its volume? (b) Is it made of pure gold?

19. What is the volume of a boy weighing 125 lb. who can barely float in water?

20. A piece of soap weighs 100 gwt., and it floats with one-tenth of its volume above water. What is its weight-density?

21′. An iron ball weighing 136 gwt., and having a weight-density of 7.80 gwt./cm.³, floats in mercury of weight-density 13.6 gwt./cm.³ How many cubic centimeters are above the surface?

22′. A meter stick of weight-density 0.70 gwt./cm.³ floats in a liquid, three-quarters submerged. What is the weight-density of the liquid?

23′. A spike 1/100 in.² in cross-sectional area is pushed through a hole in the rubber stopper of a bottle filled with water. (a) If a force of 2.0 lb. were exerted on the spike, what would be the increase in pressure in the liquid? (b) If the bottom of the bottle has an area of 2.00 in.², what is the force exerted against it?

24. What is the volume of a block of copper weighing 1,000 gwt. (weight-density = 8.93 gwt./cm.³)?

25. Water has a weight-density of 62 lb./ft.³ The specific gravity of iron is 7.5. How much will 5.0 ft.³ of iron weigh?

26. Five grams of water are mixed with 3.95 grams of ethyl alcohol. Neglecting the small change in volume of each as they are mixed, calculate the weight-density of the mixture.

27. A diver descended to a depth of 290 ft. in water having a weight-density of 64 lb./ft.³ What was the pressure at the outside of his diving suit?

28. When a 125-lb. man stepped into a canoe, it sank 1.20 in. farther into the water. Find the cross-sectional area of the canoe at the water surface.

29″. A pump in the basement of a garage is used to operate a hydraulic jack on the first floor. The areas of the two pistons are 1.00 in.² and 60 in.² respectively, and the large piston is 10 ft. higher than the other one. How great a load can be lifted by a force of 24.33 lb. applied to the lower piston? (Neglect friction.)

30. (a) What is the pressure in gram-weights per cubic centimeter at the bottom of a column of mercury 76 cm. high? (b) How high would a column of water have to be to exert the same pressure?

31. (a) A board 12 in. wide and 1.00 in. thick stands on end. It weighs 30 lb. What pressure does it exert? (b) The area of the point of a needle is 0.00015 cm.² What is the pressure when the force pushing the needle into a body is 300 gwt.?

32. What force would be required to hold 500 cm.³ of iron (weight-density =7.5 gwt./cm.³) under mercury (weight-density = 13.6 gwt./cm.³)?

33″. A uniform wooden cylinder 10.0 cm. long and 2.0 cm.² in cross section barely floats in gasoline of weight-density 0.80 gwt./cm.³ What fraction of the cylinder's volume will be above the surface when it floats in salt water of weight-density 1.10 gwt./cm.³?

34″. How heavy a stone can a boy lift under water if he can lift a 30.8-lb. stone in air? The weight-density of the stone is 312 lb./ft.³

35″. A crown made of silver and gold weighs 1,600 gwt. in air, and 1,500 gwt. in water. What are (a) the volume of the silver, (b) its weight, and (c) the percentage of silver in the crown? Weight-density of gold = 19.32 gwt./cm.³; of silver 10.53 gwt./cm.³

CHAPTER XVI

PRESSURES IN GASES

The Ocean of Air. Weigh a liter flask, first when evacuated, and then after it is opened to the atmosphere. The increase is more than 1 gwt. This simple experiment proves that air, like all other forms of matter, has weight. The air in a small classroom weighs several hundred pounds; that in a large lecture hall more than a ton. Because of its small density, the air causes little friction and usually we are not conscious of its existence. In times of storm we see plenty of evidence that air can have momentum and that great winds can exert forces and do damage. We live at the bottom of a vast ocean of air having currents and storms like those of the Atlantic Ocean. Three differences should be noted, namely: In the Atlantic the surface waters only are disturbed, but in the great atmospheric ocean, storms occur only in the lowest seven miles or so. Above this layer are regions of relative calm. A second difference is that the density of water varies little with depth, but in the atmosphere the air decreases in density as we go to higher elevations. Lastly, the ocean has a well-defined surface, but the atmosphere has no definite upper limit.

134. The Buoyancy of Air. Air and all other gases have weight, hence they produce buoyant effects like those of liquids. Archimedes' principle holds for gases. That is:

A body surrounded by a gas is buoyed up by a force equal to the weight of the gas which it displaces.

Since the weight-densities of gases are relatively small, their buoyant effects are often negligible. To show the up-push of the atmosphere, suspend a hollow brass sphere from one arm of a balance and counterpoise it by a suitable weight. Place the balance under the bell

FIG. 1.—The apparent weight of the ball increases when the jar is evacuated.

jar of an air pump, evacuate the jar, and the sphere will move downward as the buoyancy decreases (Fig. 1).

Archimedes' principle explains why a balloon rises in the air. It displaces an amount of fluid weighing more than the balloon itself. The extra load which can be lifted is the difference between the weight of the displaced fluid and that of the object. The "pay load" of a balloon is rather small because of the great weight of the balloon fabric, of the basket, and of the gas. Hydrogen is desirable for inflating balloons because of its low density, but it is highly flammable and so helium is often used, sacrificing pay load for safety.

Example. A balloon has a volume of 1,000 m.³ and, together with the basket, it weighs 800 kgwt. What is the pay load it can carry (*a*) if filled with hydrogen of weight-density 0.090 kgwt./m.³ and (*b*) if filled with helium, which is twice as dense? The weight-density of air = 1.20 kgwt./m.³, hence the buoyancy is 1,200 kgwt.

(*a*)   Weight of hydrogen   =   90 kgwt.
                      of basket, etc. = 800   "
                      of pay load   = 310   "

                                       1,200 kgwt.

(*b*)   Weight of helium   = 180 kgwt.
                      of basket, etc. = 800   "
                      of pay load   = 220   "

                                       1,200 kgwt.

A piece of cork, released under water, continues to rise until it reaches the surface. The weight-density of the water and hence its buoyant effect vary but slightly with depth. When a balloon rises in the atmosphere, on the contrary, the weight-density of the air decreases with

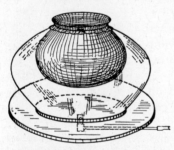

elevation, and eventually a position is reached where the buoyancy is exactly equal to the weight of the balloon, which cannot go higher than this "ceiling."

135. The Pressure of the Atmosphere. Stretch a rubber membrane over the upper opening of a glass jar open to the atmosphere. The membrane will be flat because the air pressure is equal on both sides. Pump air out of the enclosure, and the diaphragm will bulge inward because of the difference in pressure (Fig. 2). If an empty varnish can is evacuated, the force of the atmosphere pushing against the sides is sufficient to crush it.

FIG. 2.—The rubber is pushed inward when the jar is evacuated.

The huge forces which can be exerted by atmospheric pressures are demonstrated by the Magdeburg hemispheres, invented by Otto von Guericke, 300 years ago. He designed two iron vessels, each 22 in. in diameter, which could be put together forming an air-tight spherical enclosure (Fig. 3). When the interior was evacuated by means of an air pump, great forces were required to separate the hemispheres. Von Guericke must have been a good showman, for he arranged a clever public demonstration at which six-teen horses, eight on each side, pulled against each other in a tug of war, and failed to separate the hemispheres. The force required to part them can easily be calcu-lated. Replace one of the hemi-

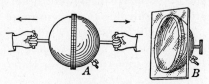

Fig. 3.—Magdeburg hemispheres.

spheres by a flat metal plate. The area of the circular opening is about 380 in.^{2} If the barometric pressure is 14.7 lb./in.^{2}, the horizontal force against the plate is about 5,600 lb. The surface area of the hemisphere is greater than that of the flat plate, but the forces acting on this surface are not all in the same direction, and the total resultant force on this side is equal and opposite to that on the flat plate, in accord with Newton's third law.

The cause of the air pressure is easily understood if we consider that we live at the bottom of an ocean of air many miles deep. If a tightly closed empty can were at the bottom of a lake, forces would act on it because of the weight of the water above it. These forces would decrease if the can were raised to the surface. Similarly, the air above an object causes pressure, and it is to be expected that, when a balloon rises to greater eleva-tions, the air pressure will decrease.

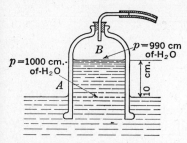

Fig. 4.—The pressure at A is caused partly by the weight of the water and partly by the pressure of the confined air.

136. Why Does Water Rise in an Evacuated Tube? Pump air out of a bell jar, the bottom of which dips into a vessel of water (Fig. 4). Then the water will rise higher and higher in the enclosure as the pumping progresses. To see why this is, consider the down-ward push of the air at the water sur-face outside. A force of about 1,000 gwt. acts on each square centimeter of the surface, and the pressure must be the same inside the jar. After-ward when the air pressure inside is diminished, the water is forced up into the jar by the push of the atmosphere. This fact has been known since ancient times, and the Greeks used to explain it by saying that nature abhors a vacuum. Three centuries ago, the Duke of Tuscany had a deep well dug, and it was found that no available pump could lift the water higher than 34 ft. Torricelli, a friend and follower of Galileo, was greatly interested in the reason for this, and he asked Galileo's opinion. The old man replied jestingly that probably nature's abhorrence of a vacuum did not extend beyond 34 ft.! The difficulty did not stop Torricelli, but rather stimulated him to further endeavors, from which came the invention of the barometer.

Torricelli wondered whether nature's "abhorrence of a vacuum" depended upon the density of the liquid used. He thought that mercury, being 13.6 times as dense as water, might be pumped only to a smaller

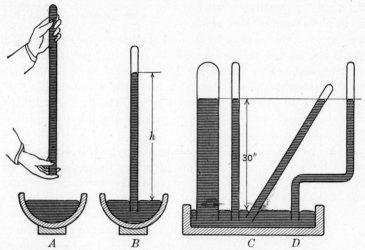

FIG. 5.—The height of the mercury does not depend upon the shape of the tube or its tilt.

height, that is, 34/13.6 ft., or about 30 in. Instead of using a pump to exhaust the air from a pipe, he filled a long glass tube with mercury, closed the open end with his thumb, and, inverting the tube, placed the end thus closed under the surface of a pool of mercury contained in a dish (Fig. 5A). When he removed his thumb, mercury escaped from the tube until the upper surface in it was about 30 in. above the level in the dish. Later experiments showed that the vertical height of the column was independent of the width of the tube and of its angle of tilt Fig. 5C.

137. Barometric Pressure and Altitude. When the news of Torricelli's invention reached Paris, Pascal suggested that if atmospheric pressure is caused by the weight of the ocean of air, the barometric pressure should decrease with elevation, just as the water pressure in a lake decreases as one rises nearer the surface. Accordingly, at his request, a relative in the country carried a barometer to the top of a mountain and found that the reading decreased more than an inch. These results confirmed the view that atmospheric pressure is caused by the weight of the atmosphere.

138. The Aneroid Barometer. Torricelli's barometer, as will be shown later, is very useful, for observations of the rise and fall of the mercury enable mariners and others to foretell the weather. Another application is in the measurement of heights of mountains. Today barometers are used to determine altitudes in airplane flights. In altitude measurements "aneroid" barometers (Greek, *anaeros*, "without air") are commonly used. An accordion-like metal vessel *A* with thin, fluted walls supports a lever which is pivoted as shown in Fig. 6. If the barometric pressure decreases, the air confined in the vessel ex-

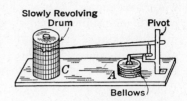

FIG. 6.—An aneroid recording barometer.

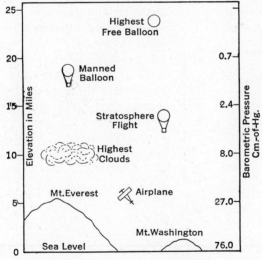

FIG. 7.—Pressure and altitude.

pands, and the top rises. The pointer at the free end of a second lever moves downward, thus indicating a decrease of pressure. In some instruments a fixed scale is provided to indicate the pressure, but in others the pointer traces a wavy line on a cylinder which is driven by clockwork. Recording barometers like this are especially useful to aviators attempting to break the record for altitude.

139. The Depth of the Ocean of Air. If the atmosphere had the same density all the way up that it has at the surface, the depth of the at-

mospheric ocean could be estimated with little difficulty. At sea level
the water barometer reads about 34 ft. and the atmosphere is about
1/700 as dense as water. It follows that, if the air were of constant
density, the height of the air column would be 700 times that of a
water barometer. This is 23,800 ft., or about 4½ miles, and the tops
of high mountains would protrude above the atmosphere like islands
in mid-Atlantic. In fact, the atmosphere decreases in density as the
altitude increases, tending toward zero as the pressure diminishes.
Hence the atmosphere has no definite outer boundary. In recent
stratosphere flights, balloons have risen to elevations greater than 14
miles, where the air pressures are less than 0.1 that at sea level (Fig. 7).

140. Pressure "Due to the Liquid" and "Total Pressure." In the
preceding chapter, we were concerned with pressures produced by the
weights of liquids, paying little attention to the pressure produced by
the weight of the atmosphere above. For example, we found that the
pressure "due to the liquid," at a point 100 cm. below the surface of a
lake, was 100 gwt./cm.² We know that this was, in fact, the excess
pressure, above atmospheric. To determine the *total* pressure, that of
the barometer (say 75 cm.-of-mercury or 1,020 gwt./cm.²) must be
added. The total pressure is therefore
1,120 gwt./cm.² When the excess pressure
in an automobile tire is 30 lb./in.² and the
barometric pressure is 15 lb./in.², the
total pressure is the sum of these quantities, namely, 45 lb./in.²

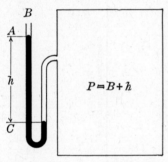

FIG. 8.—An open-tube manometer.

141. The Open-Tube Manometer. The
pressure of a confined body of gas may be
measured by an open-tube manometer
(Fig. 8). This consists of a U-shaped tube
containing a liquid of known weight-
density. One end of the tube is connected
to the reservoir; the other is open to the
atmosphere. The pressure at A in the open tube is the barometric
pressure B and at C there is an additional pressure h due to the weight
of the liquid. The total pressure P is the sum of the two, that is

$$P = B + h$$

Example. The reading of an open-tube water manometer connected to an il-
luminating-gas system is 10 cm.-of-water, and the barometric pressure is 74 cm.-
of-mercury. What is the total pressure?

$$P = 74 \text{ cm.-of-mercury} + 10 \text{ cm.-of-water}$$
$$= 74 \times 13.6 \text{ gwt./cm.}^2 + 10 \text{ gwt./cm.}^2$$
$$= 1,010 \text{ gwt./cm.}^2 = 1,010 \text{ cm.-of-water}$$

142. The Closed-Tube Manometer. The open-tube manometer is inconvenient because the barometric pressure, being variable, must be determined at frequent intervals. The closed-tube manometer is preferable because the difference in the mercury levels indicates the correct pressure directly. In this device (Fig. 9), the end E is sealed, and the space above the column of mercury is highly evacuated like that in the tube of a barometer. The liquid column DE is supported entirely by the pressure of the gas confined in the tank. Thus the pressure is equal to that produced by this column of liquid of height h.

143. The Bourdon Gage. A type of pressure gage very commonly used is represented in Fig. 10. A flattened, thin-walled, metal tube is bent so as to lie along the arc of a circle. When the tube is evacuated, it curls into a smaller circle as the flattened walls are gradu-

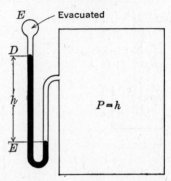

FIG. 9.—A closed-tube manometer.

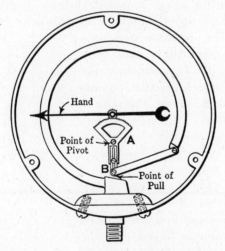

FIG. 10.—Bourdon pressure gage. The curved tube straightens when the pressure within it increases.

ally forced together by the push of the atmosphere. When the pressure of the enclosed air is greater than the barometer reading, the walls bulge out and the tube tends to straighten. A gear attached to the tube causes the pointer to rotate so that its position measures the pressure. Usually such gages indicate the excess of the gas pressure above that of the atmosphere. Thus if a pressure gage for automobile

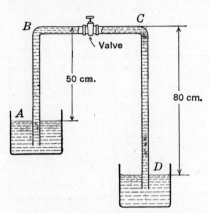

FIG. 11.—A siphon enables water to flow from a higher to a lower level.

tires reads 40 lb./in.², the total pressure is this value plus the barometric pressure.

144. The Siphon. A person can withdraw the gasoline from the tank of a car by means of a bent tube, called a siphon. To understand its action, consider a tube which is completely filled with water and has a valve preventing flow (Fig. 11). At the water surface in each open vessel, the pressure is atmospheric, and inside the tubes the pressure decreases with elevation above the open vessels. The water column in the tube

CD is longer than in the short one, hence the pressure is less at C than at B. When the valve is opened, therefore, water will flow from B toward C and the upper vessel will be emptied.

145. Pumps. The operation of the ordinary "suction" pump will be made clear by studying Fig. 12. The first up-stroke of the piston produces a partial vacuum in the cylinder of the pump. The push of the atmosphere forces water upward from the cistern through the valve at the base of the cylinder. When the piston moves downward, this lower valve shuts, preventing the down-flow of the water. Meanwhile, a second valve which is in the piston itself opens and first the trapped air, then the water is forced into the

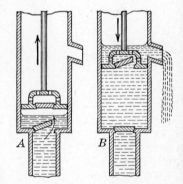

FIG. 12.—A lift pump.

space above the piston. At the next upward stroke, the water which has been trapped above the piston is lifted and escapes at the spout. This type of pump will not operate if the piston is more than 34 ft. above the water surface in the cistern. (Why?)

In deep wells force pumps are used (Fig. 13). The cylinder and piston are located in the well near the water surface. When the piston is raised, water is forced up into the cylinder just as in the lift pump. A downward motion of the piston forces the water out through a valve in the wall of the cylinder and into a pipe through which it can be forced to great elevations.

146. Rotary Pumps. The most familiar form of rotary pump is of the centrifugal type and is used to circulate air in the ventilating systems of factories and offices (Fig. 14). The air enters the pump at B near the axis of the wheel and it is thrown outward by the revolving vanes, escaping at C. Rotary pumps are used for circulating liquids as well as gases. They are very efficient when the desired change of pressure is small.

Another kind of rotary pump is used in laboratories for producing high vacua (Fig. 15). It consists essentially of an iron cylinder, fitted with four vanes sliding in slots, which rotates in a larger cylindrical opening.

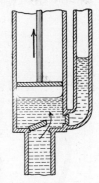

FIG. 13.—
A force pump.

Each vane is pushed outward from the axis by a spring. As the cylinder rotates, gas entering at the inlet C is trapped in the space between two vanes, is carried around and forced out at the outlet. Two or three such pumps are often operated in series, and together they give vacua as low as three millionths of an atmosphere.

147. The Diffusion Pump. The mercury diffusion pump is the simplest of all for it has no pistons or other mechanically moving parts (Fig. 16). Combined with a rotary pump, it can produce a vacuum as low as a billionth of an atmosphere. Mercury is boiled in the large flask and the vapor rushes upward through the

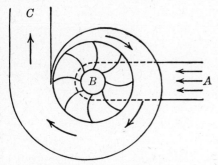

FIG. 14.—A centrifugal pump.

vertical tube. Molecules from the vessel to be evacuated enter the mercury-vapor stream and are driven forward through the curved tube. Then the mercury vapor is chilled by a water jacket, liquefies, and returns to the flask. The gas, remaining behind, is pumped out through a side tube. This device will not operate at ordinary pressures. An auxiliary pump is used to lower the pressure to a millimeter-of-mercury or so, and the diffusion pump can reduce it to an extremely low value.

148. The Human Heart. The human heart is a double pump. One section forces the blood through the lungs and thence to the other section, from which it is driven to different parts of the body. The blood

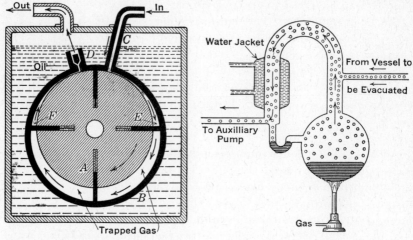

FIG. 15.—A rotary pump used to produce high vacua.

FIG. 16.—A diffusion pump.

enters the right auricle *RA* (Fig. 17), and passes down through the mitral valve into the right ventricle. The valve closes, the heart mus-

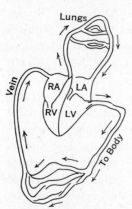

FIG. 17.—The circulation of blood.

cles contract, and the blood is forced upward through the bicuspid valve into an artery leading to the lungs. From there it returns to the left auricle and thence flows to the left ventricle, whence it is pumped to distant parts of the body. The contractions of the heart cause a rhythmic variation of the blood pressure, the increase when the left ventricle contracts being about 13 cm.-of-mercury. This increase occurs in about 1/15 sec. If the walls of the arteries were rigid, the pressure variations would be enormous, but in fact the walls expand and contract as the pressure changes. In disease, sometimes, the arteries harden, causing serious trouble because of the great pressures that occur.

149. Determining Blood Pressures. Blood pressure is measured by means of a closed rubber tube like the inner tube of a bicycle which is snugly strapped around the upper arm of the patient. Air is forced in by means of a small pump until the artery is just closed and no pulse beat can be detected by the physician as he listens with the aid of a stethoscope. The pressure of the air is then measured by means of an open-tube manometer or a Bourdon gage.

SUMMARY

Archimedes' principle applies to gases as well as to liquids.

Liquids rise in evacuated tubes because of the pressure of the atmosphere.

REVIEW QUESTIONS

1. State Archimedes' principle, and give an example in terms of the lifting ability of a balloon.

2. Why are our bodies not crushed by the enormous forces exerted by the atmosphere?

3. How can you compute the amount of pull required to separate two Magdeburg hemispheres when the system is evacuated?

4. Why does water rise in a tube when the air is pumped out of it?

5. Why does water not escape freely when a jug is suddenly inverted?

6. How should the reading of a mercury barometer with a very large bore compare with that of one having a very narrow one? Why?

7. Why does air enter the lungs when a person inhales?

8. An automobile driver notes that the pressure gage reads 46 lb./in.^{2} when he tests one of the tires of his car while at a mountain pass. Later, when he is in a valley, the tire gage reads 45 lb./in.^{2} Explain.

9. If, on a long journey, the reading of the barometer on an airplane remains constant, can the aviator be certain that his elevation also remains constant? Why?

10. In very accurate weighing, must the buoyancy of the air be considered?

11. Discuss the saying, "Nature abhors a vacuum."

12. Describe an open-arm mercury manometer and a closed-arm manometer, telling how the pressure may be calculated for each instrument.

13. Explain why water flows through a siphon. How high can water be siphoned?

PROBLEMS

1′. What is the force acting on one side of a cubical can, 5.0 in. on each side, if the water barometer height is 34 ft.?

2′. If the volume of a 100-gram block of metal is 12 cm.^{3}, find the buoyancy, the weight-density of the air being 1.23 gwt./liter.

3″. A balloon contains 10,000 ft.^{3} of hydrogen of weight-density 0.0056 lb./ft.^{3}, and the weight-density of the air is 0.080 lb./ft.^{3} If the balloon itself, with basket, weighs 500 lb. (*a*) what is the "pay load" that it can raise? (*b*) How much pay load could it lift if the hydrogen were replaced with helium which is twice as dense?

4′. If the mercury barometer reads 74 cm., what is the reading (*a*) of a water barometer, and (*b*) of one filled with glycerine of density 1.26 gwt./cm.^{3}?

5. When a mercury barometer is vertical, the length of the liquid column is 76 cm. What would be the length of the column if the tube were at an angle of 60° with the vertical?

6′. A pair of Magdeburg hemispheres is 2.0 in. in diameter. The barometric pressure is 29 in.-of-mercury. What force is required to separate them (*a*) if the interior is completely evacuated, and (*b*) if the pressure inside is 9.7 in.-of-mercury?

7′. At what depth below the surface of a lake would the pressure be twice that of the atmosphere? (Barometer reading equals 29 in.-of-mercury.)

8′. The height of a mercury barometer is 74 cm. What is the pressure at a point 24 cm. above the mercury level in the reservoir?

9″. A vertical cylinder is closed at its upper end by an 8.0-lb. piston which is 4.0 in.² in cross section. If the atmospheric pressure is 14.7 lb./in.², what is the pressure of the confined air?

10′. What is the buoyancy, due to the atmosphere, on a 75.0-kgwt. man if the mean weight-density of his body is 1.00 gwt./cm.³, and that of the air is 0.00130 gwt./cm.³?

11″. A siphon, like that depicted in Fig. 11, is used to empty a tank filled with oil of weight-density 0.90 gwt./cm.³ When the valve is closed, what is the pressure on each side of it, the lengths of the two vertical columns being 110 cm. and 220 cm. respectively? The barometer reading is 73.5 cm.-of-mercury.

12. How high is an airplane when the barometric pressure is 10.0 cm.-of-mercury less than at the earth's surface. The average weight-density of the air is 0.00123 gwt./cm.³

13″. The average weight-density of the air in a skyscraper is 0.00120 gwt./cm.³, and the barometer reads 74.0 cm. at the street level. (*a*) How much will it read at the roof, 300 m. above the ground? (*b*) What will be the increase in the force exerted on the drum of a man's ear, area = 0.30 cm.², when he descends from the roof to the street level?

CHAPTER XVII

FLUIDS IN MOTION

In the two preceding chapters fluids at rest were considered. In this condition the pressures are the same at all points at the same elevation. This law no longer holds if the fluid is moving. When water flows in a uniform horizontal pipe, there is a fall of pressure along the pipe in the direction in which the water travels. The reason is that force is required to overcome friction in the fluid. In order to study frictional effects in a moving liquid, keep a large reservoir filled with water and

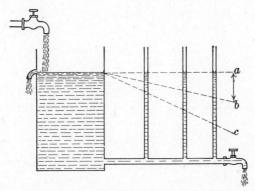

FIG. 1.—Friction causes a fall of pressure along a tube through which a liquid flows

connect it to a horizontal pipe, fitted with vertical tubes (Fig. 1). When the valve is closed, the water seeks its level and rises to the same elevation in each vertical tube. When the valve is opened slightly so as to permit a small rate of flow, the water level falls in each tube so as to show a progressive decrease of pressure along the horizontal pipe. Open the valve farther, so as to double the rate of flow, and the pressure drop is twice as great as before. It can be shown that the pressure drop and the rate of flow are proportional.

Frictional effects are very important when fluids are transported long distances. Petroleum is forced through pipe lines from Texas to the eastern states. Powerful pumps at the starting point raise the pressure of the liquid to several hundred pounds per square inch. If there were no flow, the pressure would be the same at all points along the pipe (assuming that it is horizontal). In fact, the pressure decreases with distance because of the friction of the flowing oil, and pumps are installed at several places along the route in order to renew the pressure and maintain the flow. The same practice applies to the transfer of natural gas. Most familiar of all is the flow of water to supply the residences of a city. In hilly regions the reservoirs, located at great elevations, provide ample supplies of water for the most distant buildings. On level plains it is usual to construct stand pipes or reservoirs but little higher than the roofs of the buildings. There usually is sufficient supply of water for the distant residences at night when little water is used by the community, but during the daytime the water supply may be insufficient to meet the demand.

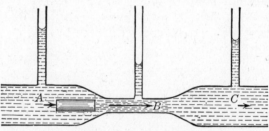

Fig. 2.—The velocity of the fluid increases as it moves from A to B because the pressure at A is greater than that at B.

150. Pressure and Velocity. When a river flows through a wide, level plain, the water travels slowly, but in going through a narrow gorge its speed increases. Similarly, when water flows through a pipe which has a narrow constriction (Fig. 2), the water speeds up as it approaches the "narrows." Hence the velocity of any molecule must increase as it moves from A to B. To cause this acceleration the pressure at A must be greater than that at B. To understand the why of this, suppose that a wooden cylinder is carried forward in the stream. It will be accelerated when it enters the narrow part of the tube. In order to cause this acceleration, the force on the rear end of the cylinder must be greater than the opposing force acting on the front end. Hence the pressure at A must exceed that at B.

This is an example of a general rule:

Whenever the velocity of a horizontally moving stream of fluid increases owing to a constriction, the pressure must decrease. High velocity is associated with low pressure, and vice versa.

There are numerous examples of variations of pressure with velocity,

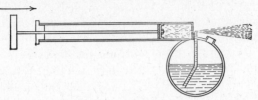

FIG. 3.—An atomizer.

the most striking being those occurring in air streams. One of the simplest illustrations is had when one holds a thin sheet of paper horizontally before the lips and blows past its upper surface. Then the pressure in the rapidly moving air stream is less than that of the air around it, and the paper is forced upward. The fluttering of a flag in a breeze can be explained in the same manner.

A second example is the ordinary "atomizer" or sprayer (Fig. 3). When the piston is moved inward, air rushes past the upper end of the small vertical tube. The velocity of the air in the jet is so great that the reduction in pressure is considerable, hence liquid is forced upward in the vertical tube, enters the jet, and is carried forward as spray.

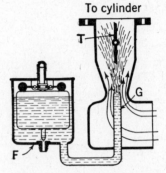

FIG. 4.—Carburetor of an automobile (from Steam, Air and Gas Power by Severns and Degler—John Wiley & Sons).

The carburetor of an automobile operates in the same manner. The level of the gasoline in the vessel (Fig. 4) is kept constant by a float which actuates a needle valve. When the engine is running, air is drawn through the carburetor. As it rushes past the nozzle the pressure is reduced. In consequence a spray of gasoline is formed which mingles with the air, producing an explosive mixture. To start the engine in cold weather, a "choke" valve (not shown) is partly closed, partly shutting off the air supply. In this way the pressure at the nozzle is further reduced, more gasoline is forced into the stream, increasing the "richness" of the mixture which explodes more readily.

FIG. 5.—The pressure at B is less than at A. Hence the ball curves to the left.

151. The Curving Baseball. A baseball having a spinning motion about a horizontal axis is thrown upward as shown in Fig. 5. The air rushes past the ball as indicated by the arrows. The spinning baseball produces a small "whirlpool" of air which opposes the wind at one side of the ball, and reinforces it at the other side. In consequence, the air velocity is greater at B than at A. The pressure at B is lowered because of the high velocity, and the baseball curves to the reader's left. If the direction of spin were reversed, the pressure at A would be diminished the more and the ball would curve oppositely, to the right. A skillful tennis player can cause the ball to spin so as to curve downward very sharply, and a golf player can increase the range of the golf ball by causing it to spin so as to curve upward (Fig. 6).

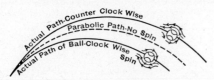

FIG. 6.—Spin may increase or decrease the distance traveled by a ball.

152. The Velocity of a Liquid Jet. The velocity of the liquid in a jet from an orifice can be found by using the law of the conservation of energy. Allow water to escape from an opening B in a tank (Fig. 7). Each gram of liquid entering at the top has the same amount of energy

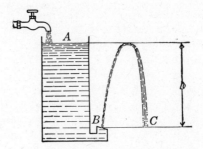

FIG. 7.—The jet rises to the elevation A.

as a gram escaping at B. That is, a gram of water at A has potential energy equal to the kinetic energy of a gram at B. It is as if the water coming from the opening had fallen directly through a frictionless pipe. If frictional effects are negligibly small, the jet rises to the same elevation as the water surface in the reservoir.

In finding the velocity of the jet, note that the energy of the water at A is potential and that the amount possessed by a particle of weight W is Wh. At B a particle has kinetic energy, its value being $\frac{1}{2}(W/g)v^2$. The two are equal, and

$$\frac{1}{2}(W/g)v^2 = Wh$$
$$v^2 = 2gh$$
$$v = \sqrt{2gh}$$

The velocity as stated is precisely that which a particle would acquire in falling through a vertical distance h. It follows that

If friction is negligible, the velocity with which a liquid issues from an orifice equals that which it would have after falling a vertical distance equal to the depth of the liquid (Torricelli's theorem).

Example. With what speed will water issue from the openings at B and C (Fig. 8), the distances below the upper water surface being 4 ft. and 16 ft. respectively?

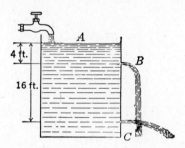

FIG. 8.—The speed of the water escaping at B is smaller than that at C. Why?

A stone would require 0.5 sec. to fall a vertical distance of 4.0 ft., and 1 sec. to fall 16 ft. The velocities acquired would be 16 ft./sec. and 32 ft./sec., respectively. Hence these are the speeds of the water in the two jets.

SUMMARY

When the velocity of a horizontal fluid stream increases, the pressure in it decreases.

The velocity of the water in a jet of liquid issuing from an orifice in an open tank equals that which a freely falling body would acquire in falling through a vertical distance equal to the depth of the liquid at the orifice.

REVIEW QUESTIONS

1. State two laws of fluid pressure applying to fluids at rest but not to those which are moving.

2. Why does the water-flow from a faucet decrease when someone opens another faucet in the same building?

3. Discuss the effect of change of velocity on the pressure in a fluid stream.

4. Explain (*a*) the action of an atomizer, and (*b*) the curving of a baseball.

5. When a baseball is thrown northward, rotating clockwise as viewed from above, does it curve to the pitcher's right or to his left?

6. A tennis ball travels northward. As viewed from the west, how must it rotate so as to curve downward?

7. How does the velocity of a jet depend upon the depth of liquid in the tank from which the liquid flows?

8. A reservoir of mercury and one of water have orifices each 4 ft. below the upper surface. With what velocity will the liquids flow from each?

PROBLEM

1. The pressure at an orifice in a water tank is 490 gwt./cm.² What is the depth of the water and with what velocity does the water escape?

CHAPTER XVIII

MOLECULAR MOTIONS

It is the intuition of unity amid diversity which impels the mind to form a science.
—F. S. HOFFMAN.

Diffusion of Gases. Remove the stopper of an ammonia bottle, and after a few minutes the odor of ammonia may be noticed in all parts of the room. This is because the ammonia molecules have considerable velocities, and they dart hither and thither through the air. Their average speed is several hundred feet per second. The relatively low rate of diffusion is somewhat surprising. It is easily understood, however, when we consider that a molecule does not "make a beeline" or travel on a straight line. On the contrary, it collides with other molecules at irregular intervals and moves about in random directions (Fig. 1). Like a person idly wandering in a crowd, with no particular objective, it progresses very slowly.

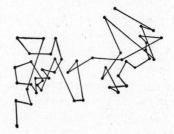

FIG. 1.—Path of an air molecule. (Exaggerated).

153. Diffusion Rates Depend on Molecular Sizes and Speeds. Gases and vapors which are composed of relatively large and massive molecules diffuse more slowly than smaller ones. For example, chloroform vapor diffuses more slowly than hydrogen. There are two reasons for this difference: first, the more massive molecules have smaller average speeds; and secondly, being more bulky, they make more collisions with other molecules in traveling a given distance.

The difference in the diffusion rates of air and of hydrogen may be demonstrated using an unglazed porcelain cup closed by a rubber stopper which is fitted with a vertical glass tube, the lower end of which is submerged in water. Air diffuses slowly through the pores in the walls of the vessel. The rates of diffusion inward and outward are the same, so that the pressure inside equals that of the barometer. Next, place an inverted glass bottle over the cup and flood it with hydrogen. The hydrogen molecules have higher speeds than those of the confined air, hence the inward diffusion of hydrogen is greater than the outward diffusion of the air. In consequence, the pressure inside the cup increases and bubbles escape at the lower end of the glass tube. Remove the glass bottle after a few minutes. Now the hydrogen which has accumulated in the cup escapes more rapidly than the air enters, and the pressure inside diminishes so that water rises in the glass tube.

154. Diffusion of Liquids and Solids. Put a few crystals of copper sulfate into a jar containing water. The crystals dissolve and the water near the bottom becomes blue. After several days, the entire volume of the liquid becomes equally tinted, showing that the dissolved substance is equally distributed. This dispersion is not caused by gravity, for the copper sulfate is denser than the water and, in accord with Archimedes' principle, it should remain at the bottom. The true explanation is that the particles diffuse through the liquid, as does ammonia through the air. The rate of diffusion is small because the molecules of the water are so densely packed together that they greatly hinder the wandering of the particles of copper sulfate.

In solids, the atoms are not free to wander, and each of them oscillates or vibrates about a fixed position. However, occasionally an atom breaks free from its moorings and diffuses. If a film of gold is laid on a piece of lead, and the metal is heated, the gold slowly penetrates the lead.

155. Osmosis. Pour water into the two compartments represented in Fig. 2. The partition separating the two is made of parchment through which water diffuses slowly. Put a trace of dye into one compartment, and eventually the two bodies of water become equally colored. This coloration proves that diffusion is occurring. The two water surfaces remain at the same level, showing that the diffusion rate is the same in each direction. Suppose instead that sugar is dissolved in the water in compartment B. The sugar molecules, perhaps because of their larger sizes, do not pass through the membrane, and they tend to block the passage of neighboring water molecules. For this reason the diffusion of water molecules from B is diminished and the diffusion into it is not affected. Water, therefore, accumulates in B, Fig. 3. This process continues until the excess pressure due to the

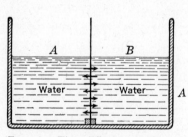

FIG. 2.—The diffusion rates are equal when the same fluid fills both compartments.

column of liquid is sufficient to equalize the two diffusion rates. This process is called **osmosis** (Greek, *osmose* = "pushing").

Osmosis is the diffusing of a liquid through a membrane into a mixture containing a constituent that cannot pass through the membrane.

156. Osmotic Pressures. Osmosis is studied using a thimble-shaped membrane attached to the large end of a funnel or "thistle" tube mounted as in Fig. 4. The solution of sugar or other substance is placed in the thimble, and

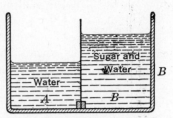

FIG. 3.—Osmosis causes the pressure to be greater in *B* than in *A*.

the pure liquid, for example water, is in the glass vessel. As osmosis continues, the liquid rises higher in the vertical tube until the excess pressure in the enclosure is sufficient to equalize the diffusion rates.

The pressure necessary to equalize the diffusion rates measures the osmotic pressure of the solution.

With sugars and many other substances, the osmotic pressure is directly proportional to the concentration. For example, a 1 per cent solution of sugar in water at 0°C. causes an osmotic pressure of 53.5 cm.-of-mercury. With a 2 per cent solution at the same temperature, the pressure is twice as great, that is, 107.0 cm.-of-mercury.

157. Examples of Osmosis. Cut a grapefruit into halves and sprinkle sugar on the cut surface. A syrup accumulates because the sugar opposes the diffusion of the water away from the surface. Salt sprinkled on a piece of meat has the same effect. A raisin placed in water soon becomes plump because water diffusing into it dissolves the sugar there which retards the diffusion of the water out of the raisin.

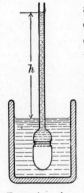

FIG. 4.—Apparatus to measure osmotic pressures.

Some of the most interesting examples of diffusion are from biology. In digestion, as food passes through the intestines, nutriment diffuses through the walls of blood vessels and enters the blood stream by which it is carried to the cells of the body. Oxygen from the blood diffuses through the cell walls, and carbon dioxide diffuses outward from the cells into the stream. The maximum rate at which a muscle can continue to work is probably determined by the rates of diffusion of oxygen and of carbon dioxide through the walls of the muscle cells. Researches indicate that this limit has nearly been attained and that no long-distance runner can much exceed the records of Nurmi and of other athletes. It is well known that the drinking of salt water increases thirst. The explanation in terms of diffusion is very simple. The salt decreases the diffusion rate of the water from the intestine into the blood stream so that more water leaves the blood than enters it. Certain remedies for obesity are merely Epsom's salts or Glauber's salts which prevent water from entering the blood.

158. Molecular Bombardment Causes Gas Pressures. A stream of water from a hose, striking a window pane, exerts a force and causes pressure. Picture a swarm of bees confined in a cage. They fly about, bumping against one another and against the walls of the enclosure. The impacts against any wall are so numerous as to exert against it a

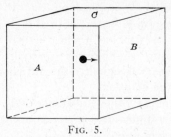

FIG. 5.

nearly constant force. The magnitude of this force will depend upon the speeds of the insects. If the speeds increase, there will be more impacts per second and at each impact a greater impulse will be delivered to the wall. Suppose, also, that the size of the enclosure is diminished so as to crowd the bees into closer quarters. Then there would be more impacts against the wall and the force exerted would increase. Thus the force exerted against the wall depends upon both the speeds of the bees and the size of the enclosure. The pressure of a gas is produced, similarly, by the bombardment of the molecules. Consider a cubical box, the length of each side of which is l (Fig. 5). Suppose that it contains a large number of oxygen molecules. These molecules continually move about with average speeds of hundreds of meters per second. They bump against each other and against the walls of the enclosure, hence the pressure of the gas.

159. Pressure Proportional to Density. Suppose that the number of molecules per unit volume is doubled, thus doubling the density. Then if the average speed is constant, there will be twice as many hits per second against the wall B, the force exerted against it will be doubled, as will also the pressure. Hence, **the pressure of a gas is proportional to its density.**

160. Pressure and Molecular Speed. If the average speed of the molecules is doubled, the force exerted against the wall B will be quadrupled. At the doubled speed, each molecule will make twice as many hits against B per unit time. Moreover, at each impact it will deliver twice as great an impulse. Since both factors are doubled, it follows that the force against the face B, and also the pressure of the gas, are quadrupled.

If the number of molecules per unit volume is n, the mass of each molecule is m, and the average speed is c, the pressure p is given approximately by:

$$p = \tfrac{1}{3} \, (nmc^2) \tag{1}$$

161. Proof of the Pressure Formula. The pressure formula is of great interest and importance because it enables us to deduce the mean speed of the molecules of a gas. The following proof is the most difficult one given in the book and may well be omitted by those students who do not enjoy algebraic manipulations.

162. The Change of Momentum per Unit Time. Suppose that a certain molecule of mass m and velocity c moves to and fro striking the face B (Fig. 5) at right angles. When it hits the wall, the velocity changes from a negative value $-c$ to a positive one $+c$. Hence the **change** of velocity is $2c$ and the change of momentum **per impact** is $2mc$.

If the width of the box is l, the distance moved by the molecule between successive impacts against B is $2l$. The number of impacts per unit time is velocity/distance $= c/2l$. Thus the total change of momentum at B per unit time is

$$\text{Change per impact} \times \text{Impacts/Unit time} \tag{2}$$
$$2mc \times c/2l = mc^2/l$$

In accord with Newton's laws of motion, the force acting on a body may be defined either as **mass times acceleration** or as the **rate of change of its momentum.** By the latter definition, the average force F exerted on the molecule by B is

$$F = mc^2/l \tag{3}$$

Thus far we have assumed that only one molecule is in the box and that it continues to move to and fro, striking B normally. Let us go a step farther and assume that there are N molecules and that one-third of them move sidewise striking B, one-third move up and down, and the remainder strike the front and back faces of the box. Since only one-third of the particles pound against B, the force is

$$F = \tfrac{1}{3} \, (Nmc^2/l) \tag{4}$$

The area of the surface B is l^2, hence the pressure is given by

$$p = F/A = \frac{\frac{1}{3}(Nmc^2)}{l^2 \times l} = \frac{1}{3}\frac{Nmc^2}{\text{Volume}} \tag{5}$$

But $N/$(Volume) is the number of molecules per unit volume which we represent by n, hence

$$p = \frac{1}{3}(nmc^2) \tag{6}$$

163. How to Compute Molecular Speeds. No one has ever seen a molecule or can hope to see one, hence it is interesting to see how simply average molecular speeds may be determined. In equation (1); nm is the mass of the gas per unit volume, that is, the mass-density d. Hence

$$p = \frac{1}{3}(dc^2) \tag{7}$$

Using this expression, we now compute the mean molecular speed of oxygen at 32°F. or 0°C. (Masses are expressed in grams, forces in dynes, and pressures in dynes per square centimeter.) Let the pressure be 75 cm.-of-mercury or 1,000,000 dynes/cm.² The density d under these conditions is 0.00143 gram/cm.³ and

$$p = \frac{1}{3}(dc^2)$$
$$1,000,000 \text{ dynes/cm.}^2 = \frac{1}{3}(0.00143 \text{ gram/cm.}^3 \times c^2)$$
$$c = 46,000 \text{ cm./sec.}$$
$$= 460 \text{ m./sec. or about 3/10 mi./sec.}$$

164. Molecular Kinetic Energy. Suppose that two equal boxes contain oxygen and hydrogen, respectively, at the same temperature and pressure. Let n, m, and c refer to hydrogen while N, M, and C are corresponding values for oxygen. Thus

$$P_1 = 1/3(nmc^2) = P_2 = 1/3(NMC^2) \tag{8}$$

There is abundant evidence (beyond the scope of this course) that the number of molecules per unit volume in each box is equal. Hence

$$1/3(mc^2) = 1/3(MC^2) \tag{9}$$

and

$$\frac{1}{2}mc^2 = \frac{1}{2}MC^2 \tag{10}$$

Thus the average translational kinetic energy of an oxygen molecule equals that of a hydrogen molecule at the same temperature. This statement holds for all gases and liquids. It holds even for mammoth colloidal particles visible through a microscope. However, molecules can possess additional energy of rotation and of vibration.

SUMMARY

The molecules in a gas diffuse slowly because each molecule collides with others and moves at random.

The rate of diffusion of a gas increases with molecular speed and decreases with increase of the size of the molecules.

The diffusion rates in liquids are smaller than those of gases because the molecules in liquids are more closely packed together.

The osmotic pressure of a solution (in many instances) is directly proportional to the concentration of the dissolved substance.

The pressure of a gas is produced by molecular bombardment. The pressure is proportional to the density of the gas and to the square of the mean molecular speed.

The mean molecular speed of a gas is found by means of the formula $p = \frac{1}{3}(dc^2)$.

REVIEW QUESTIONS

1. Explain why gases diffuse more rapidly than liquids.
2. Upon what factors does the rate of diffusion of a gas depend?
3. Describe an experiment proving that gases diffuse at different rates.
4. What is osmosis? Osmotic pressure?
5. How may the osmotic pressure of a liquid be measured?
6. (a) State several examples of osmosis, preferably including some not mentioned in the text. (b) If blood is mixed with water, the walls of the blood cells burst, but if a salt solution of proper concentration is used, the blood cells are not damaged. Explain.
7. Explain how the pressure of a gas is produced, and state three factors on which it depends.
8. Show why the pressure of a gas varies as the square of the mean molecular speed.
9. How can the mean molecular speed of a gas be determined?
10. How do the mean molecular speeds of gases depend upon their densities?
11. Compare the status of the molecular hypothesis 2,000 years ago with that in 1800 and in 1900 A.D.
12. When does a hypothesis become a theory?
13. Prove that when two gases are at the same temperature the mean (translational) kinetic energy of a hydrogen molecule equals that of an oxygen molecule.

CHAPTER XIX

TEMPERATURE

165. Temperature. Our first ideas of the difference between "hot" and "cold" are secured by means of physiological sensations. It is easy to compare the temperatures of two pieces of iron by touching first one and then the other. This method in many instances is quite unreliable. For example, on a cold winter day, a piece of iron seems colder than a piece of wood though both are at the same temperature.

Although it is difficult, at this point, to define temperature, we can state a qualitative definition of **temperature difference.** If a hot poker is dipped into a bucket of water, heat passes from the hot poker to the cold water. In general, **heat tends to flow from hotter bodies to colder ones.** It follows that, if two objects at the same temperature are brought together, neither will gain heat at the expense of the other.

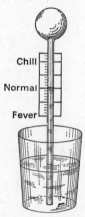

Fig. 1.—Galileo's fever thermometer.

166. Thermometers. A thermometer is a device for measuring temperatures. The first one, constructed by Galileo in 1593, was a very crude affair (Fig. 1). It consisted of a bulb attached to a glass tube the lower end of which was submerged in a vessel of water. When the bulb was heated, some of the air was expelled from it, and, as the air cooled again, water was forced upward into the tube. This thermometer was of great service to physicians and was the ancestor of the clinical thermometers of today. To use it, the physician first placed the bulb in his own mouth. As the confined air was heated, the water level in the tube moved downward to a point which was marked. Next the bulb was placed in the patient's mouth, and if the water level moved to the same position as before, the doctor reasoned, "This man's temperature is the same as mine; so it must be normal!"

Galileo attached a scale to his thermometer in order to measure the heights of the water column, but he could not trust the accuracy of the readings for variations in barometric pressure caused the water in the tube to rise and fall. After about 50 years a great improvement was made. The Grand Duke of Tuscany needed a reliable thermometer for experiments on the artificial incubation of eggs. He wanted an instrument which could be relied upon from day to day, not being affected by varying barometric pressures. He therefore inverted Galileo's bulb and tube, filled it with alcohol to a certain level, and sealed the upper end. In this improved thermometer, temperature variations were indicated by the rise and fall of the liquid surface caused by the expansion or contraction of the alcohol. The stem was marked off in degrees, forming the thermometer essentially as we know it. However, there was no accepted thermometric scale, and each experimenter set his own standard.

167. The Fahrenheit and Centigrade Scales. About a century after Galileo's invention, Fahrenheit of Danzig made improvements in thermometers, one of which was the substitution of mercury for alcohol. He is remembered principally because he devised a thermometric scale which is commonly used today. Fahrenheit wished to avoid negative readings and therefore chose for the zero point a temperature colder than the ordinary winter temperatures of his locality. He sent a thermometer to a friend in Iceland who made weather observations during the winter of 1709 and reported the lowest observed temperature. This point was selected as the zero of the new scale. Fahrenheit found that he could produce it at will by using a mixture of a salt (ammonium chloride) and ice in certain stated proportions.

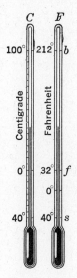

FIG. 2.—The centigrade and Fahrenheit temperature scales.

As a second fixed point on the scale, Fahrenheit may have used the normal temperature of the human body as 100°. On the thermometers of today, the value is 98.6°F. The temperature of the body is no longer used in standardizing thermometers, since it varies considerably even in healthy individuals. The upper fixed point is the temperature of boiling water, at "normal" pressure (76 cm.-of-mercury), which by definition is 212°F. For the lower point, the melting point of ice is taken as 32°F.

Centigrade thermometers are generally employed in scientific laboratories. In calibrating them, the freezing point of water is taken as 0° and the normal boiling point as 100° (Fig. 2).

168. Conversion from One Temperature Scale to the Other. In converting Fahrenheit temperature readings to centigrade, and vice versa, one should keep in mind that the 180° on the Fahrenheit scale from the freezing point to the normal boiling point of water are equal to 100° on the centigrade scale (Fig. 3). Hence

$$\frac{\text{Fahrenheit degrees above freezing}}{180\text{F.}^\circ} = \frac{\text{Centigrade degrees above freezing}}{100\text{C.}^\circ}$$

or

$$\frac{\text{Fahrenheit temperature} - 32\text{F.}^\circ}{180\text{F.}^\circ} = \frac{\text{Centigrade temperature} - 0\text{C.}^\circ}{100\text{C.}^\circ}$$

That is,

$$5/9(\text{Fahrenheit temperature} - 32\text{F.}^\circ) = \text{Centigrade temperature}$$

Example. The temperature of a room is 70°F. What is the reading of a centigrade thermometer?

$$\frac{70°\text{F.} - 32\text{F.}^\circ}{180\text{F.}^\circ} = \frac{t_\text{C.} - 0\text{C.}^\circ}{100\text{C.}^\circ}$$

$$t_\text{C.} = 21.1°\text{C.}$$

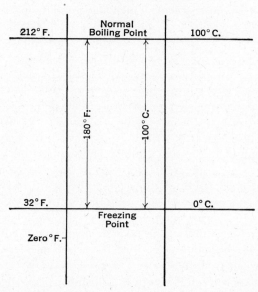

FIG. 3.—The relationship between Fahrenheit and centigrade temperatures.

169. The Expansion of Gases—Boyle's Law. The volume of a body of gas depends to a marked degree upon both its temperature and its pressure. In studying the expansion of a gas, it is convenient first to keep the temperature constant, observing the variation of the volume as the pressure is changed. The relationship was first studied by Robert Boyle about 1660. He used a J-shaped tube (Fig. 4), into which mercury was poured, trapping air in the closed, shorter end. When the mercury surfaces in both sides were at the same level, the pressure

TABLE I

Pressure cm.-of-Hg	Volume, cm.³	Pressure × Volume (cm.-of-Hg × cm.³)
75.0	1.00	75.0
150.0	0.503	75.4
225.0	0.332	74.7
300.0	0.251	75.3

of the confined air equaled that of the atmosphere, for example, 76 cm.-of-mercury. Boyle then poured mercury into the open arm until the volume of the confined air was reduced to one-half of its previous value. In this condition, with the temperature unchanged, the mercury surface in the open tube was 76 cm. above that in the closed tube, giving a pressure of 152 cm.-of-mercury. In other words, the pressure of the confined gas was doubled. Boyle found that when the pressure was tripled the volume was reduced to one-third. He made numerous other measurements, using widely different pressures.

Typical results for an experiment using simple apparatus are shown in Table I.

On the basis of such findings, Boyle stated his well-known law, as follows:

When the temperature is constant, the volume of a body of gas varies inversely as the pressure.

That is, if a body of gas of volume v_1 at a pressure p_1 is compressed to a volume v_2 at a pressure p_2 (the temperature being constant),

$$p_1/p_2 = v_2/v_1$$

or

$$p_1v_1 = p_2v_2 \quad \text{(Boyle's law)}$$

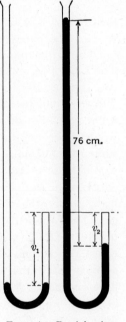

FIG. 4.—Boyle's law tube.

170. Boyle's Law is Not Absolutely True.

The reader may well object that the pressure-volume products in the table are not constant and, hence, that Boyle's law is not correct. This illustrates a common truth in scientific investigations. Most laws hold approximately, and under certain limited conditions. If the experiment is repeated using better apparatus, the errors are reduced, but they never become zero. Moreover, where the gas pressure is high, the molecules are so closely crowded together that Boyle's law does not hold even approximately.

171. Boyle's Law and Molecular Bombardment. Suppose that 2 in.³ of air at a pressure of 15 lb./in.² are confined in a cylinder closed by a sliding piston (Fig. 5). When the piston is pushed inward, reducing the volume to 1 in.³, the density of the gas is doubled. Further, if the

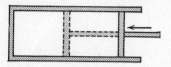

temperature of the gas is the same as before, the molecules have the same average speed. Since the density is doubled, there are twice as many hits per second against the piston and the pressure is doubled in accord with Boyle's law.

FIG. 5.—Compressing a gas increases the density and the pressure.

172. Volume and Temperature. Let 273 cm.³ of dry air at 0°C. be confined in a long cylinder closed by a sliding piston (Fig. 6). Let the pressure of the air be constant and the temperature be raised 1°C. Then the confined air will expand 1 cm.³, that is, 1/273 of the initial volume at 0°C. The rate of expansion is constant when the temperature is raised farther, and at 100°C. the volume is 373 cm.³

Suppose that instead of raising the temperature it had been lowered. Then the air would have continued to contract at the same rate for many degrees. Eventually, it would liquefy and cease to behave like a gas. Let the same experiment be performed using some other gas, for instance, hydrogen. Then the expansion per degree is very nearly the same as before, namely, 1/273 times the volume at 0°C. **All gases have approximately the same coefficient of volume expansion.** Moreover, all gases liquefy at low temperatures. It is convenient to imagine an "ideal" gas which would not liquefy but would continue to contract at

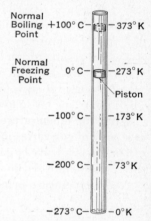

FIG. 6.—Expansion of a gas at constant pressure.

the same rate even at very low temperatures. The volume of this gas would be 173 cm.³ at −100°C. At −200°C. it would be 73 cm.³, at −272°C. it would be 1 cm.³, and at −273°C. it would be zero.

173. The Kelvin or Absolute Temperatures. In dealing with gases, it is very helpful to use the **Kelvin** temperature scale on which the boiling point of water is 373°, the freezing point is 273°, and the zero is −273°C. (more accurately −273.181°C.). One great advantage of this scale is that the volume of a gas at constant pressure is proportional to its Kelvin temperature. This rule holds for most gases at ordinary temperatures and pressures, and, by definition, it would hold for an ideal gas at any temperature.

Example. A cylinder closed by a piston contains 500 cm.³ of air at 76 cm.-of-mercury and 0°C. At what temperature would the volume be 1,500 cm.³ if the pressure remained constant?

The initial temperature is 0°C. or 273°K.

$$p_1/p_2 = T_1/T_2$$
$$\frac{500 \text{ cm.}^3}{1,500 \text{ cm.}^3} = \frac{273°K.}{T.}$$
$$T = 819°K.$$
$$819°K. - 273°K. = 546°C.$$

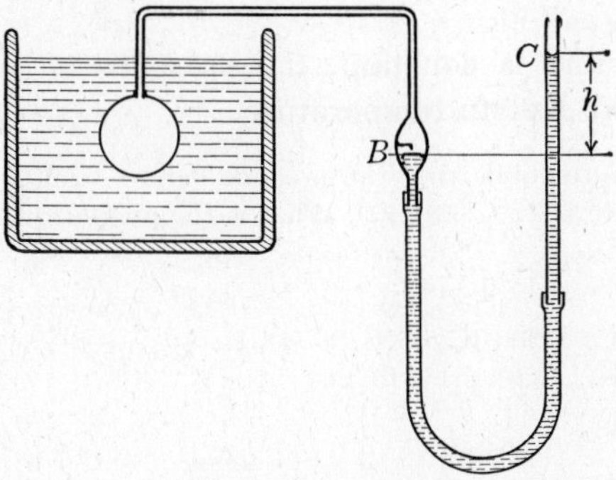

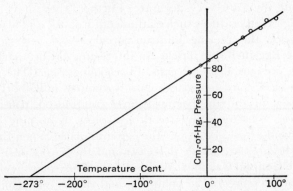

Fig. 7.—A constant-volume gas thermometer.

Pressure at Constant Volume—Charles' Law. When the volume of a gas remains constant, the pressure increases with rising tempera-

Fig. 8.—The variation of pressure with temperature, at constant volume.

ture. The variation may be determined using the apparatus represented in Fig. 7. The bulb containing the gas is connected to a rubber tube filled with mercury, one end being attached to a glass tube C. When the tube is raised, mercury is forced upward until it touches a marker wire at B. The device serves as an open-air manometer, and the pressure of the confined gas is $B + h$, where B is the barometric pressure. When the temperature increases, the gas expands. Then the open tube is raised so as to restore the volume to its previous value and the pressure and temperature are noted as before.

The results of such an experiment are shown in Fig. 8. It will be noted that all the points lie along a straight line. This line if extended cuts the horizontal axis at $-273°$C. This means that, if the gas were cooled sufficiently, and if it continued to behave in the same manner, its pressure would become zero at $-273°$C., that is, at the Kelvin zero.

Charles' law is as follows:

When the volume is constant, the pressure of an "ideal" gas is proportional to the Kelvin temperature.

Example. In an automobile tire, the pressure (above atmospheric) is 30 lb./in.² when the temperature is 27°C. (81°F.). What is the pressure when the temperature rises to 45°C. (113°F.)?

Barometric pressure = 15 lb./in.²

$$27°C. = 300°K., \quad 45°C. = 318°K.$$
$$\frac{300°K.}{318°K.} = \frac{(30 + 15) \text{ lb./in.}^2}{X}$$
$$X = 47.7 \text{ lb./in.}^2 \quad \text{Excess pressure} = 32.7 \text{ lb./in.}^2$$

The Gas Thermometer. Devices like that shown in Fig. 7 are often used in research work for the accurate measurements of temperatures and are called gas thermometers. They are cumbersome and inconvenient, but they are very accurate. Further, they may be used to measure high temperatures such as those of furnaces, and also temperatures far below the freezing point of mercury.

174. The Egg-in-Bottle Trick. An interesting bit of "parlor magic" utilizes the pressure decrease caused by cooling a gas. The problem is to get a peeled, hard-boiled egg into an empty milk bottle. Try to push the egg in, and the confined air is compressed, causing an opposing force. A better way is to drop a piece of burning paper into the bottle, and afterward to put the egg into place. When the confined air cools, the pressure inside decreases and the egg is pushed in.

175. The General Gas Law. We have been studying the relationships between the pressure p, the volume v, and the Kelvin temperature T of a gas, and have considered three special laws, namely:

v varies as $1/p$, when T is constant (Boyle's law)
v varies as T, when p is constant
p varies as T, when v is constant (Charles' law)

These three special laws can be combined into a general law expressed by the following equation:

$$\frac{p_1 v_1}{T_1} = \frac{p_2 v_2}{T_2}$$

The reader will note that if $T_1 = T_2$ this equation yields Boyle's law and that if $v_1 = v_2$ it expresses the law of Charles.

This equation is very convenient in solving problems.

Example. When a balloon left the earth in a stratosphere flight, the volume of the gas was 100,000 ft.³, the pressure was 74 cm.-of-mercury, and the temperature was 27°C. or 300°K. Find the volume of the gas at an elevation where $p = 14.8$ cm.-of-mercury and $t = -73°C. = 200°K$.

$$\frac{p_1 v_1}{T_1} = \frac{p_2 v_2}{T_2}$$

$$\frac{74 \text{ cm.-of-Hg} \times 100,000 \text{ ft.}^3}{300°K.} = \frac{14.8 \text{ cm.-of-Hg} \times v}{200°K.}$$

$$v = 333,000 \text{ ft.}^3$$

SUMMARY

Heat tends to flow from points of higher to those of lower temperatures.

On the Fahrenheit scale, the normal boiling point of water, at 76 cm.-of-mercury, is 212°, and the freezing point is 32°. On the centigrade scale, the corresponding values are 100°C. and 0°C.

If a gas is cooled, the volume being constant, the change of pressure per degree is constant over a considerable range. If this decrease per degree remained constant, the pressure would become zero at $-273°C$. Consequently, we take this point as the zero of a new "Kelvin" temperature scale on which 273° is the freezing point of water and 373° its normal boiling point.

To transform centigrade temperatures into Fahrenheit, or vice versa, use the relation

$$\frac{(t_F. - 32 \text{ F.}°)}{180 \text{F.}°} = \frac{t_C. - 0 \text{C.}°}{100 \text{C.}°}$$

Boyle's law states that, when the temperature is constant, the product of the pressure and volume of a gas is constant. That is, pressure is inversely proportional to volume.

Charles' law is as follows: The pressure of a gas, at constant volume, is proportional to its Kelvin temperature.

The pressure, volume, and temperature of an ideal gas are interrelated by

$$\frac{p_1 v_1}{T_1} = \frac{p_2 v_2}{T_2}$$

REVIEW QUESTIONS

1. Define temperature difference.

2. Describe Galileo's thermometer, and state at least two of its disadvantages.

3. Describe the improvements made by Fahrenheit, and discuss the fixed point used by him in calibrating thermometers.

4. Discuss the relative advantages of the centigrade and the Fahrenheit scales.

5. Derive an equation interrelating corresponding Fahrenheit and centigrade thermometer readings.

6. State advantages and disadvantages of mercury as a thermometric substance.

7. Make a sketch of a gas thermometer, and show how it may be used. State its advantages and disadvantages.

8. State Boyle's law, and describe an experiment for testing its validity. To what extent is it a valid statement?

9. Show how Boyle's law might be derived from the equation $p = 1/3nmc^2$.

10. Discuss the variation of gas volume with temperature if the pressure is constant. Define "ideal gas," "Kelvin zero," "Kelvin temperature."

11. Discuss the variation of gas pressure with temperature when the volume is constant. State Charles' law.

12. What advantage has the Kelvin temperature scale over the centigrade scale?

13. If a gas meter reads correctly at 70°F., will the customer gain or lose when the temperature is 100°F.?

PROBLEMS

1. Reduce the following Fahrenheit temperatures to centigrade: (a) blood temperature, 98.6°F.; (b) the freezing point of mercury, −39.°F.; (c) a room temperature, 68°F.; (d) the surface temperature of the sun, 11,000°F.

2. Reduce the following to Fahrenheit readings: (a) the melting point of gold, 1,063°C.; (b) the boiling point of mercury, 357°C.; (c) the boiling point of helium, −267°C.; (d) the boiling point of nitrogen, −195°C.

3′. At what temperature does a Fahrenheit thermometer read the same as a centigrade thermometer?

4′. What is the reading of a Fahrenheit thermometer when the reading on the centigrade scale is one-half as great?

5′. The volume of the inner tube of an automobile tire is 2,000 in.³ If the pressure, above atmospheric, is 30 lb./in.² and the barometric pressure is 15 lb./in.² what volume will the air occupy if the tire bursts, assuming that the temperature is constant?

6′. How many cubic inches of air at atmospheric pressure must be pumped into the tire described in the preceding problem in order to raise the pressure above atmospheric from 30 lb./in.² to 45 lb./in.²?

7′. A cylinder with a sliding piston contains 3,000 cm.³ of air at 27°C. Find the volume at 127°C., if the pressure remains constant.

8. Motorists often believe that tires burst on hot days because of the increase in pressure caused by a rise of temperature. Criticize this belief, and suggest a more probable explanation after solving the following problem:

9′. An automobile tire at 27°C. contains air at a pressure of 45 lb./in.² (above atmospheric). The barometric pressure is 15 lb./in.² Find the pressure increase if the temperature rises 20 C.° (36 F.°).

10. In 1 hr., 1,000 ft.³ of air at 17°C. pass into a hot-air furnace and the temperature is raised 10 C.° Find the volume of air escaping per hour at the hot-air registers.

11′. If the temperature of 1 cm.³ of an "ideal" gas were raised from −272°C. to −270°C., how much would it expand if the pressure were constant?

12′. A chemistry student collects 280 cm.³ of carbon dioxide gas at a pressure of 75 cm.-of-mercury and a temperature of 27°C. Find the volume of the gas at standard temperature and pressure (0°C. and 76 cm.-of-mercury).

13′. The density of air at 0°C. and 76 cm.-of-mercury is 1.29 gm./liter. Find its density at 27°C. and 100 cm.-of-mercury.

14′. When the bulb of a gas thermometer (Fig. 7) was at 0°C., the height h was 24 cm. and the barometer reading was 76 cm. When the bulb was in a certain furnace, h was 224 cm. Find the temperature of the furnace.

15″. What is absolute zero on the Fahrenheit scale?

16′. The volume of a certain steel hydrogen tank is ¼ m.³ How much hydrogen will it contain at 20 atmospheres if the density of hydrogen at 1 atmosphere pressure is 90 grams/m.³ (temperature constant)?

17. How many cubic feet of helium at a pressure of 60 atmospheres are required to fill a balloon of volume 200,000 ft.³ at a pressure of 1 atmosphere (temperature constant)?

$$\text{Thermal capacity} = \frac{1 \text{ calory}}{1 \text{ gm/c}^\circ}$$

$$\text{Thermal capacity of water} = \frac{1 \text{ B.T.U.}}{1 \text{ lb. } 32^\circ F}$$

Standard conditio

760 mm (of mercury)
at 0° c

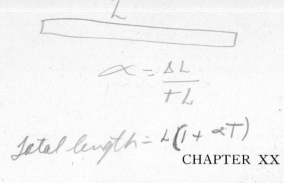

$$\alpha = \frac{\Delta L}{TL}$$

Total length $= L(1 + \alpha T)$

CHAPTER XX

EXPANSION OF SOLIDS AND LIQUIDS

When a solid body is heated, the kinetic energies of its atoms increase and they vibrate or oscillate with greater average speeds. The atoms push one another away so that the body expands. There are numerous familiar examples of expansions and contractions caused by variations in temperature. When cement sidewalks are laid, gaps are sometimes left between adjacent blocks in order to permit expansion. Hot water poured into a thick glass tumbler sometimes fractures the glass because the surface layers near the water expand before the outer layers have become heated. There is less danger of breaking if the walls are very thin because all parts of the glass are heated more uniformly. In constructing the steel frame of a building, the rivets are hammered while hot, and in cooling they draw the iron plates tightly together. The steel tires of locomotives, driven onto the wheels at a high temperature, contract sufficiently to grip the wheels so strongly that no rivets or bolts are required. The bulging walls of brick buildings are drawn inward by means of iron rods. In such an operation, the rod joining opposite walls is heated so that it expands. Then the nut at one end is tightened. When the rod cools, it exerts great forces which pull the walls toward each other.

176. The Coefficient of Linear Expansion. When a metal rod is heated, the expansion is proportional to the original length L of the rod, and to the rise of temperature $(t_2 - t_1)$. Thus:

$$\text{Change of length} = \alpha L(t_2 - t_1) \qquad (1)$$

In this equation α is the **coefficient of linear expansion** (or thermal expansivity) of the material. It equals the fractional expansion per degree. For example, an iron wire 1 km. (100,000 cm.) is heated 1 C.⁰ and expands 1.2 cm. The coefficient of linear expansion is 1.2 cm./(100,000 cm. $\times$ 1 C.⁰) = 0.000012/C.⁰ (see Table 1).

176

TABLE I

COEFFICIENTS OF LINEAR EXPANSION

Material	Fractional Expansion per Centigrade Degree at 20°C.	Expansion in Centimeters per Kilometer per Centigrade Degree
A. LINEAR		
Aluminum.................	0.000022	2.2
Brass.....................	0.000019	1.9
Copper...................	0.000017	1.7
Glass, ordinary............	0.0000090	0.90
Glass, Pyrex..............	0.0000040	0.40
"Invar" alloy (nickel-steel)..	0.0000009	0.09
Iron......................	0.000012	1.2
Platinum.................	0.0000090	0.90
Fused quartz..............	0.00000059	0.059
Steel.....................	0.000013	1.3
Tungsten.................	0.0000034	0.34
B. VOLUME		
Ethyl alcohol..............	0.00101	
Mercury..................	0.000182	

Example. One of the steel cables supporting a suspension bridge is 1000 m. long. Find its expansion when the temperature changes from 0°C. to 40°C.

Linear expansion = 0.000013/C.° ×
  100,000 cm. × 40 C.° = 52 cm.

177. Correcting for Expansion.

If a surveyor uses a steel tape which is correct at 70°F. and the actual temperature is 100°F., the tape will be longer than the length marked upon it, and errors arise. When tapes are made of invar, a nickel-iron alloy, the errors are about one-fourteenth as great and are neglected in ordinary work. The pendulum rod of a clock expands when the temperature rises, and the clock loses time. Sometimes a vessel of mercury is used as a bob (Fig. 1). The expansion of the rod tends to increase the effective length of the pendulum, and the expansion of the mercury, relatively much greater, tends to raise the center of gravity, decreasing the length. With careful design, the two changes can be made practically to neutralize each other so that the clock keeps time more accurately.

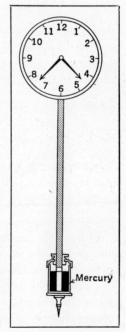

FIG. 1.—A compensated clock pendulum.

178. Unequal Expansion. Rivet a bar of iron and one of brass together as in Fig. 2A and heat the bimetallic bar in a flame. The brass expands more than the iron and the bar bends. Many thermostats for

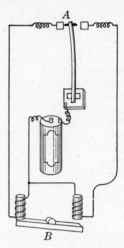

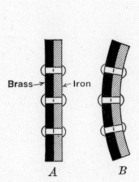

FIG. 2.—Differential expansion.

FIG. 3.—A temperature-control device.

controlling furnaces and electrical heating devices utilize such bimetallic bars. In Fig. 3, the bar is mounted between two electrical contact points. If the temperature of the room falls, the bar moves sidewise until it touches a contact, closing an electric circuit and energizing an electromagnet which opens the drafts or the gas-supply valve. As the room heats again, the bar moves backward until it touches a second contact, closing another circuit which adjusts the drafts or shuts off the gas. In many automobiles thermostats are placed in the tubes through which water flows from the engine to the radiator (Fig. 4). As the water cools, the

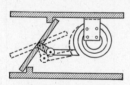

FIG. 4.—An automobile thermostat.

bimetallic strip moves, closing the valve and preventing the flow of water from the engine. When the water gets hot, the valve is opened wide permitting maximum flow through the radiator.

179. Volume Expansion. When a block of iron is heated, not only does the length increase, but also the width and thickness, and the volume increases with temperature. The laws for computing the volume change are similar to those for linear expansion. We define the volume coefficient of expansion as **the change of volume per unit volume per degree change of temperature.**

For example, if 1 cm.³ of iron expands 0.000036 cm.³ when the temperature is raised 1 C.° the coefficient of volume expansion is 36/(1,000,000 C.°).

Let the initial volume of a substance be v, the rise of temperature $(t_2 - t_1)$, and the coefficient of volume expansion β. Then

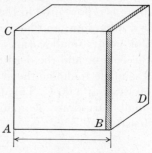

$$\text{Volume expansion} = \beta v (t_2 - t_1) \quad (2)$$

The volume coefficients of solid substances are not given in reference books because they can be found by merely multiplying the linear coefficients by 3. The explanation follows: Suppose that a cubical block of glass, 1 cm. on each edge, is heated 1 C.° and the expansion of the edge AB is 0.0000040 cm. (Fig. 5). Thus, the coefficient

FIG. 5.—When heated, the cube expands equally along AB, AC, and BD.

of *linear* expansion is 0.0000040/C.° Now, if the height and depth of the cube did not change, the volume expansion would likewise be 0.0000040/C.° In fact, the change of each of these dimensions is equal to that along AB, so that the volume change is 0.000012 cm.³ Hence, **the volume coefficient is thrice the linear coefficient.**

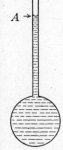

Place water in a glass bulb (Fig. 6), and plunge the bulb into hot water. At first the liquid surface at A moves downward and afterward it rises. The initial fall of the surface is produced because the expanding glass walls increase the volume of the bulb. Later, when the liquid itself is heated, it expands and the level at A rises. The expansion of the glass decreases the upward motion of the surface, and the apparent increase equals the difference between the increase in volume of the liquid and that of the container.

FIG. 6.

Example. The brass gasoline tank of a car has a volume of 15 gal. It is filled to the brim with gasoline, the average coefficient of expansion of which is 0.00096/C.° What volume will overflow if the temperature rises 20C.°?

Expansion of gasoline	= 15 gal. × 0.00096/C.° × 20 C.°
	= 0.29 gal.
Linear expansion coefficient of brass	= 0.19 × 10⁻⁴/C.°
Cubical expansion coefficient of brass	= 0.57 × 10⁻⁴/C.°
Expansion of brass container	= 15 gal. × 0.57 × 10⁻⁴/C.° × 20 C.°
	= 0.017 gal.

Hence,

Overflow = 0.290 gal. − 0.017 gal. = 0.27 gal. approximately.

180. The Maximum Density of Water. If a bulb (Fig. 6) contains water initially at 0°C., the liquid in the tube at first descends and then rises even when it is heated slowly. The explanation is that water contracts when its temperature rises from 0°C. to 4°C., and afterwards expands as most other liquids do. The expansion of water with temperature is represented in Fig. 7. It will be noted that, at 4°C., the volume is a minimum, and hence that the density is a maximum. Further, at this point, small variations in temperature produce little effect upon the volume and the density. In devising the metric system, an attempt was made to define the gram so that it should equal the mass of 1 cm.³ of water at 4.00°C. This temperature was chosen because at this point small variations of temperature produce very small variations in density.

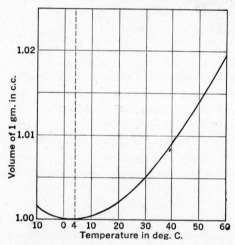

Fig. 7.—Water contracts when its temperature increases from 0° to 4, 0°C.

The fact that water is denser at 4°C. than at the freezing point is of very great importance, for otherwise the water in lakes and rivers would freeze first at the bottom and the ice would accumulate there. This ice, protected by the water above it, might not all melt during the following summer. Eventually, the northern lakes and oceans might be frozen solidly. Not only would the fish be killed, but also the effects on climate would be profound.

SUMMARY

Substances generally expand on heating.

The coefficient of linear expansion of a substance is the fractional expansion per degree rise of temperature.

The coefficient of cubical expansion of a solid substance equals three times its linear coefficient of expansion.

$$F_L = L(1 + \alpha T)$$

REVIEW QUESTIONS

1. Give several instances of expansion, including some not mentioned in the text.
2. Define "coefficient of linear expansion" and "coefficient of cubical expansion."
3. Prove that thrice the coefficient of linear expansion of a substance equals its coefficient of cubical expansion.
4. Describe the change of volume of water with temperature, and show why this is important regarding the freezing of lakes and rivers.
5. An iron rod connects the opposite sides of a circular iron hoop. If the system is equally heated, will the hoop remain circular?
6. After studying the table of coefficients of linear expansion, explain why a glass is more likely to crack when cooled quickly than a utensil made of quartz.
7. Why is it desirable in filling teeth to use some material that has almost the same coefficient of expansion as the teeth?
8. What kind of wire would be suitable for sealing into Pyrex glass, and what kind into ordinary glass?

PROBLEMS

1. A steel wagon tire is 16 ft. in circumference at 220°C. when it is put onto a wagon wheel. How much will the circumference shrink in cooling to 20°C.?
2''. Estimate from Fig. 7 the coefficients of cubical expansion of water at 20°C. and at 60°C.
3'. A spherical cavity in a block of copper has a volume of 1.000 cm.³ when the block is at 20°C. Find the volume of the cavity at 80°C.
4. When a steel rail was first rolled at a steel mill, its length was 40 ft., and its temperature was 520°C. Find its contraction in cooling to 20°C.
5. If steel rails 10 m. long are laid, just touching each other, at 40°C., what will be their separation at −10°C.?
6. An iron rod 1,000 cm. long expands 1.44 mm. when heated from 0°C. to 12°C. What is its linear coefficient of expansion?
7'. A glass flask of volume 1,000 cm.³ is full of mercury at 20°C. How many cubic centimeters will overflow when the temperature is raised to 50°C.? (The coefficient of linear expansion of glass is 0.0000092/C.° The volume coefficient of mercury is 0.000182/C.°)
8''. An iron rod 1.00 cm.² in cross-sectional area and 500 cm. long is used to pull the bulging wall of a building back into position. The rod is heated 50 C.° above room temperature and is then bolted tightly between the two opposite walls of the building. When the rod cools (a) how much would it contract if there were no tension, and (b) how much force would be exerted on the walls if they did not yield? (Use Young's modulus of elasticity 15.3 × 10⁸ gwt./cm.²)

$$V_F = L^3(1 + 3\alpha T)$$

$$V_F = V_0(1 + Bt) \text{ where } B = \text{coef of vol exp.}$$

$$V_F = 1000 cm^3(1 + ($$

(4)

CHAPTER XXI

CALORIES AND BRITISH THERMAL UNITS

The heat of a body is the kinetic energy due to the disorderly, chaotic motions of the molecules. This energy might be expressed in foot-pounds or in joules. More often it is given in British thermal units or in calories.

The British thermal unit (B.t.u.) is the amount of heat required to raise the temperature of 1 pound-mass of water 1 F.°

For example, 50 B.t.u. of heat are necessary to raise the temperature of 10 pounds of water from 70°F. to 75°F.

The calorie is the amount of heat required to raise the temperature of 1 gram-mass of water 1 C.°

Often in biology and in physiology the kilogram calorie is used. It equals 1,000 calories.

The amount of heat required to cause unit temperature rise in unit mass of water varies slightly with temperature, and for exactness it is necessary to specify the temperature range. Thus the calorie is usually defined as the amount of heat required to raise the temperature of 1 gram of water from 15°C. to 16°C.

181. Specific Heat. Heat a pound of iron and a pound of water (in a suitable vessel) separately over two equal Bunsen flames. The iron becomes so hot in a few minutes that water boils when a few drops are sprinkled on the upper surface of the block. Meanwhile, the water in the vessel is heated so slightly that one's hand may be placed in it without discomfort. This simple experiment shows that a given mass of water requires more heat per degree rise of temperature than does an equal mass of iron.

The specific heat of a substance is the heat absorbed per unit mass per unit rise of temperature.

The heat H required to raise the temperature of a body of mass M and specific heat S from a temperature t_1 to t_2 is given by

$$H = MS (t_2 - t_1).$$

182

TABLE I

SPECIFIC HEATS IN CALORIES/(Gram-C.°) or in B.t.u./(Pound-F.°)

SOLIDS

Aluminum	0.212
Brass	0.090
Carbon (graphite) at −50°C	0.114
at 11°C	0.160
Copper	0.092
Glass (soda)	0.016
Gold	0.0316
Ice	0.51
Iron	0.115–0.119
Lead	0.030
Silver	0.056
Zinc	0.093

LIQUIDS

Alcohol, ethyl	0.60
Mercury	0.033
Water (by definition)	1.00

Gases	At Constant Volume	At Constant Pressure
Air	0.162	0.237
Hydrogen	2.42	3.41

182. The Calorimeter—Water Equivalent.

Heat measurements in the laboratory are made using calorimeters of the form shown in Fig. 1. A small metal cup K is supported inside a larger vessel, by means of a fiber disk. The purpose of the arrangement is to insulate the inner vessel so as to minimize the loss or gain of heat to or from the surroundings. Usually water is contained in the inner cup, and, when heat is added, part goes to the water and part to the container. It is convenient, in such measurements, to consider the **water equivalent** of the calorimeter, that is, the mass of water which would absorb just as much heat per degree as does the container. This value is easily found. For example, the specific heat of copper is about one-eleventh that of water, so that 100 grams of copper are equivalent to about 9.0 grams of water.

FIG. 1.—A calorimeter.

The equation for computing the water equivalent of the calorimeter of mass m is as follows:

$$W.E. = (s/s_w)m$$

s being the specific heat of the metal, and s_w that of water.

The heat H added to a calorimeter of water equivalent $W.E.$ containing a mass of water m is given by

$$H = s_w(m + W.E.)(t_2 - t_1)$$

in which s_w represents the specific heat of water and $(t_2 - t_1)$ is the rise of temperature.

Example. One hundred grams of water are contained in a brass calorimeter of mass 200 grams. How much heat is required to raise the temperature 5.0 C.°? The specific heat of brass is 0.090 cal./(gram-C.°).

$$W.E. = 0.090 \times 200 \text{ grams.} = 18 \text{ grams.}$$
Heat loss by hot body = heat gain by cold body.
$$1.00 \text{ cal./gram-C.°}(100 \text{ grams} + 18 \text{ grams}) \times 5.0 \text{ C.°} = 590 \text{ cal.}$$

183. Heats of Combustion of Fuels and Foods. When large quantities of coal are purchased, it is customary to specify the minimum

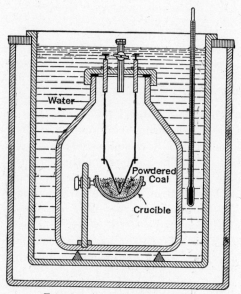

FIG. 2.—A bomb calorimeter.

heat of combustion, that is, the amount of heat evolved per unit mass of coal burned. This quantity is difficult to measure since in ordinary stoves much energy is lost, and usually part of the fuel is unburned.

A type of calorimeter used for determining heats of combustion of fuels and foods is represented in Fig. 2. It consists of a massive steel "bomb" containing a crucible filled with a known quantity of test substance, coal for example. A thin iron wire, suspended from two electrically insulated rods, is buried in the coal. After the cover is screwed on tightly, oxygen from a tank is added until the pressure is about 25 atmospheres. The bomb is then placed in a large calorimeter containing water, and the initial temperature is carefully read. An electric current, sent through the fine iron wire, heats it red hot and ignites the material, which burns violently until all the carbon is oxidized. The heat of combustion causes a rise of the temperature of the calorimeter. This rise is noted, and the heat evolved is computed in the usual manner (Table II).

TABLE II

Heats of Combustion of Fuels and Foods

Fuels	Calories per Gram	Foods	Calories per Gram
Alcohol, ethyl.........	7,180	Apples....................	290
methyl..............	5,300	Butter....................	3,030
Coal, anthracite........	7,400	Buttermilk...............	160
bituminous..........	5,500– 7,000	Beans, navy...............	1,600
Coke.................	8,000	Cream....................	865
Water gas.............	3,000– 6,000	Lard.....................	4,080
Coke-oven gas........	4,000– 6,000	Milk......................	310
Natural gas...........	8,000–12,000	Sugar, granulated.........	1,860
Gasoline.............	11,000	White bread..............	1,215
Hydrogen.............	34,000		
Wood (oak)..........	4,000		

184. Atomic Heats. In comparing the specific heats of different metals listed in Table I, it will be noted that elements of large atomic weight have relatively small specific heats. For example, the atomic weight of lead is about twice that of silver, and the specific heat is about one-half as large. For many elements in solid state at ordinary temperatures, the product of the specific heat by the atomic weight has approximately the same value. This product is the "atomic heat" of the substance.

The fact that 27.0 grams of aluminum and 207.2 grams of lead absorb heat nearly equally when their temperatures are raised is highly significant, for each of the two bodies of metal contains the same number of atoms. Hence each atom of the aluminum and of the lead absorbs about the same amount of heat.

185. The Specific Heat of a Gas When the Volume is Constant is Smaller Than That When the Pressure is Constant. Confine equal masses of air in two cylinders fitted with pistons (Fig. 3), and raise the temperature of each system equally. Permit the piston of B to move freely so that the pressure is constant, but lock that of A in its first position so that the volume is constant. When the temperature is raised, the gas in each cylinder absorbs an equal quantity of heat in

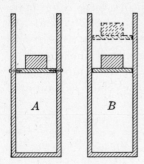

making the molecules move faster. In A the volume is constant and no external work is done, but in B work must be done in raising the piston. Hence more energy must be supplied to B, to cause the expansion and **the specific heat at constant pressure is greater than that at constant volume**. (See Table I.)

FIG. 3.—The gas in B is permitted to expand. More heat is absorbed per degree rise of temperature than in A, the volume of which is constant.

SUMMARY

Heat is molecular kinetic energy.

The calorie is the amount of heat required to raise the temperature of 1 gram-mass of water 1C.° The British thermal unit is the amount of heat required to raise the temperature of 1 pound-mass of water 1F.°

The specific heat of a substance is the amount of heat absorbed per unit mass per degree rise of temperature. It is expressed in calories per gram-centigrade-degree or in British thermal units per pound-Fahrenheit-degree.

The water equivalent of a body is the mass of water that will absorb the same heat per degree rise of temperature as does the body.

The atomic heat of an element is the heat absorbed per gram-atom per degree rise of temperature. It equals the product of the specific heat and the atomic weight.

The specific heat of a gas at constant pressure is greater than that at constant volume.

REVIEW QUESTIONS

1. Define "calorie," "British thermal unit."
2. Define "specific heat," and state a unit in which it may be expressed.
3. Define "water equivalent," and state an illustrative problem with its solution.
4. Define "heat of combustion," and state a unit in which it is expressed.
5. Discuss "atomic heat."
6. (a) Discuss the two specific heats of a gas. (b) Why is the specific heat of a solid at constant pressure approximately equal to that at constant volume?
7. Would you expect the specific heat of hydrogen at constant volume to be greater than, less than, or equal to, that of oxygen? Why? (The heat absorbed *per molecule* is the same in each gas.)

PROBLEMS

1. How many calories are required to heat 800 grams of water from 18°C. to 23°C.?
2. A copper calorimeter of mass 100 grams contains 100 grams of water. How many calories are required to raise the temperature from 16°C. to 22°C.?

3. Compute the number of calories in 1 B.t.u.

4'. A 10-gram nickel ball is removed from a furnace and is dropped into a copper calorimeter of mass 200 grams containing 100 grams of water at 18°C. If, afterward, the temperature of the water rose to 22°C., find the temperature of the furnace. Specific heat of nickel = 0.113 cal./gram-C.°

5''. How much bituminous coal must be burned to heat a bathtub full of water from 10°C. to 50°C., if the water has a mass of 40,000 grams? Find the cost of heating the water if bituminous coal costing 0.8 cent per kilogram is used. The efficiency of the heater is 50 per cent, and the heat of combustion is 6,000 cal./gram.

6. When 100 grams of water at 15°C. were mixed with water at 30°C., the temperature of the mixture was 25°C. How much hot water was there?

7'. A 20-gram mouse is placed in a closed calorimeter and is supplied with air through an inlet tube. The water equivalent of the calorimeter and its contents is 100 grams. If the temperature rises 0.15C.°/min., how much heat is evolved per hour?

8'. What fraction of its own weight of white bread must the mouse eat per day to supply this heat?

9. (a) If the average density of the air is 1,200 grams/m.³, how much heat is required to heat 3,000 m.³ of air at constant pressure from 15°C. to 25°C.? (b) How much bituminous coal, heat of combustion 6,000 cal./gram, would supply the needed energy if the stove is 50 per cent efficient?

10'. A classroom is 30 ft. by 20 ft. by 12 ft. How much heat is required to raise the temperature of the air it initially contains from 60°F. to 70°F. at constant pressure? Density of air at 60°F. = 0.070 pound/ft.³

11'. How much coal, heat of combustion = 10,000 B.t.u./pound, must be burned to supply the heat needed in Problem 10? Efficiency of the furnace = 25 per cent.

12'. One thousand grams of boiling water at 100°C. are poured into an aluminum tea kettle at 20°C., after which the temperature of the two is 86°C. Find (a) the water equivalent of the tea kettle, and (b) its mass.

13. Find the water equivalent of an iron bathtub having a mass of 100 pounds. The specific heat of the iron is 0.116 B.t.u./pound-F°.

14'. Two hundred grams of lead shot at 50°C. are poured into 180 grams of water at 10°C. in a calorimeter having a water equivalent of 20.0 grams. Find the temperature of the "mixture."

15. (a) How many B.t.u. are required to raise the temperature of 1 ft.³ of water 1.00 F.°? (b) How many calories are required to raise the temperature of 1.00 cm.³ of water 1.00C.°?

16. What change in temperature will 1 cal. of heat produce in 1.00 gram of (a) mercury, (b) lead, (c) aluminum, (d) hydrogen at constant pressure?

17''. The heat of combustion of butter is 3,030 cal./gram. Find the value in B.t.u. per pound.

CHAPTER XXII

HEAT TRANSFER AND RADIATION

Conservation of Fuel. The hardy pioneers, in the days of the covered wagon, endured living conditions that we would find very harsh if not intolerable. Their log cabins, open to the winter breezes, were poorly heated even by the roaring log fires. Today, in contrast, we are concerned that the heat for our dwellings be produced economically, that it be transferred to the desired location efficiently, and that the outer walls of the dwelling be insulated so as to reduce the rate of heat loss. In order to understand how these aims are accomplished, we shall consider the transfer of energy by **conduction,** by **convection,** and by **radiation.**

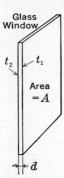

FIG. 1.—The heat transferred per second through a glass window pane depends on its area, the temperature difference, the thickness, and the thermal conductivity of the glass.

CONDUCTION

186. What Is Conduction? When one end of an iron rod is inserted into a mass of burning coal, the other end becomes warm, showing that heat has been transmitted along the rod. The explanation is that the molecules of the iron at the end nearer to the flame become heated and oscillate more violently than before. These molecules, colliding with their neighbors, transfer kinetic energy to them, and this energy is passed onward as heat toward the end of the rod. The important thing about conduction is that **heat alone is transferred; matter is not.**

187. Thermal Conductivity. In winter weather, considerable heat escapes from a heated room by conduction through the glass window panes. The amount transmitted per unit time depends upon several factors. They are the cross-sectional area A of the glass, its thickness d, the temperature difference $(t_2 - t_1)$ between the two surfaces, and the thermal conductivity K of the substance (Fig. 1). In general, for any large flat body like this,

Heat transferred/Time is proportional to A, to $(t_2 - t_1)$, and to $1/d$, so that:

$$\text{Heat/Time} = KA(t_2 - t_1)/d$$

188

The thermal conductivity expresses the **amount of heat that will flow per unit time through a unit area of a plate of unit thickness, the temperature difference between the faces being 1°.**

TABLE I

THERMAL CONDUCTIVITIES OF MATERIALS IN CAL./(SEC. × CM. × C.°)*

A. Metals	K	B. Non-metallic Solids	K	C. Liquids and Gases	K
Aluminum.	0.50	Asbestos paper.	0.0004	Alcohol, ethyl, at 20°C.	0.00057
Copper....	0.99	Concrete......	0.0020	Water at 20°C........	0.0014
Iron......	0.163	Cork board....	0.00011	Air at 0°C............	0.000057
Lead......	0.083	Glass, window .	0.0025	Hydrogen at 0°C......	0.00041
Silver.....	1.005	Wool felt.....	0.00010		
		Ice...........	0.0050		
		Glass wool.....	0.00015		
		Rock wool.....	0.00010		
		Wood........	0.0004		
		Soil, moist.....	0.0037		
		Snow........	0.00026		

The gases generally are the poorest conductors of all. To this hydrogen is an exception, its conductivity being greater than that of asbestos paper or of cork.

188. Heat Insulation. The furry coats of the fox or of the polar bear have small thermal conductivities largely because of the air which is

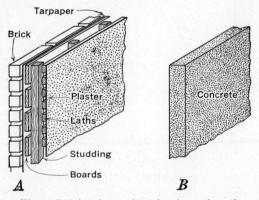

FIG. 2.—The wall A is a better heat insulator than the wall B.

entrapped between adjacent hairs. The layer of heat insulation thus provided decreases the rate of heat loss in winter weather. Man is so poorly protected that he could not survive in cold climates if he did not use clothing. The walls of refrigerators are heat insulated by suc-

* To get conductivities in B.t.u./(sec. × ft. × F.°), multiply values by 0.067.

cessive layers of cork or by layers of mineral wool. Most refrigerators are very wasteful not only because householders are not willing to pay for good insulation, but also because, in buying refrigerators, they pay more attention to "gleaming white porcelain" than to heat insulation. The cost of operating such refrigerators would be greatly decreased if they were better designed.

Residences are heat insulated in order to keep the heat from escaping in winter as well as to keep it from entering in summer. Fortunately, both aims may be attained by the same means. Usually the heat insulation is achieved by using several layers of material, sometimes porous, separated by small air spaces. In Fig. 2A, there are six layers of different materials. Such a wall conducts less than one-fourth as much heat as an equal wall of solid concrete like that in Fig. 2B. The insulation may be further improved by filling the spaces between the studding with asbestos or with mineral wool.

189. The Davy Safety Lamp. Many extremely useful inventions involve simple applications of physical laws. In the early nineteenth

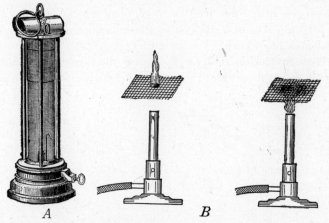

A   B

FIG. 3.—(A) Davy safety lamp. The flame cannot ignite the gas outside the screen. (B) Illustrating the principle of the Davy lamp.

century many miners were killed in the coal mines of Great Britain because the explosive gases were ignited by the flames of the miners' lamps. Sir Humphry Davy found how to avoid the danger by enclosing the lamps in screens of wire gauze (Fig. 3A). In the presence of the explosive gases, combustion occurred inside the gauze, but the gases outside were not ignited. The explanation for this is that, when a flame burns at one side of a wire gauze, the wires conduct the heat away and the gas at the other side does not burn. The conducting away of heat by a metal may be illustrated by the following "parlor magic." Place a glowing cigarette in contact with a handkerchief pressed against a silver coin (Fig. 4). The cloth is not scorched because silver is a good conductor and the heat is conducted away by the metal.

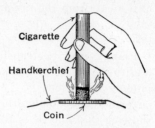

FIG. 4.—The glowing cigarette does not singe the handkerchief.

CONVECTION

If a rectangular glass tube filled with water is held in a flame as shown in Fig. 5 the liquid column above A expands and becomes less dense than that above B. Hence, the pressure at A is less than that at B and the hot water flows upward causing circulation. **In convection heat and matter are transferred together.**

Numerous other examples of convection will occur to the student. In the hot-air furnace, Fig. 6, the air is heated, rises to the room

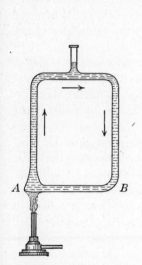

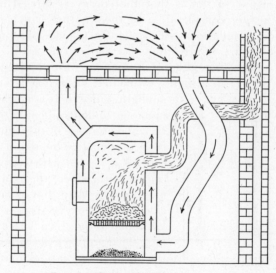

FIG. 5.—Causing convection in a liquid.

FIG. 6.—Convection of air.

through hot-air registers, and, after cooling, descends again through the cold-air return pipes. In automobile engines the cylinders are cooled by streams of water which are pumped from the engine through channels in the "radiator" and thence back to the engine. As it goes through the radiator, the water is cooled, giving up heat to a stream of air. The heat is carried from the engine by convection of water, is conducted through walls of the channels just mentioned, and is carried away from the radiator principally by convection of the air.

RADIATION

Energy may be transferred by **conduction** and by **convection.** In addition, there is another extremely important mode of transfer, namely, **radiation.**

A hand held under the bulb of an incandescent lamp feels warm, showing that energy is absorbed. The energy is not carried by convection since heated air moves upward, and it is not transferred by conduction since air, like other gases, is a poor conductor of heat. In a somewhat similar manner, if a thermometer is placed in direct sunlight it is heated. In this experiment, it is even more evident that conduction and convection are not important factors. In fact, since there are no molecules in the depths of space, no energy can possibly come to us by conduction or by convection. How, then, is it transferred? The answer to this is that the energy is carried by radiations like light. Further consideration of their nature will be given later. When the sun's radiations are incident on a piece of stone, the molecules of the stone are agitated and the temperature rises.

190. Absorption of Radiation. Mount two thermometers A and B (Fig. 7) in a highly evacuated flask, and let this be placed in direct

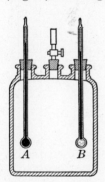

sunlight. Since there is no gas in the bottle, the thermometer bulbs are heated by radiation only. If the thermometers are of the same dimensions and structure, they will be heated at the same rate. If, however, A is coated with lampblack or soot, and B is coated with silver, the temperature of A will rise more rapidly than that of B because more of the incident radiation is absorbed and less is reflected. Lampblack, then, is a better absorber than silver. In fact, the lampblack absorbs more than 97 per cent of the incident radiation, and an untarnished silver surface absorbs less than 10 per cent. A body which would absorb *all* the incident radiation is called a **perfectly black body** or, more briefly, a **black body.**

FIG. 7.—The blackened thermometer absorbs more energy than the silver-coated one does.

191. Good Absorbers are Good Emitters. If the two thermometers mounted in the evacuated bottle are at the same temperature and are transferred to a cool room, the temperature of the blackened thermometer falls more rapidly than that of the other. In general, **the blacker body or the**

better absorber is also the better emitter. This principle of physics has many applications.

In painting the hot-water radiators of a residence one should choose a coating which is highly emissive. A chromium-plated radiator, for example, would be much less effective than one painted black. Strange as it may seem, white lead paint is a good absorber and emitter of invisible, infra-red radiations though it is a good reflector of visible light, and it is a good covering for radiators. It is estimated that a radiator covered with white lead paint will deliver 15 per cent more energy than one covered with a bronze or aluminum paint.

Frequently furnace hot-air pipes in cellars are coated with a single layer of thin asbestos paper, the purpose being to prevent loss of energy. In fact, the paper actually increases the energy loss. Because it is so thin, it has small effect in decreasing conduction losses of heat. Let us consider the effect on losses due to radiation. The brightly tinned surfaces of the bare pipe are poor absorbers and hence poor emitters of radiation. The asbestos surface, on the contrary, is, like lead paint, an excellent emitter, and more energy is lost than before. It is claimed that a layer of solid asbestos more than $\frac{1}{4}$ in. thick would be required to reduce the energy loss to that of the bare, shiny pipe.

The housewife is justified, from a scientific standpoint, in using pots and kettles with shining walls, since there is little radiation from them. For higher efficiency, however, the bottoms of the kettles should be blackened, since the amount of energy absorbed from the flame would be increased.

The **emissivity** of a surface is the ratio of its radiation output to that of an equal black body at the same temperature. For example, the emissivity of a black body is 100 per cent, that of lampblack is 97 per cent, and that of untarnished silver about 10 per cent.

TABLE II

EMISSIVITIES OF SURFACES AT 100°C.

"Black body" (by definition)	1.00
Asbestos paper	0.93
White canvas	0.88
Window glass	0.88
Galvanized iron, tarnished	0.50
Aluminum bronze paint	0.28
Galvanized iron, bright	0.15
Copper, polished	0.070
Aluminum foil, polished silver	0.060

Dirigible airships are usually coated with aluminum paint in order to secure low absorption and also low emission. When the airship thus coated goes into the shadow of a cloud, it cools slowly because its surface is a poor emitter. When it passes from the shadow into full sunlight, it heats slowly because the surface is a poor absorber. Because the temperature of the gas changes slowly, rapid variations of pressure are avoided.

192. Aluminum Insulation. Since aluminum is a good conductor of heat, it is somewhat surprising that it is used instead of cork for the thermal insulation of refrigerators. In practice, instead of a solid block of cork, several parallel sheets of aluminum foil are mounted close together, separated by thin, narrow strips of asbestos. There are two reasons why little energy is transferred across the system. First, the aluminum surfaces are poor emitters of radiant energy, and, second, the temperature difference between adjacent sheets is small. For example, if there are eleven sheets of aluminum with ten air spaces, and the total temperature difference is 20 F.°, then the temperature difference between adjacent sheets is only 2 F.°

193. The Dewar Flask or Thermos Bottle. This device, which is now commonly used, was invented by a physicist to serve as a container for liquid air. It is interesting to note the various means used in its structure to decrease energy losses. As shown in Fig. 8, the flask is double-walled. The interspace is highly evacuated, and there is little conduction and little convection. One of the most important features is the coating of silver on the surfaces of the two walls. When a hot liquid is placed in the flask, little radiation escapes because of the low emission of these surfaces. Silver is a poorer emitter than glass (see Table II), and the energy radiated is diminished to about 1/40 of its previous value. If the flask contains a cold liquid, little energy enters because the surfaces are poor absorbers, and they reflect most of the incident radiations.

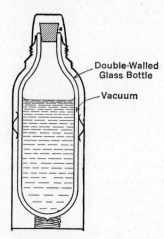

Double-Walled Glass Bottle

Vacuum

FIG. 8.—Dewar or thermos flask. Its walls are good reflectors and poor emitters of radiant energy.

194. Radiation and Temperature. When a fire is kindled in a stove, the amount of energy emitted per second increases with rising temperature. The rate of energy emission of a "black body" depends on the absolute temperature T of the surface and its area A and is given by

Calories/sec. $= kAT^4$ (Stefan's law)

For a black body the constant k has a value 1.36×10^{-12} cal./(cm.^{2} − sec. − K.°^{4}). For other surfaces, the values can be found using Table II.

Example. Find the energy radiated per second by a black body which is a sphere of area 10 cm.² at a temperature 27°C. or 300°K.

Cal./sec. $= 1.36 \times 10^{-12}$ cal./(cm.² K°.⁴) $\times$ 10 cm.² $\times$ (300 °K.)⁴ $= 0.111$ cal./sec.

When one stands near a hot stove his body is warmed by the radiations which he receives, but when he stands near a block of ice he feels chilled. In view of this fact, it is surprising to learn that the ice, being above the Kelvin zero, is emitting radiant energy. The ice seems chilly because it is absorbing more energy than it emits, and the stove seems warm for the opposite reason.

SUMMARY

Conduction and Convection. In conduction, heat energy is passed from molecule to molecule without transfer of matter.

The heat transfer per unit time through a plate of substance equals $KA\ (t_2 - t_1)/d$, K being the coefficient of thermal conductivity, A the area of the plate, $(t_2 - t_1)$ the temperature difference between the faces, and d the distance between them.

In convection, matter and heat are transferred together. Convection is illustrated by the hot-air furnace and by the cooling system of an automobile.

Radiation. In radiations such as light, energy is transferred without molecular motion.

The percentages of incident radiations which are absorbed by different surfaces vary widely. A **black body** is one which absorbs all the incident radiant energy. The greater the absorptivity of a surface, the greater its emissivity. Therefore **a black body is a maximum emitter of radiation.**

The rate of energy emission of a black body of area A is expressed by

$$\text{Energy/Time} = kA(T)^4$$

REVIEW QUESTIONS

1. Define "conduction" and "convection," and differentiate between them.

2. State several examples of conduction in solids and liquids.

3. State several examples of convection in liquids and gases, and, if possible, one in solids.

4. How could you decrease the loss of heat from a hot metal ball because of (a) conduction, and (b) convection?

5. State the equation for the heat conduction through a plate, defining each term.

6. Why is the thermal conductivity of hydrogen greater than that of oxygen?

7. Why does a chimney "draw" poorly when a fire is first kindled?

8. Why is snow a better insulator than ice?

9. Why is woolen cloth a better insulator than linen?

10. Why does iron seem colder than wood in winter weather?

11. Since air is a poorer conductor than wool, why does a cloth covering decrease the loss of heat from a hot body?

12. A film of stagnant air at the surface of the window panes of a room would have what effect on the heat loss from the room?

13. Why do firemen wear woolen clothing in summer to keep cool and in winter to keep warm?

14. Why is a hollow wall filled with sawdust a better insulator than when filled with air alone?

15. Why should hot-air pipes from a furnace to rooms on the first floor be larger than those to rooms on the second floor?

16. A piece of paper wrapped onto a brass rod may be held in a gas flame without being burned. If wrapped on a wooden rod, it burns quickly. Explain.

17. Why should the coating of ice be removed from the cooling unit of a refrigerator at frequent intervals?

18. Why do smoke and heated air rise in a chimney?

19. Why does the first layer of ice on a pond freeze more readily than successive layers?

20. In winter weather, why will a wet glove freeze to an iron bar more quickly than to a wooden one?

21. Why is the cooling unit usually placed near the top of a refrigerator?

22. Distinguish radiation from conduction and convection.

23. Strictly speaking, do we receive any heat from the sun? Why?

24. Name several instances in which highly reflecting surfaces are desirable, also others in which the surfaces should be black.

25. Why are balloons painted with aluminum paint? Would you choose it for a radiator?

26. Show why there is little energy loss from convection, conduction, and radiation when hot water is placed in a thermos flask.

27. A block of ice constantly radiates energy in warm weather, yet it melts. Explain.

PROBLEMS

1. When an automobile travels at 40 mi./hr. the flow of water through the radiator is 1 gal./sec. (8 lb./sec.). If the fall of temperature of the water as it passes through the radiator is from 180°F. to 140°F. how much heat is carried away from the engine during each second?

2. The glass in the twenty windows of a certain dwelling has a total area of 15 m.² The glass is 0.3 cm. thick, and the temperature difference between the two surfaces is 5.0 C.° (a) How much heat is transmitted in 10.0 hr., and (b) how much bituminous coal (heat of combustion equals 7,000 cal./gram) must be burned to supply this heat?

3. A pond is covered by a sheet of ice 1.00 cm. thick. The temperature of the upper surface of the ice is −10°C., and that of the lower surface is +2°C. At what rate is heat conducted through each square centimeter of ice at the surface?

4″. A factory chimney is 100 m. high, and the cross-sectional area of the opening is 1.00 m². The average weight density of the gases is 0.0011 gwt./cm.³; that of the air outside is 0.0012 gwt./cm.³ Find the difference in pressure at the base of the chimney, inside and outside. (b) If the flue at the bottom of the chimney were suddenly closed by a barrier, find the difference in the forces pushing against it from the two sides.

5. (a) The walls of a dwelling are of solid concrete. Their thickness is 30.0 cm., and the total surface area is 500 m.² If the average temperature difference, in winter, is 10 C.°, how much heat is transferred per second and per day of 86,000 sec.? (b) How much coal, of heat combustion 8,000 cal./gram, would supply this heat? (c) What would the coal cost for 100 days, at 1 cent/kg. ($10.00 per ton)?

6. A layer of snow 3.0 cm. thick covers a field. If the surface of the ground is at

$0°C.$, and the upper surface of the snow is at $-10°C.$, how much heat is transferred per hour per square meter of surface?

7. A slab of stone 50 cm. by 60 cm. and 10 cm. thick is exposed on the lower side to steam at $100°C.$ A cake of ice rests on the upper side. In 40 min., 4,800 grams of ice are melted absorbing 80 calories of heat per gram. What is the thermal conductivity of the stone?

8. The flow of heat into an aluminum cooking vessel 2.00 mm. thick is 75 (cal./sec.)/cm.^{2} If the temperature of the inside surface is $100°C.$, what is the temperature of the outside surface?

9. The hot-water pipes of a furnace in a cellar are coated with a black paint having a thermal emissivity of 0.81. The heat loss by radiation is 33,000 B.t.u./day. What would be the loss if the pipes were painted with aluminum paint, the thermal emissivity of which is 0.27?

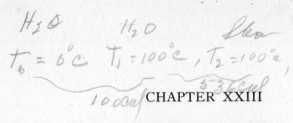

CHAPTER XXIII

CHANGE OF STATE

Nature is ever making signs to us, she is ever whispering to us the beginnings of her secrets; the scientific man must be ever on the watch, ready at once to lay hold of nature's hint, however small; to listen to her whisper, however low.—M. FOSTER.

195. Fusion and Melting. Place some snow or crushed ice, at a temperature below the freezing point, in a vessel on a stove. The temperature rises at first, showing that the molecular kinetic energy is increasing. When the melting point is reached, the temperature remains constant until all the ice is melted. Afterward, the temperature of the water begins to rise (Fig. 1).

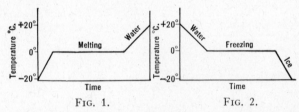

FIG. 1.

FIG. 2.

FIG. 1.—The temperature of ice remains constant while it is melting.
FIG. 2.—The temperature of water remains constant while it is freezing.

During the melting, heat was received from the stove, and so the question arises: "What becomes of this heat energy?" When water is in the solid state, the atoms are neatly arranged in space lattices. As the ice melts, the component molecules are torn from the lattice one by one, and as in the tearing down of a brick wall, work is required. During the melting, therefore, the added heat energy is utilized in "breaking up" the component parts of the ice. Place a vessel of warm water in the freezing compartment of a refrigerator, and the temperature falls until the water begins to freeze. Thereafter, the temperature remains constant until all the water is frozen. Then the temperature of the ice begins to decrease (Fig. 2). The melting point and the freezing point have the same value, namely 0°C.

The melting points of all crystalline solids such as ice, iron, or mercury have definite, constant values. In a non-crystalline substance such as butter or glass there is no definite melting point, but the substance

198

gradually softens as it is heated. The reason for this difference of behavior is that in a crystalline substance, for instance, ice, the atoms are arranged in space lattices and the same amount of work is required to tear away one atom as another. In raising the temperature of the metal, the atoms oscillate more violently and have more kinetic energy. At the melting point, they achieve sufficient energies to break away from their lattices and they do so, entering the liquid state. All the atoms are equally bound, hence the melting point is constant. The atoms of a non-crystalline substance such as butter are not arranged in lattices, and the work required to dislodge some of the molecules is greater than required for others. Hence part of the butter melts at one temperature, part at another. The substance gradually softens as the temperature rises, and it has no definite melting point.

TABLE I

Melting Points of Crystalline Substances at Normal Pressure

°C.

Alcohol, ethyl	−117.3
Aluminum	659
Ammonia	−78
Copper	1,083
Carbon dioxide	−57.0
Helium	−271.5
Gold	1,063.0
Hydrogen	−259.14
Mercury	−39.0
Oxygen	−218.4
Platinum	1,773.5
Rose metal, alloy	98.0
Tin	232
Water	0

196. Heats of Fusion. We have seen that ice in melting absorbs heat and that, when water freezes, heat is evolved. The most familiar use of this property of water is in the household refrigerator. A few pounds of ice melted per day absorb heat and keep the temperature below that of the surroundings. Sometimes, in winter, farmers place tubs of water in their cellars so that the water, in freezing, may evolve heat to keep the cellar warm enough to prevent damage to fruit and vegetables.

The heat of fusion L of a substance is defined as the amount of heat required per unit mass to melt the substance without change of temperature.

$$L = \frac{\text{Heat absorbed}}{\text{Mass of substance melted}} = \frac{H}{m}$$

The heat of fusion of water is 80 cal./gram or 144 B.t.u./Pound.

Example 1. If 200 grams of water at 40°C. are poured onto several kilograms of cracked ice at 0°C., how much ice is melted?

The final temperature is 0°C.

The heat lost by the water is $H = S_w m_w (t_2 - t_1)$

$$\frac{1 \text{ cal.}}{\text{Gram C.°}} \times 200 \text{ grams} \times 40 \text{ C.°} = 8,000 \text{ cal.}$$

Hence, the mass m of ice melted is $m = H/L$

$$= \frac{8,000 \text{ cal.}}{80 \text{ cal./gram}} = 100 \text{ grams}$$

Example 2. If 30 grams of ice at 0°C. are placed in a copper calorimeter of mass 110 grams containing 190 grams of water at 25°C., find the final temperature.

The water equivalent of the calorimeter is 10 grams.

The heat lost by "hot" body is

$$H_1 = S_w(m_w + \text{W.E.})(t_2 - X) = \frac{1 \text{ cal.}}{\text{gram C.°}}(190 \text{ grams} + 10 \text{ grams})(25°\text{C.} - X) \quad (1)$$

The heat gained by the cold body is partly used in melting the ice and partly in raising the temperature. The heat required to melt the ice of mass M is:

$$H_2 = ML = 30 \text{ grams} \times \frac{80 \text{ cal.}}{\text{Gram} - \text{C.°}} = 2,400 \text{ cal.} \quad (2)$$

To raise the temperature from 0°C. to X

$$H_3 = S_w M(X - 0\text{C.°}) \quad (3)$$
$$= 1 \text{ cal./(gram} - \text{C.°)} \times 30 \text{ grams} \times (X - 0\text{C.°})$$

Equating

$$H_1 = H_2 + H_3,$$
X is found to be 11.3°C.

The heats of fusion of several substances are listed in Table II.

TABLE II

HEATS OF FUSION

Substance	Calories per Gram	B.t.u. per Pound
Carbon dioxide ("dry ice") (including the heat of vaporization)	45.3	81.5
Iron, cast	5.5	9.9
Lead	5.4	9.7
Oxygen	3.30	5.94
Mercury	2.8	5.0
Sulfur	9.4	16.9
Water	80.	144.
Zinc	28.	50.

Notice that the heat of fusion of water is very high. Next comes carbon dioxide, which is somewhat more than one-half as great. It has been proposed that carbon dioxide (dry ice) be used in refrigerators instead of ice. One advantage would be that the air would be quite dry and that waterpans would not have to be emptied.

197. Water Expands on Freezing. Most substances contract when they solidify, but water, bismuth, and a few others expand. The increase of volume of water is nearly 10 per cent.

The water in the radiators of automobiles often freezes in winter, and the expansion bursts the channels. This expansion is an important cause of disintegration of rocks and soils. Another important consequence is that ice is less dense than water. If water contracted on freezing, the ice would sink to the bottoms of lakes and rivers. There, heat-insulated by the water, it would remain unmelted during most of the following summer, and the effects on the climate would be very pronounced.

FIG. 3.— Expan-sion oc-curs when milk freezes.

198. Supercooling. Water, freed from dissolved air by boiling and not jarred or shaken, may be cooled several degrees below the freezing point and then it solidifies suddenly (Fig. 4). The absence of dissolved air and other impurities favors this "supercooling." All plumbers know that the hot-water pipes of a vacant residence are more likely to burst than the cold-water pipes. In the latter, the liquid freezes so gradually that some of it is forced along the pipe back to the water main, and the pressure, therefore, does not rise sufficiently to do dam-

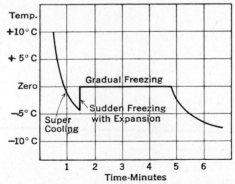

FIG. 4.—Water can be cooled below 0°C. without freezing.

age. The water in the other pipes has been freed from dissolved air and impurities by heating. It freezes suddenly, bursting the pipes.

199. Freezing Mixtures. In making ice cream, salt is added to the ice to lower its melting point. "Anti-freeze" solutions for the radiators of automobiles are made by dissolving alcohol, glycerine, etc., in the water. In general, the freezing points of liquids are lowered when foreign substances are dissolved in them. The explanation in terms of crystal structure is exemplified by the freezing of water. When a salt solution freezes, the crystals of salt and of water form separately. The salt must be driven out of the solution, and to do this requires energy. The salt therefore tends to prevent fusion and so it lowers the freezing point.

200. Evaporation. There is plenty of evidence, as we have seen, that the molecules of liquids, and of gases too, for that matter, move about with high speeds, colliding with one another and with the walls of the container. If a vessel of water is left uncovered, the water gradually evaporates. Some of the molecules near the surface, more energetic than their fellows, plunge through the elastic surface film.

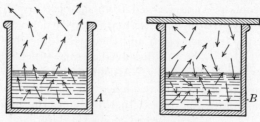

FIG. 5.—The evaporation of water.

In most solids the binding forces are so great that few molecules escape. In others, such as iodine and camphor, evaporation, or sublimation as it is termed, is appreciable. Common ice also vaporizes, for if wet clothing is exposed in zero weather, the water soon freezes, but in the course of a few hours, practically all the ice evaporates and the clothing is ready to be ironed. Dry ice or solid carbon dioxide sublimes readily at room temperatures.

201. Saturation Vapor Density. Expose water in an open vessel (Fig. 5A) and it will gradually evaporate. Some of the molecules near the surface have sufficient kinetic energies to enable them to plunge through the elastic film and to escape into the air. Then they disperse by diffusion, and the quantity of liquid gradually diminishes. Close the vessel by means of a tightly fitting lid so that the vapor cannot escape (Fig. 5B). As evaporation proceeds, the vapor above the liquid becomes more dense. But not only do molecules escape from the liquid, but also others from the vapor return to it, and there comes a time when the two rates are equal; that is, dynamic equilibrium is established. The space above the liquid is then said to be saturated. The evaporation and condensation rates are equal, and the vapor density remains constant.

When a vapor in contact with its liquid is saturated, the rates of evaporation and of condensation are equal.

Raising the temperature of a liquid causes it to vaporize more rapidly, and hence the saturation vapor density increases.

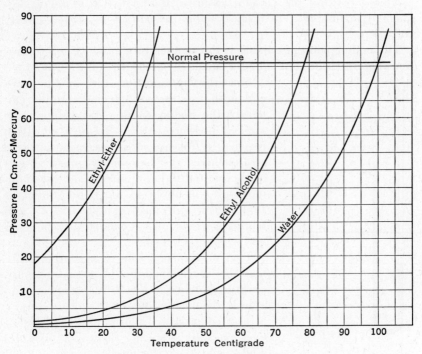

FIG. 6.—Variations of vapor pressures with temperatures.

202. Saturation Vapor Pressure Increases with Temperature. Rise of temperature causes an increase of pressure as well as density of a saturated vapor. For this there are two reasons. First, the number of molecules is greater, and second, they move faster. They exert greater forces at the walls of the enclosure because there are more impacts per unit time and also because each molecule delivers more momentum per impact. At ordinary room temperatures, the saturation vapor pressure of water is a few millimeters-of-mercury, but in a locomotive boiler the pressure is many atmospheres. The variations with temperature of saturation vapor pressures of water vapor and of other liquids are represented in Fig. 6.

203. Boiling Points. Usually evaporation of water occurs at the upper surface only, but at a certain temperature bubbles are produced inside the liquid and it boils. Thereafter, the temperature remains constant, regardless of the rate of heating. The question arises, why are no vapor bubbles produced in the liquid when it is below the boiling point? The answer is quite simple. Bubbles of vapor cannot be produced because the vapor pressure is less than that of the atmosphere. If a bubble were formed below the surface, it would quickly collapse.

The boiling point of a liquid is the temperature at which the saturation vapor pressure of the liquid equals the pressure at the surface.

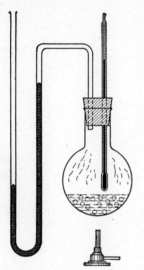

FIG. 7.—An apparatus for measuring vapor pressures.

Since the vapor pressure at the boiling point equals that at the surface of the liquid, evidently the boiling point depends upon the applied pressure. At the greatest elevation reached by Piccard in his ascension into the stratosphere, the barometric pressure was about one-tenth that at sea level and the boiling point was about 45° C. At the summit of Pike's Peak water boils at about 186° F., and boiling water is not hot enough to cook beans and some other foods.

The variation of boiling point with pressure may be determined by means of the apparatus sketched in Fig. 7. Water is boiled in a flask, the flame is removed, and the stopper is inserted at once. Then cold water is poured over the flask, lowering the vapor pressure. The steam above the liquid is condensed and the water boils vigorously until the temperature of the flask falls almost to that of the room. The temperatures of the vapor are measured by means of the thermometer, and the corresponding pressures by means of the open-tube manometer.

204. The Coffee Percolator—Geysers. The influence of pressure on the boiling point explains the operation of the ordinary percolator (Fig. 8). Near the bottom of the funnel, the boiling point is somewhat higher than that at the surface of the water (Why)? Bubbles of steam form there and rise, pushing water ahead of them in the narrow vertical tube. This liquid, rising to regions of lower pressure, is above its boiling point, and it bubbles so violently that a spray is thrown over into the coffee contained in the upper vessel. Geysers are merely gigantic percolators. The temperature of the water, deep in the earth, is far above the normal boiling point (Fig. 9). When this water begins to boil and rises toward the surface, the pressure decreases and the superheated liquid boils so violently that a jet is thrown many feet into the air. One of the best-known geysers is "Old Faithful" in Yellowstone Park. It merits this name because successive eruptions occur with clocklike regularity at intervals of an hour or more. After a jet is expelled, the temperature at the bottom of the column falls nearly to the normal value. Then the water accumulates again and a considerable period is required to heat it sufficiently to boil at the enhanced pressure caused by the column that fills the tube.

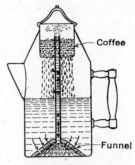

FIG. 8.—A coffee percolator.

205. The Effect of Dissolved Substances on Vapor Pressures. Place salt water and pure water in separate containers A and B under cover, and reduce the pressure (Fig. 10). Then the amount of water in B will slowly diminish and that in A will increase. The salt molecules in A, because of their great attractions, tend to prevent the evaporation of the water molecules. Thus the vapor pressure near the salt solution is less than that over the water so that vapor diffuses from B to A. In general, **any solid substance, dissolved in a liquid, lowers the vapor pressure.**

206. Cooling by Evaporation. When a liquid evaporates, the speedier molecules escape more readily than the slower ones; and each escaping molecule carries away

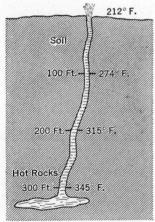

FIG. 9.—A geyser is a giant percolator.

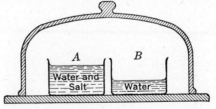

FIG 10.—The vapor pressure of a salt solution is smaller than that of pure water at the same temperature.

more than the average share of kinetic energy. For this reason, evaporation tends to cool the remaining liquid. Many examples of this phenomenon will occur to the reader. On a hot day, one fans himself in order to increase evaporation. Water vaporizes from the leaves of trees, cooling the surrounding air. In the tropics, drinking water is kept in porous vessels so that evaporation from the outer surface may cool the contents.

An effective demonstration of the cooling effect of evaporation is obtained by placing a small vessel of water under the bell jar of an air pump (Fig. 11). Under this vessel is a large glass dish containing sulfuric acid to absorb the water vapor. When the pressure is lowered sufficiently, the water boils. The rapid evaporation cools the water until it begins to freeze. While this is occurring, ice, boiling water, and steam are in contact with each other. (The pressure and temperature at which the three are in equilibrium are 0.46 cm.-of-mercury and 0.0076°C., respectively.)

Fig. 11.—Water can freeze and boil simultaneously.

207. The Heat of Vaporization. Since evaporation is a cooling process, heat must be supplied in order to keep the temperature constant when a liquid vaporizes. The amount of heat required is proportional to the mass of liquid which is evaporated.

The heat of vaporization of a liquid is the amount of heat per unit mass required to vaporize the liquid if the temperature is constant. It is expressed in calories per gram or in British thermal units per pound (See Table III).

$$\text{Heat of vaporization} = \frac{\text{Heat absorbed}}{\text{Mass vaporized}}$$

TABLE III

BOILING POINTS AND HEATS OF VAPORIZATION OF LIQUIDS AT 76 CM.-OF-MERCURY

(1 cal./gram = 1.80 B.t.u./Pound)

	Boiling Point, °C.	Heat of Vaporization, Cal./gram
Alcohol, ethyl...............	76.0	204
Ammonia...................	−33.3	302
Ether.....................	−35	83.9
Helium....................	−268.8	
Hydrogen..................	−252.8	
Mercury...................	357	
Oxygen....................	−183	
Water.....................	100.0	540
Water (at 0.4 cm.-of-mercury)..	0	597
Sulfuric acid...............	338	
Sulfur dioxide..............	−10.0	95

Example 1. How many calories are required to change 50 grams of ice at 0°C. into steam at 100°C.?

(a) To melt the ice: $H_1 = ML = 50$ grams $\times$ 80 cal./gram = 4,000 cal.

(b) To heat the water to 100°C.: $H_2 = S_w M_w (t_2 - t_1) = 1$ cal./(gram C°.) $\times$ 50 grams $\times$ 100 C.° = 5,000 cal.

(c) To vaporize the water at 100°C.:

$$H_3 = ML' = 50 \text{ grams} \times 540 \text{ cal./gram} = 27,000 \text{ cal.}$$
$$H_1 + H_2 + H_3 = 36,000 \text{ cal.}$$

Example 2. One hundred grams of steam at 100°C. are condensed in a vessel of ice water at 0°C. How much ice will be melted?

To condense the steam, $H_1 = mL' = 100$ grams $\times$ 540 cal./gram = 54,000 cal.

To cool the water to 0°C.:

$$H_2 = M_w S_w (t_2 - t_1) = 1 \text{ cal./(gram C.°)} \times 100 \text{ grams} \times 100 \text{ C.°} = 10,000 \text{ cal.}$$
$$H_1 + H_2 = 64,000 \text{ cal.} = X \times 80 \text{ cal./gram}$$
$$X = 800 \text{ grams}$$

208. Mechanical Refrigerators. In refrigerators the "working substance" is a liquid of high vapor pressure such as ammonia or sulfur dioxide. The operation of a mechanical household refrigerator will be made clear by studying Fig. 12. Liquid sulfur dioxide, enclosed by the hollow walls of the freezing chamber, evaporates, absorbing heat from the surroundings. The vapor flows down through the vertical pipe and is compressed by the rotary pump. The compression heats the vapor, which is forced through a long, spiral tube, where it is gradually cooled and it liquefies. Then the liquid is pumped back into the freezing chamber where it again evaporates, and the cycle of operations is repeated.

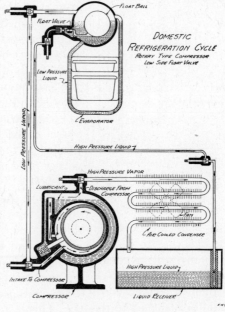

Fig. 12.—A household refrigerating unit. (Courtesy of F. H. Stiening, University of Pittsburgh.)

209. The Gas Refrigerator. In some refrigerators the motors and pumps are eliminated and a gas flame produces the cooling, without any machinery.

In explaining how they operate, at first alcohol will be used as the "working substance," which absorbs heat when it evaporates. Later, this will be replaced by the liquid ammonia which is employed in practical refrigerators.

Suppose that alcohol is poured into the opening (Fig. 13) and evaporates as it trickles through the cool bent pipe. Thus heat is absorbed and the chamber is cooled. From the lower end of the pipe, the alcohol vapor, mixed with air, enters the "absorber" chamber, where the alcohol is dissolved in a stream of water. The circulation of the mixture is caused in the following manner. The top of the absorber and the evaporator pipe are joined by a tube, and the closed space is flooded with hydrogen instead of air as just described. Notice that the bent pipe contains a mixture of alcohol vapor and hydrogen, but the absorber contains hydrogen only, for the alcohol is removed by the water. The heavy mixture in the "cooling pipe" therefore continues to flow downward while the lighter hydrogen flows upward from the absorber. In this way circulation is maintained.

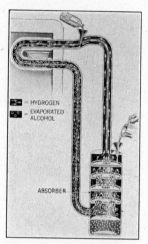

FIG. 13.—Refrigeration by evaporation of alcohol which is recovered by dissolving it in water.

In the system just described, alcohol and water must be supplied continually. Now we shall see how the solution, accumulating at the bottom of the absorber, is separated into alcohol and water which may be used again.

First the mixture is lifted into an upper vessel called the still. This lifting is accomplished just as in the coffee percolator or the geyser. The mixture flows from the absorber to a boiler (Fig. 14) where it is heated by a flame and the bubbles of vapor rise in a percolator pipe, forcing the water up into the still. Here the alcohol bubbles escape from the water which returns to the absorber to be used again. Meanwhile, the alcohol vapor, rising from the still, condenses in the horizontal part of the tube, and the liquid alcohol re-enters the "cooler" pipe. The heat given up by the alcohol in condensing is conducted away by the metal "fins" of the radiator attached to the pipe. This heat then escapes by radiation and by convection.

Thus far we have assumed that the "working substance" is alcohol, but in practice ammonia is preferred because it evaporates more readily than alcohol.

The student may well raise the question, how can the liquid that is condensed in the warm tube leading from the still evaporate at a lower temperature in the cooling chamber? In answering this question, it should be pointed out that the upper tube contains vapor only, saturated at a higher temperature. The pressure in the cooling chamber, about the same as that in the upper pipe, equals the sum of the pressures of the vapor and the hydrogen. Therefore the pressure of the vapor itself is less than that in the upper tube. It follows that the liquid will evaporate when it enters the cooling chamber, even at the lower temperature.

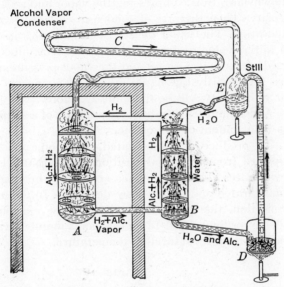

FIG. 14.—The alcohol-water solution is lifted by a percolator and then distilled to separate the two constituents.

The stages of operation which we have described are as follows:

1. The evaporation of the ammonia, absorbing heat from the refrigerator.

2. The dissolving of the ammonia vapor in water, removing the ammonia from the hydrogen.

3. The lifting of the solution by the percolator.

4. The distillation of the ammonia from the solution.

5. The condensation of the ammonia vapor.

(Notice that the dissolving of the ammonia in the water evolves heat which is removed from the absorber by an air-cooling system which is not shown in the diagrams.)

The operation of the refrigerator is automatic, being controlled by a thermostat bulb located in the cooling chamber. This bulb contains a volatile liquid. When the temperature of the refrigerator rises, the vapor pressure of the liquid increases and a diaphragm opens the gas-supply valve farther, increasing the rate of refrigeration. In this way the temperature is kept nearly constant.

210. The Pressure of a Saturated Vapor is Independent of Volume. To study the effect of volume variations on vapor pressure, suppose that a few drops of ether are placed in a long cylinder closed by a piston (Fig. 15). Some of it will evaporate, producing saturation. Push the piston downward, thus compressing the vapor and raising its pressure and density. Then the rate of condensation will be greater than that of evaporation. The vapor density will diminish rapidly until it reaches the initial value and saturation is again attained. Pull the piston upward to its first position and the vapor pressure and density will diminish temporarily but liquid ether will evaporate and, soon, the pressure and density will be the same as before.

At constant temperature the pressure of a saturated vapor is independent of its volume.

To produce an unsaturated condition, pull the piston upward from its initial position so far that all the liquid evaporates. Then on further expansion the space becomes unsaturated and the pressure decreases. In the unsaturated condition, the vapor obeys Boyle's law and Charles' law, like an ordinary gas. In fact, **a gas is merely a vapor far removed from its saturation temperature.**

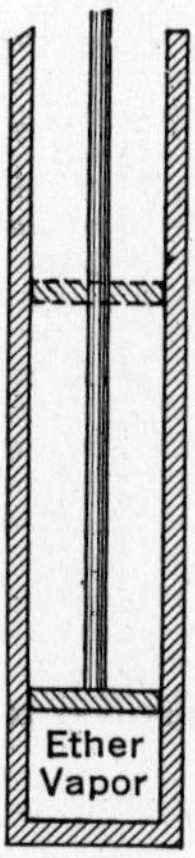

Ether Vapor

Fig. 15.— The pressure of a saturated vapor is independent of its volume.

TABLE IV

Substance	Boiling Points at Normal Pressure °C.	Critical Temperatures °C.	Critical Pressures, Atmospheres
Air.............	−194	−140	37
Ammonia........	− 33.5	132	111
Carbon dioxide...	− 80	31.1	73
Ether...........	34.5	194	35.5
Helium..........	−267	−268	2.26
Hydrogen........	−253	−240	12.8
Oxygen..........	−183	−119	50
Water...........	100	374	217

All Gases Can Be Liquefied. The vapors of many substances such as water, alcohol, and gasoline can be liquefied at ordinary temperatures by compressing them, but the so-called "permanent" gases such as air, hydrogen, and helium must first be cooled below their "critical temperatures."

The critical temperature of a gas is that temperature above which it cannot be liquefied.

A Demonstration of the Critical Temperature. A thick-walled glass tube half filled with liquid carbon dioxide can be used to determine the critical temperature of that substance (Fig. 16).*

Immerse the tube in a beaker of water and warm it slowly. As the temperature rises, the vapor becomes more dense, the liquid less dense, and the film of the surface between the two less sharply defined. The film fades away entirely at 31.1°C. because the vapor and the liquid are equally dense. At higher temperatures, the entire space is filled with vapor (or gas) and the carbon dioxide cannot be liquefied by any pressure, however great.

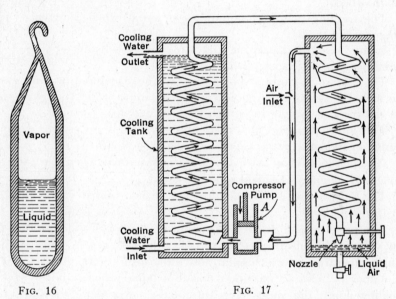

FIG. 16   FIG. 17

FIG. 16.—The surface film of a liquid disappears at the critical temperature.
FIG. 17.—A liquid-air machine, simplified.

211. Making Liquid Air. In order to liquefy air, it must be cooled below its critical temperature (−140°C.). In one often-used method, the pump A (Fig. 17) compresses air to a pressure of 200 atmospheres. Heat caused by the compression is absorbed in the cooling tank. Then the air enters the second coil and escapes through the nozzle. The

---

* The vapor pressure of carbon dioxide at the critical temperature is many atmospheres, and the tube may explode. The observers should therefore be protected by a piece of plate glass.

expansion chills the gas because of the work done against the internal forces of attraction between the molecules, after which the gas travels upward in the heat-insulated chamber. It cools the incoming air in the coil and then returns to the pump. The process continues, and the air, escaping at the nozzle, becomes colder and colder. Finally it is chilled sufficiently so that a portion of it liquefies and may be drawn off like water. Hydrogen gas is liquefied by the same method, after being chilled by passing it through a tube immersed in liquid air.

SUMMARY

Heat is evolved when a liquid freezes, and when it evaporates, heat is absorbed.

The freezing points of liquids are lowered when substances are dissolved in them.

Water, bismuth, cast iron, and a few other substances expand on solidification, but most substances contract.

The *heat of fusion* of a substance is the heat required per unit mass to melt the substance without change of temperature. It is expressed in calories per *gram* or in British thermal units per *pound*.

The more energetic molecules are more likely to escape when a liquid evaporates, hence vaporization cools a liquid.

A vapor in contact with its liquid is saturated when the rates of evaporation and of condensation are equal.

The density and the vapor pressure of a saturated vapor increase with temperature.

The pressure and density of a saturated vapor are independent of its volume. An unsaturated vapor obeys the gas laws. A gas is a vapor the temperature of which is far above the saturation point.

Vapor bubbles are produced inside a liquid when it boils. At the boiling point, the vapor pressure equals the pressure to which the liquid is subjected. Evidently, then, the boiling point of a liquid depends on the applied pressure.

In the percolator and the geyser, water is heated above its normal boiling point and boils explosively when the excess pressure is decreased.

Dissolved substances always decrease the vapor pressure of a liquid.

The density of a liquid and its saturated vapor are equal at the critical temperature and the surface film between them disappears. A gas cannot be liquefied when above its critical temperature.

REVIEW QUESTIONS

1. Draw a curve showing how the temperature of a piece of ice varies when it is placed on a heated stove.

2. Discuss supercooling.

3. Explain why salt lowers the freezing point of water.

4. Discuss the influence of pressure on the melting point.

5. What becomes of the heat energy utilized in melting ice and what is the source of the heat liberated when water freezes?

6. Show how the heat of fusion of water can be determined experimentally.

7. State advantages and a disadvantage of "dry ice" for use in ordinary refrigerators.

8. Show why evaporation cools a liquid but condensation heats it.

9. Define "saturated vapor," "vapor density," and "vapor pressure."

10. Show that the pressure and density of a saturated vapor are independent of the volume.

11. Discuss the variation of pressure with volume for an unsaturated vapor.

12. How would the presence of a gas in the space above a liquid affect (a) the saturation vapor pressure of the liquid, and (b) its rate of vaporization?

13. Define "boiling point," and discuss the influence of pressure on it.

14. Describe the operation of a percolator and of a geyser.

15. Discuss the influence of dissolved substances on the boiling point and the saturation vapor pressure of a liquid.

16. Describe an experiment proving that vaporization cools a liquid.

17. How could you determine the heat of vaporization of water?

18. Make a sketch of a mechanical refrigerator, and explain how it operates.

19. Make a sketch of a gas refrigerator, and carefully describe its operation.

20. Define critical temperature and pressure. Is critical temperature a measure of the difficulty of liquefying a gas?

21. In terms of critical temperature, distinguish between a vapor and a gas.

22. Make a suitable sketch, and show how liquid air is produced.

23. When a healthy man works in a furnace room at a temperature of 110°F., why does his temperature remain at 98.6°F.?

24. Why is it difficult to make snowballs in very cold weather?

25. If there is a little water at the top of the mercury column in a barometer tube, will the barometer read too high or too low?

26. When water boils in a tea kettle, the space near the spout is clear, and a cloud appears farther out. Explain.

27. Prove that vapor bubbles cannot be produced in water which is below the boiling point.

28. Why cannot water be heated above 100°C. at normal pressure?

29. Would you expect the heat of vaporization of water to be greater at 20°C. or at 100°C.? Why?

30. Why do liquids of high surface tensions have high boiling points and low vapor pressures?

31. A few drops of water are placed in each of two flasks containing dry air at a pressure of 76 cm.-of-mercury. One flask is evacuated; the other contains air at normal pressure. Describe the progress of evaporation in each flask, and state the value of the final pressure in each. (Saturation vapor pressure of the water is assumed to be 2.0 cm.-of-mercury.)

32. Steam enters a radiator at 100°C. and water leaves it at the same temperature. Is the room heated?

33. A vessel of pure water and one of salt water are placed in a closed box. Which liquid decreases? Why?

PROBLEMS

1. Two kilograms of ice are melted per hour in a refrigerator. How much heat enters the refrigerator per hour, the final temperature being 10°C.?

2. One hundred grams of water are supercooled to −10°C. Then a chip of ice is dropped into the water, and ice is suddenly formed. How much ice is produced?

3. What temperature results if 200 grams of ice at 0°C. are placed in 100 grams of water at 50°C.?

4″. How much heat is required to change 10.0 grams of tin at 132°C. into liquid at its melting point, 232°C.? (Sp. ht. of tin = 0.054 cal./gram C.°, heat of fusion = 13 cal./gram.)

5′. What mass of water at 100°C. must be added to 100 grams of ice in order that all the ice may be melted?

6′. A copper ball of mass 100 grams and specific heat 0.092 cal./(gram C.°) at a temperature of 160°C. is placed in a cavity in a block of ice at 0°C. How much ice will be melted?

7″. A copper calorimeter of mass 200 grams and specific heat = 0.10 cal./(gram C.°) contains 400 grams of water at 45°C. If 200 grams of ice were melted in it, the resulting temperature would be 5.0°C. Compute the heat of fusion of ice.

8′. How much heat is required to change 10.0 grams of ice at 0°C. to steam at 100°C.?

9′. How many grams of water at 20°C. can be heated to 100°C. by condensing 5 grams of steam at 100°C.?

10. How much ammonia must be evaporated in a refrigerator to absorb sufficient heat to freeze 1,000 grams of water at 0°C.? (Neglect the heat required to warm the vapor.)

11. What mass of steam at 100°C. must be added to 100 grams of ice in order to melt it?

12. Coal with a heat combustion of 14,000 B.t.u./pound is used in a boiler having an efficiency of 60 per cent. How many pounds of water at 62°F. can be turned into steam at 212°F. for each pound of coal burned?

CHAPTER XXIV

HEAT, WORK, AND ENGINES

The history of man is dominated by and reflects the amount of available energy.

Until the middle of the nineteenth century, the view was commonly held that heat was a tenuous substance, called caloric, which permeated all bodies and could be forced out by friction. It was believed that, when a wire is bent to and fro, it becomes hot because heat is squeezed out of it like water from a sponge. Though this view was generally favored, many physicists believed that heat is a form of energy. The first experiments strongly favoring this view were made by Benjamin Thompson who later became Count Rumford. Thompson was an American Loyalist or Tory who was driven from his Massachusetts home soon after the Battle of Lexington. He fought in the British army, and later in Europe he was quite successful as a soldier of fortune and executive. Rumford was placed in charge of an arsenal at Munich, where his famous experiments on heat and work were performed in 1798. He noticed that a great deal of heat was produced while a cannon was being bored, and he wished to see if the supply of "caloric" in the iron could be exhausted by long-continued boring. He purposely blunted the tool so that it would not cut the metal and found that heat could be produced, hour after hour, almost indefinitely. Rumford reasoned that, since heat was evolved from the iron almost without limit, it could not be a form of matter. Further, he argued, to get heat from the iron one had to put in energy, so that **heat is a form of energy.**

Rumford's statement is as follows:

"It is hardly necessary to add that anything which an isolated body or system of bodies can continue to furnish without limitation, cannot possibly be a material substance."

212. How Much Work Will Produce a Calorie of Heat? Though, in our opinion, the caloric theory was thoroughly discredited by the work of Rumford, it was not abandoned for forty-five years or so, when the British physicist Joule determined the amount of work required to produce 1 B.t.u. of heat. The apparatus used was essentially a churn, the paddles of which were driven by falling weights (Fig. 1). The stirring of the water produced heat, and the amount generated was found, as usual, by noting the rise in temperature of a known mass of water (taking into account the water equivalent of the apparatus). The work input was the product of the weight W of the falling body and the total distance through which it moved.

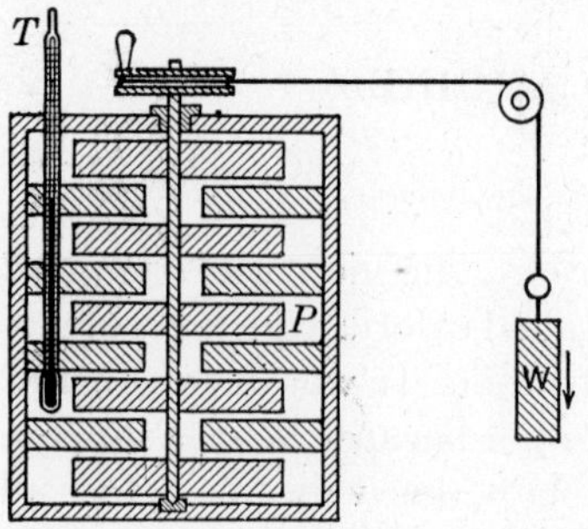

Joule's results were within 1 per cent of the value accepted today, which is:

$$778 \text{ ft-lb.} \qquad = 1 \text{ B.t.u.}$$

$$\left.\begin{array}{l} 42,600 \text{ gwt.-cm.} \\ 4.183 \text{ joules} \\ 41.83 \text{ million ergs} \end{array}\right\} = 1 \text{ cal.}$$

$$(252 \text{ cal.} = 1 \text{ B.t.u.})$$

FIG. 1.—Determining the number of foot-pounds of work required to produce 1 B.t.u. of heat.

Joule found the same "mechanical equivalent" for heat otherwise produced, as by the friction of solid surfaces. Another observer, Hirn, shortly afterward determined the mechanical equivalent by noting the heat evolved when a falling weight struck a piece of lead. His results agreed well with those of Joule, and the caloric theory was finally abandoned.

Example 1. The falls at Niagara are 180 ft. high. How much is each pound of water heated when it passes over the cataract?

Energy transformed = 180 ft-lb.
Heat produced   = 180 ft-lb./(778 ft-lb./B.t.u.) = 0.231 B.t.u.
Rise of temperature = 0.231 F.°

Example 2. A 4.90-gram lead rifle bullet has a velocity of 10^5 cm./sec. (1 km./sec.). How many degrees does the temperature rise when the bullet strikes a target if one-tenth of the heat remains in the bullet?

K.E. $= \frac{1}{2}(W/g)v^2 = \frac{1}{2}$ 4.90 gwt./(980 cm./sec.^{2}) $\times$ (10^5 cm./sec.)^2
     $= 25,000,000$ gwt-cm.

Heat $= \dfrac{25 \times 10^6 \text{ gwt-cm.}}{42,600 \text{ gwt-cm./cal.}} = 587$ cal.

Heat remaining in bullet = 58.7 cal.

Let t = rise of temperature:

$$58.7 \text{ cal.} = 0.030 \text{ cal./gram-C.}° \times 4.90 \text{ grams} \times t$$
$$t = 399 \text{ C.}°$$

213. Steam Engines. The first practical steam engine was constructed more than two centuries ago by Newcomen and was used in pumping water from coal mines in England. Its operation will be understood by studying Fig. 2. Steam from the boiler enters the cylinder and pushes up the piston A, thus operating a lever which lowers the piston B of the pump. When the steam piston reaches the top of the cylinder, the steam supply is cut off, and by opening a valve D, water is jetted into the cylinder. This water condenses the steam, causing a partial vacuum. The pressure of the atmosphere forces the piston to descend. By reversing the valves C and D, the cycle of operation is then repeated. It will be noted that in this engine the valves must be adjusted after each motion of the piston. There is a story that this operation was made automatic by a boy named Humphrey Potter who was employed to shift the valves. He noticed that they had to

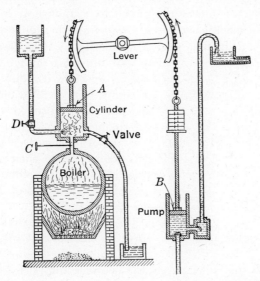

FIG. 2.—Newcomen's steam engine was used to pump water.

be reversed whenever the piston arrived at its extreme up or down position, and he devised a system of cords and pulleys connected to the oscillating lever. The story is that when the foreman found young Humphrey playing marbles while the engine ran itself, he discharged him. If so, this is one of the first examples of technological unemployment in which a worker lost his job because of improvements in machinery. However, seldom does a man invent the particular machine that displaces him.

The Newcomen engine was very crude, but it was used for fifty years before there was a great improvement. About 1745 James Watt, an instrument maker at the University of Glasgow, was asked to repair a model of a Newcomen engine and became interested in developing it. He noticed that, when the jet of water was thrown into the cylinder, the walls were cooled and a great deal of heat was wasted. To prevent this, a separate chamber, called a condenser, was provided which was cooled by a stream of water flowing through a coil of pipe. When the piston reached its topmost position, the valve C was closed as before, the valve E was opened, and the steam rushed into the box where it was chilled and condensed. Whereas the efficiency of the Newcomen engine was about 1.5 per cent, that of Watt's new engine and its condenser was twice as great.

The Newcomen engine was used only for pumping water, but Watt devised means to connect the piston to a crankshaft so as to turn a wheel to drive machinery. He also invented the double-acting engine in which the steam first pushes on one face of the piston and then on the other face, giving the steam engine as we know it today. The new age of industrial civilization dates from Watt's first improved engine which was made in 1763, thirteen years before the American Declaration of Independence. Since then the steam engine, the internal-combustion engine, and the electric motor have become the slaves of men.

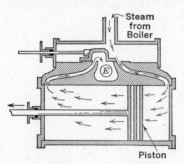

Fig. 3.—Cylinder and piston of a modern steam engine.

214. A Modern Steam Engine. Steam engines have been improved enormously since the days of Watt. In Fig. 3, steam from the boiler enters the cylinder and pushes the piston to the left. Meanwhile, steam on the other side of the piston is forced out through E into the exhaust pipe. After the piston has moved to the left sufficiently, the slide valve is automatically shifted so as to make the steam enter the space at the other side of the piston, thus reversing the motion.

215. The Steam Turbine. The turbine engine resembles a water wheel or a windmill. Jets of steam are directed against the blades or "buckets" of the turbine, exerting forces on the blades so as to keep the wheel in motion. The single-impulse turbine (Fig. 4) has only one wheel. It is very wasteful of energy unless it is operated at high speed. The reason is that, when the blades move slowly, the steam molecules rebound with but small change of speed, and hence the steam gives up little of its energy. This defect is remedied in turbines having several wheels on the same shaft. Fixed blades are mounted between adjacent moving wheels (Fig. 5). The steam jet strikes against the first set of moving buckets and rebounds, giving up some of its

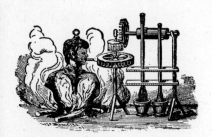

FIG. 4*A*.—A steam turbine of long ago.

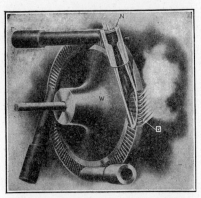

4*B*. A single impulse-wheel turbine.

energy. Then the jet is reversed by the fixed blades mounted on the turbine casing. Then the steam strikes the next revolving wheel and rebounds with further diminished energy. In this manner it "worms" its way through the turbine, and emerges with greatly reduced velocity, energy, and pressure. Because of the diminished pressure, the steam expands as it travels through the turbines, and so the last sets of wheels are made larger than the first (Fig. 6).

216. The Internal Combustion Engine. In the internal-combustion engine, the heating occurs within the cylinder itself, and no boiler or firebox is necessary. The

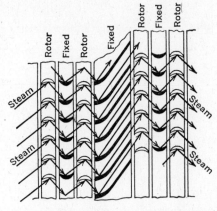

FIG. 5.—Several impulse wheels mounted on the same shaft. The steam worms its way through, giving up its energy to the moving buckets.

four stages in the operation of such a motor are represented in Fig. 7.

(*a*) **The "intake" stroke.** An explosive mixture of air and gasoline vapor is drawn into the cylinder.

(*b*) **The "compression" stroke.** The intake valve is closed and the piston moves upward, compressing the mixture.

(*c*) **The "power" stroke.** Just before the piston reaches the end of its upward journey, the mixture is ignited by an electric spark, and

FIG. 6.—A 50,000 horsepower steam turbine. Imagine how much space 50,000 horses would occupy! (Courtesy of Westinghouse)

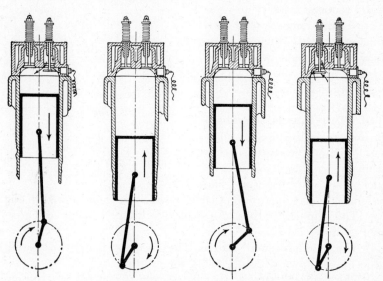

(From Severns and Degler, "Steam, Air, and Gas Power.")

FIG. 7.—A four-cycle internal-combustion engine.

the pressure increases to several hundred pounds per square inch. The piston is then driven downward, work is done, and the gas is cooled by the expansion.

(d) **The "exhaust" stroke.** The exhaust valve opens, the piston moves upward and the gases are expelled.

The four stages are then repeated.

Many small gasoline engines have only one cylinder; the energy is delivered during only one stroke out of each four, that is, once for each two revolutions of the shaft. A massive flywheel keeps the system going during the three stages when no energy is delivered. In automobile engines, several cylinders are mounted side by side, their pistons being connected to the same shaft so that the "power" strokes occur more often and the motion is more uniform.

Retarding the Spark. If the explosion is deferred until the piston has moved part way down in the power stroke, less work will be done in pushing the piston and energy will be wasted. Furthermore, the gas, having done less work, will be hotter when it enters the exhaust. Thus the engine tends to heat excessively when the spark is retarded. To prevent this waste, the spark is "advanced" as far as possible so that the spark occurs just before the piston reaches the top of the cylinder during the compression stroke. Formerly, this adjustment was made by the driver, but now the "advancing of the spark" is accomplished automatically.

217. High Compression. During the compression stroke, the explosive mixture is heated to a degree depending upon the ratio of the initial and final volumes. In high-compression engines, the reduction in volume is more than sixfold. The advantage of higher compression is that greater efficiency is achieved. The disadvantage is that sometimes the mixture burns so suddenly that "knocking" results.

218. The Diesel Engine. The Diesel engine has the same four stages of operation as the ordinary gasoline engine, but it has neither carburetor nor electric spark ignition. At the input stroke, air, instead of an explosive mixture, is drawn into the cylinder. During the next stroke it is compressed much more than in the gasoline engine and, therefore, is very highly heated. A jet of oil, forced into this heated air, ignites and, in burning, supplies energy to drive the piston downward.

The Diesel engine is more efficient than the gasoline engine and it burns heavy, inexpensive oils. Its use is rapidly increasing, but thus far the great weight and high cost have prevented its adoption for automobiles. Another important obstacle is that the device for injecting just the right amount of oil into the hot gas has not yet been developed so as to work well at all speeds.

219. The Degradation of Energy. The belief that energy is never created or destroyed is very comforting and might encourage us to exploit coal fields and oil deposits. However, there is another belief that warns us to be careful. This belief is that there is a "downhill" tendency in nature, that, though energy is not destroyed, it tends to become less and less available. Suppose that the gasoline in the tank of a car is accidentally ignited and burns. Then the energy that is set free escapes and is wasted. But suppose that the gasoline is burned in the cylinders of the engine. In this case, useful work is done in propelling the automobile along a highway. However, in this case, also, heat is produced in overcoming friction, and the final condition of the energy is the same. Many experiments lead to the conviction that **all other forms of energy tend to be converted into heat.** In a sense, therefore, heat is the most "low down" form of energy.

220. The Death of Heat. It is important to inquire into the tendencies of heat itself. One fact to be noted is that the amount is constantly increasing as other forms of energy are transformed into it. The next is that heat tends to flow "downhill," and become less available. That is, it flows from hotter bodies to colder ones just as water flows from higher to lower levels. Hotter bodies tend to become cooler, and as time goes on we approach more nearly to an ultimate stagnant state. Then the sun and the stars would be cold, unchanging bodies, all at the same temperature. The dismal condition when all parts of the universe will be at the same temperature is called the death of heat because no energy could be transferred. It follows that no heat engine could be operated, for engines always receive heat from a hotter source such as a boiler, utilize part of it in doing work, and throw out waste heat into a colder "sink" or "exhaust."

It is comforting to believe that the death of heat probably is many billions of years away and that on our own little earth human life may persist for millions of years. It should be kept in mind, also, that the law of the degradation of energy may not always apply, since it is justified merely by our past experience.

Two laws of thermodynamics embody the law of the conservation of energy and that of its dissipation. They are as follows:

1. When heat is produced by the expenditure of work, and vice versa, the ratio of work done to heat produced is constant. (The ratio is 4.18 joules/cal. or 778 ft-lb./B.t.u.)

2. In all natural processes involving the transfer of energy, some of it becomes less available.

221. The Sun is the Source of Our Energy. Our most bountiful, direct source of energy is the radiation of the sun. On a clear day when the sun is directly overhead, each acre of ground receives energy at a rate of more than 5,000 hp. If purchased at 3 cents/kw-hr. this energy would cost more than $100/hr.

Unfortunately, we have no efficient means of harnessing the sun's energy to our engines. Most of it is reradiated into space. A little is used in evaporating water which, falling as rain, supplies our rivers which can turn water wheels. Some of the energy stirs up winds which can drive windmills. Most important of all is the energy stored in growing plants, providing fuel to maintain animal life. Part was stored in the fossilized remains of plants and animals millions of years ago, and this energy we thoughtlessly expend in maintaining our industrial civilization.

In America we have used our petroleum resources lavishly. It has been so easy to locate new supplies that old fields are abandoned when less than half of the oil has been extracted. Then, too, the gas which forces the oil from the pores of the sandstone has been permitted to escape, leaving the oil forever imprisoned in the rocks. So wasteful are we that probably in a score of years most of our oil will be exhausted. The mining of coal is more difficult, the reserves are larger, and a century or so will elapse before our supplies are seriously depleted. When these carbon deposits are gone, we can use water power, but if all the available falls were utilized, they would take care of only about one-tenth of our present needs.

222. Efficiencies of Engines. The engines of today are much more efficient than Newcomen's, yet the best of them waste about 60 per cent of the heat energy which they receive from the boilers. What of the future? Will the efficiencies gradually increase and approach 100 per cent?

Before answering this question, we consider a somewhat similar situation regarding the efficiency of a waterfall.

Suppose that a water wheel is supplied from a reservoir A which is 400 ft. above sea level and delivers water to a lake which is 300 ft. above sea level (Fig. 8). What is the greatest possible efficiency?

At the reservoir each pound of water has 400 ft-lb. of potential energy, and at the water wheel, 100 ft. below, the potential energy is 300 ft-lb. Hence each pound of water can do at most 100 ft-lb. of work in turning the wheel. Therefore, the maximum possible efficiency is

$$\frac{\text{Energy output}}{\text{Energy input}} = \frac{100 \text{ ft-lb.}}{400 \text{ ft-lb.}} = 25 \text{ per cent}$$

The maximum efficiency of a steam engine can be found by similar considerations. The steam in the boiler is at a high temperature and has a great deal of potential energy. It is cooled in the cylinder of the engine doing work. Then the remainder of the heat is wasted, being thrown out in the exhaust.

Suppose that an engine receives steam from a boiler at a temperature $T_2 = 127°C$. or $400°K$. Part of the heat is used in pushing the

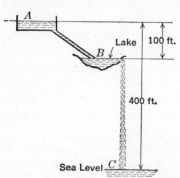

FIG. 8.—Only one-fourth of the energy of the water at A is available to turn a water wheel at B.

piston of the engine, and the remainder is delivered to the exhaust or "sink" at a temperature $T_1 = 23°C$. or $300°K$. By complicated reasoning, it can be shown that the maximum possible efficiency of the engine is given by

$$\text{Efficiency} = (T_2 - T_1)/T_2 \quad (1)$$

that is, in this example, 25 per cent.

In order to secure high efficiency, the boiler temperature T_2 should be high and the exhaust or "sink" temperature T_1 should be low. Thus, because of its higher boiling point, water is a better working substance than alcohol. In recent years, turbine engines have been devised to use mercury as a working substance. High efficiencies are secured because of its high boiling point. (The hot liquid mercury from the exhaust is used in a steam boiler to evaporate water and thus much of its energy is utilized.)

In the internal-combustion engine the temperature of the burning gases is higher than that attained in steam boilers, hence these engines are correspondingly more efficient.

223. Overall Efficiency. As applied to engines and machinery, the word efficiency has several distinct meanings. For example, the "boiler efficiency" tells us what fraction of the heat of the fuel is delivered as energy of the steam. The "engine efficiency" tells what fraction of the energy supplied to the engine is converted into mechanical energy, and "overall efficiency" means the ratio of the useful mechanical energy to that of the fuel. This value is often very low. The energy losses for a certain automobile traveling at 30 mi./hr. on a level road are shown in Fig. 9. Notice that less than 5 per cent of the energy is used in overcoming road friction. Most of the remainder is wasted in the cooling system and in the exhaust gases.

TYPICAL ENGINE EFFICIENCIES

	Per Cent
Steam, reciprocating type..............	12–27
turbine.........................	32–38
Automobile engine...................	15–20
Diesel engine.......................	30–40
(The human body)...................	13–20

224. The Human Body—a Heat Engine? In several ways, our bodies resemble heat engines. When a steam engine is at rest or when

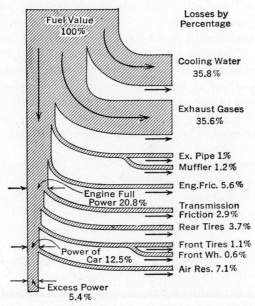

FIG. 9.—Energy losses in operating an automobile.

it runs without doing useful work, all the energy is wasted. Similarly, when a person is resting or moving about without doing anything useful, his energy is dissipated. A man lying in a hammock on a hot summer day loses energy at a rate of about 70 watts or 50 ft-lb./sec. When a person does work, his muscle tissue is oxidized more rapidly and the heat of combustion supplies the energy. Notwithstanding these similarities, the body is not a heat engine, for if it were, energy would be received from a "boiler" or other hot source and some of it would be delivered to a "sink" at a lower temperature. The difference of temperature would have to be much higher than that which can actually exist.

Example. If the normal temperature at which energy is delivered by a heat engine is that of the human body ($T_1 = 98.6°F. = 37°C. = 310°K.$), what is the minimum temperature T_2 of the boiler from which the heat is received, if the efficiency is 20 per cent?

$$\text{Maximum efficiency} = \frac{T_2 - T_1}{T_2} = 20 \text{ per cent}$$

$$= \frac{T_2 - 310°K.}{T_2} \quad \text{or} \quad T_2 = 388°K. = 115°C. = 239°F.$$

SUMMARY

The work of Rumford, Joule, and others has convinced scientists that heat is a form of energy.

Forty-two million ergs or 42,600 gwt-cm. of work are required to produce 1 cal. of heat, and 778 ft-lb. to produce 1 B.t.u.

Heat engines are used to convert heat energy into mechanical energy.

When the spark of an automobile engine is "retarded," the engine tends to overheat because less energy is utilized in pushing the pistons.

The law of the conservation of energy asserts that energy is never created or destroyed. The law has no theoretical justification and is based on experiment.

The first law of thermodynamics asserts in effect that whenever heat is produced by the expenditure of work, or vice versa, the same amount of work is always performed for each unit of heat.

All other forms of energy tend to be converted into heat, which is therefore the lowest form of energy. All bodies tend to approach the same common temperature.

The second law of thermodynamics asserts that the energy of the universe tends to become less and less available.

The theoretical maximum efficiency of an engine supplied with heat from a source at temperature T_2 and delivering heat to a "sink" at temperature T_1 is given by:

$$\text{Efficiency} = (T_2 - T_1)/T_2$$

REVIEW QUESTIONS

1. Describe the caloric theory of the nature of heat, and show how Rumford's results tended to disprove it.

2. Describe Joule's experiments, and show in what respects they afforded better evidence regarding the nature of heat than earlier ones.

3. In your opinion, was the invention of the steam engine a blessing?

4. Make a sketch of a Newcomen engine, showing the necessary valves, and explain how it operates.

5. Describe an improvement which Watt devised for the steam engine, and show why the efficiency was increased.

6. Make a sketch of a steam engine, showing the slide valve.

7. Describe a "single-impulse" turbine and one having several impulse wheels.

8. State several advantages of turbines over reciprocating-type steam engines.

9. Make sketches of a 4-stroke cycle gasoline engine showing the positions of the valves during each of the four strokes.

10. Why does the engine tend to overheat when the spark is retarded?

11. What are the advantages and disadvantages of high-compression engines?

12. Explain the operation of a Diesel engine, and state some of its advantages and disadvantages.

13. State the law of the conservation of energy.

14. State several sources of energy, including some that are not mentioned in the text.

15. State the first law of thermodynamics. Discuss the "degradation" of energy.

16. Discuss the influence of temperatures on the efficiencies of engines.

PROBLEMS

$$(g = 32 \text{ ft./sec.}^2 = 980 \text{ cm./sec.}^2)$$

1'. In turning an ice-cream freezer, a man exerts an average force of 10 lb., and his hand travels on a circle 2.0 ft. in circumference. He turns the crank at a rate of 1 rev./sec. for 100 sec. (a) How much work does he do? (b) What is his horsepower? (c) How much heat does the stirring produce in the 100 sec.?

2. A boy weighing 100 lb. slides down a rope 20.0 ft. long, arriving at the ground with zero speed. (a) How much work was done by friction, and (b) how much heat was produced?

3''. An automobile weighs 3,200 lb., and its speed is 90 ft./sec. (about 60 mi./hr.). It is stopped in 4.00 sec. (a) What was its initial kinetic energy? (b) What was the horsepower of the brakes (i.e., at what rate did they absorb energy)? (c) How much heat was produced?

4. The burning of 1 gal. of gasoline liberates about 30,000,000 cal. of heat or about 125,000,000 joules = 93,000,000 ft-lb. To what elevation would this amount of energy lift a car weighing 3,000 lb.?

5'. A man when resting expends energy at a rate of 70 watts. When working, his power consumption is doubled. How much bread per hour would he need to afford the energy, the heat of combustion being 8,000 cal./gram?

6. A man weighing 156 lb. climbs a mountain 10,000 ft. high. (a) How much work is done, and how much is its heat equivalent? (b) How many soda biscuits each of mass 1/100 pound having a heat combustion of 100,000 B.t.u./pound would supply this amount of energy?

CHAPTER XXV

THE PHYSICS OF THE WEATHER

When ye see a cloud rise out of the west, ye say, "There cometh a storm," and so it is.—The Bible.

Charles Dudley Warner once remarked that everyone talks about the weather yet no one does anything about it. In a sense this is true, for man has achieved no control of the elements. However, he has learned to predict the weather and so can prepare to meet it.

The most important properties of the weather at any place and time are the **temperature, wind, barometric pressure, humidity,** and **precipitation** or **rainfall.** Each of these is influenced by many factors, the most important of which will be discussed.

225. Temperature. The average annual temperature in any region depends partly upon the rate at which radiation is received from the sun. A screen 1 cm.^{2} in cross section, placed normal to the sun's rays, at the outer borders of the atmosphere, would receive nearly 2 cal. of energy per minute. A great deal of the radiant energy is reflected by the atmosphere or is absorbed, so that even on clear days less than 50 per cent reaches the earth's surface. A little of this energy is stored by growing plants, but most of it is radiated into space. Century by century, the earth is in thermal equilibrium, receiving and radiating energy at nearly the same rate with very small variations in average temperature.

The absorption of the atmosphere is due principally to the water vapor, carbon dioxide, fog, and dust that it contains. Of these by far the most variable constituent is the dust. Much of it is thrown into the atmosphere by volcanoes where it remains suspended for months and even years. During the past two centuries, there have been numerous instances of cool summers which can be explained by volcanic eruptions. The year 1816 is variously known as "the year without a summer," "poverty year," and "eighteen hundred and froze to death." Snow fell in New England every month of the year. The cold weather was caused by atmospheric absorption of the sun's radiations by dust ejected by an explosion of the volcano Tomboro. In more recent years cool summers have followed eruptions of Krakatoa in 1883, Mont Pelée in 1902, and Katmai in 1912.

The radiation received by a unit area of the earth's surface depends upon the angle of incidence of the sun's rays. The surface AC (Fig. 1), on which the rays are incident normally, receives energy at a rate twice that at which the equal surface AB receives it.

The two factors which we have just discussed are chiefly responsible for the difference in temperature between the arctic regions and the tropics. A beam of sunlight incident near the north pole must penetrate a greater depth of atmosphere than an equal beam incident near the equator (Fig. 2). Further, the first beam is incident obliquely and hence is distributed over a larger area than the second. For both these reasons, less radiation is received per unit area at the pole than at the equator.

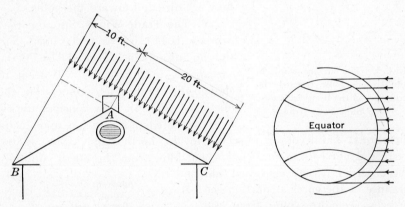

FIG. 1.—The surface AC receives twice as much radiant energy as AB.
FIG. 2.—The arctic regions receive less energy than the tropics because the radiations are incident at an acute angle.

226. The Influence of Bodies of Water. The climate of Great Britain which is near the ocean is much more temperate than that of the plains of Canada or of central Russia. The temperature variations in Great Britain are small for several reasons—first, the water acts as an immense reservoir absorbing energy and emitting it with relatively small changes of surface temperature. This is because the specific heat of water is large and also because heat is convected to considerable depths by currents and by waves. Second, the water absorbs heat in evaporating, and emits heat in condensing. Lastly, fogs and clouds form readily near the ocean and have a blanketing effect, preventing the gain or loss of heat by the earth.

227. The Winds. The temperatures at various parts of the earth's surface depend not only upon the amount of radiation received and upon the presence of bodies of water, but also upon the prevailing winds. These huge convection currents in the air are caused by the unequal heating of the atmosphere. The air near the equator expands

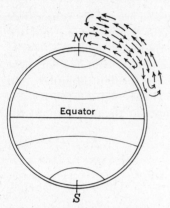

FIG. 3.—The surface winds in the tropics blow toward the equator. In the temperate zone they blow away from it.

and rises like the gases in a chimney, travels to the arctic regions, descends, and returns to the tropics (Fig. 3). Notice that there is also a surface wind blowing from the tropics toward the pole. (The reasons for this behavior are too complex to be presented here.) Keep in mind that **the surface winds in the tropics blow toward the equator, but in the temperate zones they are directed toward the poles.**

228. The Trade Winds. Suppose that a breeze is blowing from the north and that an automobile is headed east. As the car speeds up, the wind will seem to change direction and to come from the northeast (Fig. 4). Now consider the effect of the earth's rotation upon wind directions. Think of an observer in the north tropic zone. If the earth did not rotate, the wind would blow from the north. Actually the observer travels eastward and because of the earth's rotation the breezes seem to come from the northeast. In the days of the sailing ships, these winds were very useful in navigation, and so they were called the "trade" winds.

229. The Westerlies. The winds in the temperate zones are much more erratic than those of the tropics, but careful observations show that their prevailing direction is from the west or southwest. To understand the reason for this, study Fig. 3 again and notice that the winds in the temperate zones are

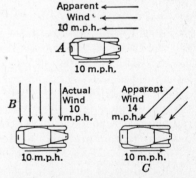

FIG. 4.—The wind blows from the north and the automobile travels east. The wind seems to come from the northeast.

directed toward the poles and are opposite to the trade winds. Hence in the United States they blow from the south. Then consider carefully the effect of the earth's rotation. The air at all points south of your position is carried eastward because of the earth's rotation. Its east-velocity is greater than yours. Hence the prevailing winds come from the southwest and they are called westerlies. These winds are very important in explaining the climates of the United States.

230. Land and Sea Breezes. The westerly sea breezes from the Pacific Ocean, traveling over California, Oregon, and Washington, account for the relatively mild and uniform climates in these sections. Along the eastern coasts of America, the climate is much more variable, because the westerlies pass over great land areas where the temperatures fluctuate widely.

The breezes at the seashore often vary with the time of day. The land heats rapidly during daylight, and the air, being heated, rises like the gases in a chimney. Then the air moves in from the ocean, and this constitutes the sea breeze. At night the land surface cools quickly, the cold air descends, and a breeze blows out over the ocean.

231. Hurricanes. The hurricanes of the tropics are huge whirlwinds 100 to 200 miles in diameter. They are produced over the oceans, and are caused, like other winds, by the unequal heating of the atmosphere. An extended region of the ocean's surface becomes thoroughly heated, and the air above it rises. Then air from the surrounding regions streams in toward the center. In this way gigantic whirlpools are formed which in the northern hemi-

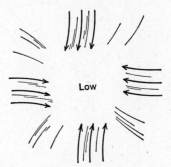

Fig. 5.—Direction of the winds in a hurricane.

sphere are always directed counter-clockwise as viewed from above. Fig. 5 represents the motion of the winds in a hurricane. The air from the south has a greater velocity toward the east than the center of the storm. Hence the wind "gets ahead." The air from the north has a smaller velocity and it falls behind. In this manner the spiral motion is produced.

232. Tornadoes or "Twisters." In the temperate zones, violent local storms called tornadoes or "twisters" occur which resemble hurricanes but are much smaller in area. These whirlwinds are funnel-shaped and vary from a few feet to a mile in diameter. They sweep out paths of destruction from 20 to 300 miles long. At the center of the spiraling whirlpool of air the barometric pressure is greatly reduced. Sometimes in a tornado the atmospheric pressure decreases 10 per cent in less than a minute and houses are destroyed by the sudden expansion of the air imprisoned in them.

233. Cyclones. The word "cyclone" is popularly used to signify a tornado; but to weather forecasters, it means an enormous spirally moving air stream much less violent than the hurricane or tornado.

Cyclones are located by means of simultaneous nationwide observations of the winds and of the barometric pressure. As will be explained later, reports are telegraphed to central stations where weather maps are made. On those maps are drawn heavy lines called "isobars" which connect points where the barometric pressure is the same (Fig. 6).

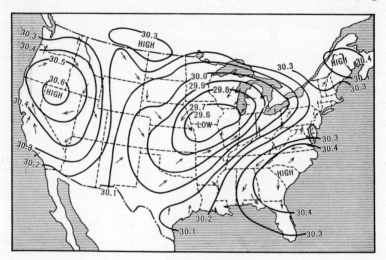

FIG. 6.—Weather map.

Arrows are drawn indicating wind directions. The weather maps always show at least one region encircled by isobars, where the barometric pressure is a minimum. The wind is directed spirally around this "low," indicating that it is the center of a gigantic whirlpool of air. On the northern hemisphere the cyclones are always directed counterclockwise like a hurricane, and for the same reason.

234. The Anticyclone or "High." The maps also reveal other regions called anticyclones or "highs" where the barometric pressures have maximum values, and these regions, likewise, are located by isobars (Fig. 6). In the northern hemisphere, the winds about the center of the high are always directed clockwise. The center of the high is a region where the air streams downward and then spreads out laterally in all directions. The air moving southward seems to come from the northeast for the same reason that the trade wind does, and that which moves north seems to blow from the southwest like the westerlies.

Successive weather observations show that the highs and lows follow one another in a majestic procession across the continent. The rates of travel vary widely, their average speed in the United States being 30 mi./hr., or about the speed of automobile travel.

235. Humidity. One of the most important properties of the weather is the dampness or relative humidity. By this expression is meant the ratio of the amount of water vapor in unit volume to the amount that would be contained if the space were saturated. That is:

$$\text{Relative humidity} = \frac{\textbf{Density of water vapor}}{\textbf{Density if the space were saturated}}$$

For example, if the actual vapor density is 10 grams/m.^{3}, and the saturation vapor density is 20 grams/m.^{3}, the relative humidity is 50 per cent.

236. The Dew Point. In winter weather, accidents occur because moisture collects on the inner surfaces of the windshields of automo-

TABLE I

SATURATION VAPOR DENSITIES AND PRESSURES

Temperature, °C.	°F.	Vapor Density, grams/m.^{3}	Vapor Pressure, mm.-of-mercury
−10	14.0	2.16	1.96
0	32	4.85	4.58
5	41.0	6.80	6.54
10	50	9.41	9.21
11	51.8	10.02	9.85
12	53.6	10.66	10.52
13	55.4	11.23	11.29
14	57.2	12.07	11.99
15	59.0	12.83	12.79
20	68	17.30	17.55
40	104	51.1	55.4
60	140	130.5	149.6
80	176	293.8	355.4
100	212	598	760
200	392	7,840	11,650

biles, preventing good vision. The temperature of the glass is low and the air near it is cooled enough to become supersaturated, so that water is deposited on the surface. One remedy is to warm the glass. Another is to open the windows of the car so that the air inside, damp with the moisture of the passengers' breaths, may be replaced by fresh air, containing less moisture.

The temperature at which the water vapor in a space is saturated is called the "dew point." It may be determined by placing a little warm water in a silver cup and adding ice until a film of dew first appears on the surface of the cup. The temperature of the water is then noted on a thermometer. Dew point observations are used in determining relative humidities. The method will be understood from the following example.

Example. What is the relative humidity if the outdoor temperature is 20°C. and the dew point is 15°C.?

From Table I the saturation vapor density of water at 15°C. is found to be 12.83 grams/m.³ This is the amount of vapor actually present per unit volume. From the table we also ascertain how much water vapor would be present if the space were saturated at 20°C., namely, 17.30 grams/m.³ Hence the relative humidity is (12.83 grams/m.³)/(17.30 grams/m.³) = 0.742 = 74.2 per cent.

237. Hygrometers. In determining relative humidities, weather observers use hygrometers. One type consists of two thermometers, the bulb of one being covered by a cloth or wick moistened with water. If the space were saturated, there would be no evaporation from the cloth and the two thermometers would indicate the same temperature. When the air is unsaturated, water evaporates from the wet bulb and it is cooled. Moreover, the drier the air the greater is the rate of evaporation, and hence the greater the temperature difference of the two thermometers. A table provided with the instrument shows the relative humidity corresponding to any pair of temperature readings. Hair hygrometers (Fig. 7) are convenient for household use. Their essential part is a strand of hair which contracts when it absorbs moisture. This contraction moves the pointer that indicates the relative humidity on a scale.

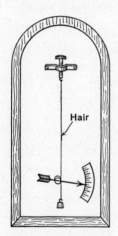

Fig. 7.—A hair hygrometer.

238. Dew, Fog, and Clouds. Water is deposited as dew when moisture-laden air comes into contact with objects which are at temperatures below the dew point. When this temperature is below freezing, the vapor is deposited as frost.

Fogs and clouds are produced when the atmosphere is cooled below the dew point. This cooling may be caused by the mixture of colder air with moist, warm, air, when winds blow from the sea over land.

A second method of cooling is by expansion. As air rises, the temperature falls about 1 C.° for each 185 ft. increase in elevation, so that eventually, at a certain level, the air is cooled to the dew point, becomes saturated, and fog or clouds form. On calm, sultry summer days many small puffy "wool pack" or "cumulus" clouds may be seen (Fig. 8). Each small cloud reveals the presence beneath it of a vertical air stream. These rising winds carry moisture, which condenses when cooled to the dew point. Soaring birds use these air streams to maintain their elevations for considerable periods without muscular exertion. Pilots, flying with engineless airplanes or gliders, travel for scores of miles. The planes are carried

FIG. 8.—Cumulus clouds.

upward in the successive "air fountains," and they glide down from each column to the next (Fig. 9).

239. Rain. The formation of fog is readily explained, but the production of comparatively large raindrops is more difficult to understand. The question is: How can the multitude of microscopic fog particles in a cloud be merged into a very few raindrops? One hypothesis

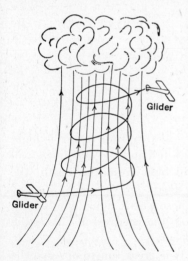

FIG. 9.—A glider takes advantage of rising air streams.

is that, when a cloud is carried upward by a wind, most of the heavier droplets are left behind. The air, cooled by expansion as it rises, becomes supersaturated. Water vapor condenses on the few droplets, which rapidly increase in size. Later these droplets falling through the air pick up other small droplets and become still larger.

240. Scientific Weather Forecasting. Those who live out-of-doors become expert in predicting the weather for the next day or so, but most of us rely upon the forecasts of the United States Government. These are based on observations made twice daily at 8:00 A.M. and 8:00 P.M., Eastern Standard Time, at about 200 stations in North America. Observations are also received from other countries, and radio messages from vessels at sea. Each observer reports the barometric reading, wind velocity, temperature, relative humidity, cloudiness, and the precipitation of the preceding 24 hours. All these messages are received at each of several forecasting centers where maps like that in Fig. 6 are prepared. The forecaster then predicts the weather for his own district and sends out copies of the map, as well as telegraphic forecasts and sometimes special warnings of dangerous storms and "cold waves." All this is accomplished within 2 hours of the time when the observations were made.

In foretelling the weather, the positions of the "lows" or regions of minimum pressure are of paramount importance. To understand this consider Fig. 10, which represents a huge low advancing toward the

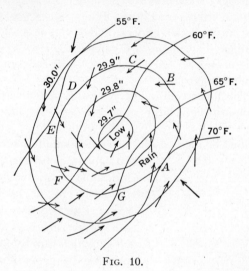

FIG. 10.

east. At A the wind is from the south, and the temperature is high. As the low approaches, the barometer will fall and the cloudiness will increase. After it passes, the winds will blow from the north, the barometer will rise, and the clouds clear away.

The most interesting region is at G, where warm, moist winds from the south first mix with cooler winds from the northwest. This is the region where storms are most likely to occur.

241. Locating the Position of a Low. It is great fun to observe the veering of the wind as a storm approaches. To locate the low keep in mind that the wind spirals around it in a counterclockwise direction. Stand with your back to the wind and point forward with your right hand, palm down. Then your thumb will point toward the probable position of the low.

242. Weather Lore. The weather is of unending interest, not only because of its influence on our comfort and well-being, but also because the drama of the skies holds our attention. In earlier days men lived more in the open than we do and were much more affected by the winds and storms. They had fewer diversions to distract them, and so they were more mindful of the weather than we are.

The ancient forecaster was handicapped because all his observations were qualitative. He had no thermometers, barometers, or hygrometers. Furthermore, his observations were local and he could not know the weather conditions over wide areas. His crude attempts to set up simple weather laws give interesting examples of primitive applications of scientific method. First, patiently, year after year, the weather observer noted the winds and clouds and rain; then he set up certain simple generalizations or laws which were handed down from father to son, and they were constantly tested by experience. Some of the most nearly valid survive to this day. A good deal of chaff has been preserved with the wheat. Notable among these errors are the cherished beliefs that the moon affects the weather. Thousands of farmers are careful to plant their crops in the "dark of the moon," though meteorological studies fail to show any real relationship between the moon's phases and the weather.

> The moon and the weather
> May change together,
> But change in the moon
> Won't change the weather.

243. Rules for Predicting the Weather. The following well-founded rules for forecasting are embodied in weather proverbs.

1. When the western sky is clear in the evening, fair weather is expected. Rain clouds in the west presage storms.

This is because storms usually travel from west to east.

> Golden sunset at night,
> Sailors delight.

"When ye see a cloud rise out of the west, ye say, 'There cometh a storm,' and so it is."

2. Low-lying huge cumulus clouds indicate high humidity and foretell rain.

> When the clouds appear like rocks and towers,
> The earth's refreshed by frequent showers.

Other signs of high humidity presaging rain are: (*a*) rheumatic pains; (*b*) "sweating" walls of dwellings, caused by dew; (*c*) falling smoke from chimneys. (This is because water vapor condenses on the smoke particles, increasing their weight.)

3. When the humidity is low and the clouds clear up early in the morning, fair weather is predicted; otherwise rain.

> Mists descending on the plain,
>   Scatter away the clouds and rain.
> But when they hang on mountain tops,
>   They'll soon descend in copious drops.

4. When hair-like cirrus clouds at very high elevations are visible, the sky is clear and fair weather is to be expected for twenty-four hours.

> The higher the sky, the fairer the weather.

5. When very high "mackerel" clouds are seen, cold air and warm air are mixing and rain is to be expected within twenty-four hours.

> Mackerel sky, rain is nigh.

> Mackerel sky and mares' tails
> Cause the sailor to furl the sails.

244. Artificial Weather. All attempts at controlling the weather have failed, but we have learned to protect ourselves from the elements by better clothing, shelter, and heating so that winter today has few terrors. The great improvements in heating methods have brought with them certain disadvantages. The temperatures of dwellings heated by open fireplaces were usually fairly low, and the relative humidities were high. When central heating is used, temperatures are often as high as 80°F., and the relative humidities are greatly diminished. In consequence the membranes of the nasal passages become dry and the susceptibility to colds increases. Attempts to improve this condition are made by the evaporation of water. The difficulty is that, for an ordinary dwelling in zero weather, about 1 gal. of water per day per room is required to keep the relative humidity at a proper value. Further, when the humidity is maintained in this manner, water deposits on the window panes and trickles downward, forming pools on the sills below. This may be prevented by using double windows so that the inner glass surfaces are not cooled below the dew point.

During the summer, when the air is damp, perspiration does not evaporate readily and discomfort results. In air-conditioning systems, ventilating fans force the air of a building through sprays of water chilled by refrigeration. The air is cleaned by this process, and its temperature and humidity are lowered to desired levels.

SUMMARY

Important characteristics of the weather are: the temperature, wind, humidity, and precipitation.

Radiation from the sun is important in determining the temperature at a given location. This, in turn, depends upon the elevation of the sun and upon the amount of atmospheric absorption.

The screening effect of the atmosphere depends principally upon the content of water vapor, carbon dioxide, fog, and dust.

The temperature variations at a given locality are decreased if large bodies of water are located near by. This effect results because of the high specific heat of water, its fluidity, and the enhanced humidity which it imparts to the air.

The trade winds blow from the poles toward the equator. Because of the rotation of the earth, the trade winds seem to come from the east or northeast. In the temperate zones, the winds blow toward the poles. Because of the earth's rotation they seem to come from the west or southwest.

Because of unequal heating, breezes often blow from sea to land in the daytime and oppositely at night.

Tornadoes and hurricanes are spirally blowing, destructive winds. In the northern hemisphere they rotate counterclockwise.

Cyclones are somewhat like tornadoes but are much larger, being several hundred miles in diameter. The wind velocities usually are low.

The relative humidity of a space is the ratio of the actual water-vapor content per unit volume to the content if the space were saturated.

The dew point of air is the temperature at which the air would be saturated, keeping the water-vapor density constant.

Fogs and clouds are formed when air is cooled below the dew point.

Cumulus clouds are formed above vertically rising columns of air.

Rain is produced when a cloud rises so rapidly that most of the fog particles are left behind. The few remaining ones then grow by deposition of water vapor, forming raindrops.

When a barometric low approaches, the barometric pressure and temperature fall, the cloudiness increases, with probable rain. As the low recedes and a high approaches, the pressure rises and the skies clear, with less probability of rain.

REVIEW QUESTIONS

1. Discuss factors affecting the temperature at a given locality, including elevation of the sun, atmospheric absorption, and the presence of large bodies of water. Apply these principles to your own locality.

2. Explain the production of the trade winds and of the westerlies, showing why they blow oppositely to each other.

3. How does a tornado resemble a cyclone, and how do they differ? Which is mentioned more frequently (*a*) in the news columns, and (*b*) in the weather reports? Why?

4. Carefully explain why the cyclones rotate counterclockwise in the northern hemisphere and oppositely in the southern hemisphere.

5. What is an anticyclone, and how does it differ from a cyclone?

6. Define relative humidity, and state the factors on which it depends.

7. Define dew point, and show how it may be determined.

8. Show how the wet-bulb and dry-bulb thermometers are used to determine relative humidities.

9. Explain why the bases of several neighboring cumulus clouds usually are at about the same level. How is such a cloud produced?

10. How can a bird soar for hours without beating its wings?

11. Explain the production of rain.

12. The following statistics show maximum and minimum weather records for the United States. Why might each location be expected to "beat the record"?

1. Coldest ever −65°F. Fort Keogh, Mont., January, 1888.
2. Hottest ever 134°F. Greenland Ranch, Death Valley, July, 1913.
3. Smallest rainfall 1.65 in./yr. Greenland Ranch, Calif.
4. Largest rainfall, 131.5 in./yr. Glenora, Oregon.
(World record, 456 in. = 38 ft., Cherrapunja, India.)

13. The following verses ascribed to Erasmus Darwin, the grandfather of Charles Darwin, summarize the weatherlore of Virgil, Theophrastus, and of other ancient writers. Which, in your opinion, have inadequate scientific foundations?

The hollow winds begin to blow,
The clouds look black, the glass is low,
The soot falls down, the spaniels sleep,
And spiders from their cobwebs peep.
Last night the sun went pale to bed,
The moon in halos hid her head.
The boding shepherd heaves a sigh,
For, see! a rainbow spans the sky.
The walls are damp, the ditches smell,
Closed is the pink-eyed pimpernel.
Hark! how the chairs and tables crack,
Old Betty's joints are on the rack;
Her corns with shooting pains torment her
And to her bed untimely send her.
Loud quack the ducks, the peacocks cry,
The distant hills are looking nigh.
How restless are the snorting swine!
The busy flies disturb the kine.
Low o'er the grass the swallow wings,
The cricket, too, how shrill she sings!
Puss on the hearth, with velvet paws
Sits wiping o'er her whiskered jaws.
Through the clear stream the fishes rise
And nimbly catch th' incautious flies.
The glow-worms, numerous and bright,
Illumed the dewey dell last night.
At dusk the squalid toad was seen
Hopping and crawling o'er the green.
The whirling dust the wind obeys,
And in the rapid eddy plays.

The frog has changed his yellow vest
And in a russet coat is dressed,
- Though June, the air is cold and still,
The mellow blackbird's voice is shrill,
My dog, so altered is his taste,
Quits mutton bones on grass to feast.
And, see yon rooks, how odd their flight,
They imitate the gliding kite.
And seem precipitate to fall,
As if they felt the piercing ball.
'Twill surely rain—I see with sorrow
Our jaunt must be put off tomorrow.

14. Using the map of Fig. 6, predict the weather for the next 24 hours at Atlanta, Ga.

15. Distinguish between "weather" and "climate."

16. Explain why the earth has seasonal changes.

17. What is the difference between fog, dew, rain, and snow?

18. On a certain winter's day the dew points indoors and outdoors were the same, yet the relative humidities were different. Explain.

19. Why is the climate on the west side of the Rocky mountains rainy, though on the east side it is dry?

20. Describe the probable weather as a low approaches and as it recedes.

21. Draw a map indicating typical isobars or equal-pressure lines about a low and showing the wind directions at several points. Which parts are likely to be warm, and which cloudy? Where is rain most likely to fall? Why?

PROBLEMS

1. When the dew point is 15°C., what is the water-vapor density?

2. If the dew point is 10°C. (50°F.), what is the relative humidity (a) in a room where the temperature is 20°C. (68°F.), and (b) outdoors where it is 15°C.?

3. Suppose that outdoors on a summer's day the temperature is 20°C. and the dew point is 10°C. If the air as it rises cools 0.6°C. for each 100 m., at what elevation will clouds form?

4'. Each day 24,000 grams (6 gal.) of water are evaporated at 100°C. to humidify a dwelling. Find the cost per 30 days if gas is used costing $1.20/1,000 ft.^{3} or $10.00 per billion calories. (Assume that initial temperature of water is 20°C. and that the efficiency is 100 per cent.)

5. One wall of a lecture room is 3.0 m. by 10 m. During a storm the mercury barometer reading outdoors suddenly decreased 1.00 cm. What was the force tending to push out the wall if no air escaped?

REFERENCES

C. F. Brooks, "Why the Weather?"

W. J. Humphreys, "Physics of the Air."

W. R. Gregg, "Aeronautical Meteorology."

M. Luckiesh, "Book of the Sky."

W. J. Humphreys, "Rain Making and Other Vagaries."

W. H. Puck, "A Short Course in Elementary Meteorology."

CHAPTER XXVI

VIBRATIONS

In earlier chapters several types of motion were considered, beginning with the simplest—that of a particle moving on a straight line with constant velocity. Rectilinear motion with constant acceleration was discussed next; and, following this, the third type, that of a particle moving on a circular path with constant speed but changing velocity. The student should now be prepared to study the to-and-fro or vibrating type of motion, which is somewhat more complex than the others, yet very necessary to an understanding of sound, light, radio, and other kinds of waves. Familiar examples are the swaying of trees, the fluttering of flags, and the quiverings of the strings of musical instruments.

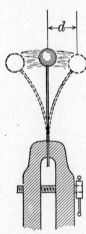

Fig. 1.—A ball and spring vibrating with simple harmonic motion.

245. Simple Harmonic Motion. The simplest type of vibration, called simple harmonic motion, is illustrated by a ball mounted on a flat spring which is supported in a vise (Fig. 1). Pull the ball sideways, distorting the spring, and you will observe an opposing force. This force becomes greater as the ball is pulled farther away from its initial position, and is proportional to the displacement d, that is the distance from the position of equilibrium. This fact distinguishes simple harmonic motion from all other kinds and affords the following definition:

Simple harmonic motion is that type of vibration in which the restoring force is proportional to the displacement and is always directed toward the position of equilibrium.

The Period of a Simple Harmonic Vibration. The period of vibration of a body means the time required for a "round trip" or a complete to-and-fro motion. This time, for a simple harmonic vibration, depends upon two factors, one, the stiffness of the spring (or other agency) that pushes the body back to its position of equilibrium, and the other, the mass of the vibrating body. The stiffness of the spring is measured by the "**force-constant,**" that is **the force necessary to cause a unit displacement.** For example, if 30 gwt. are required to displace the ball represented in Fig. 1 through a distance of 1 cm., and 60 gwt. to cause a displacement of 2 cm., the force-constant is 30 gwt./cm.

$$\text{Force-constant} = \frac{\text{Restoring force}}{\text{Displacement}}$$

If the spring is replaced by another which is 4 times as stiff, so that 120 gwt. are required to cause a displacement of 1 cm., the period is halved.

The second factor affecting the period is the mass of the vibrator. Replace the ball (Fig. 1) by one which is 4 times as massive, and the period of the system will be doubled.

These two laws are expressed by the following equation which will be derived presently.

$$\text{Period} = 2\pi \sqrt{\frac{\text{Mass}}{\text{Force-constant}}} = 2\pi \sqrt{\frac{W/g}{K}} \qquad (1)$$

Example. A 4.0-lb. ball is suspended by a light, spiral spring. A force of 2.0 lb. is required to pull the weight downward 1.00 ft. Find (a) the force-constant and (b) the period of vibration.

(a) $K = 2.0 \text{ lb.}/1.00 \text{ ft.} = 2.0 \text{ lb./ft.}$

(b) $T = 2\pi \sqrt{\dfrac{4.0 \text{ lb.}/(32 \text{ ft./sec.}^2)}{2.0 \text{ lb./ft.}}} =$

$\pi/2 \text{ sec.} = 1.57 \text{ sec.}$

246. Another Description of Simple Harmonic Motion. In considering simple harmonic motion, it is convenient to use an imaginary "reference circle." Suppose that a wheel is mounted on a horizontal axis and that a ball C is fastened to one side of its rim (Fig. 2). Let the sun be vertically overhead so that the shadow of the ball appears on the floor at C'. Turn the wheel at constant speed, and the shadow will vibrate with simple harmonic

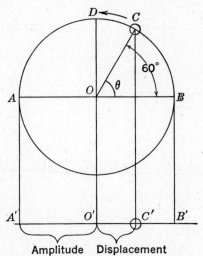

Fig. 2.—The ball C moves with uniform circular motion and C' with simple harmonic motion.

motion. The circle on which the ball travels is the "reference circle" of the vibration. This fact affords the following description of simple harmonic motion:

Simple harmonic motion is the motion of the projection on a straight line of a point which moves on a circle with constant speed. The line and the circle must be in the same plane. (The projection of a point on a line is the point where a perpendicular from that point intersects the line. Thus, in Fig. 2, C' is the projection of C.)

247. The Phase of a Vibration. Later in dealing with sound and light we shall need to use the word phase which tells us what fraction of a vibration has been completed. Usually phase is expressed in terms of the angle through which the reference particle has moved from some chosen position. For example, in Fig. 2 C has moved through 60° since leaving B. When the phase is 90°, the ball will have made one-fourth of a complete vibration.

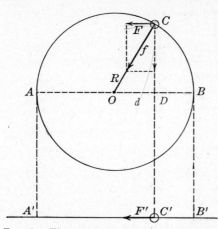

FIG. 3.—The restoring force F acting on C' equals the horizontal component of the force acting on C.

248. Derivation of the Equation for the Period of a Simple Harmonic Vibration. One advantage of this description of simple harmonic motion is that it affords a derivation of the equation for the period.

Consider the forces acting on the ball C and an equal ball C' vibrating along $A'B'$ (Fig. 3). The ball C moves on a circle with constant speed v. The centripetal force acting on it is given by

$$f = mv^2/R \tag{2}$$

The horizontal component F of this force is equal to the restoring force acting on the vibrating ball C'.

From similar triangles,

$$F/f = d/R$$
$$F = f \times d/R \tag{3}$$

From (2) and (3), $F = mv^2/R \times d/R \; = m \times v^2/R^2 \times d$

Transposing

$$R^2/v^2 = m/(F/d) = \frac{m}{\text{Force-constant, } K}$$
$$2\pi R/v = 2\pi\sqrt{m/K}$$

But $2\pi R/v$ is the time required for one revolution of the reference particle C and equals the period T of the vibrator, so that

$$T = 2\pi\sqrt{m/K}$$

249. The Pendulum. The motion of a pendulum was first studied by Galileo when he was a young man at Pisa. One day at the cathedral he whiled away the service watching the vibrations of a chandelier, set swinging by an attendant who lighted the candles. Galileo noticed that the time of the vibrations seemed to be constant as the motion gradually died down, and he verified this conclusion by timing them. He had no watch or clock, but used his own pulse to mark off the time. Later at home he performed experiments with simple pendulums made by suspending balls from strings.

The period of a "simple" pendulum consisting of a small ball of mass m suspended by a long cord of length l is given by

$$T = 2\pi\sqrt{l/g} \qquad (4)$$

g being the acceleration of gravity.

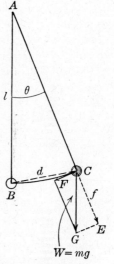

FIG. 4.—The restoring force acting on C equals $W \times d/l$.

Notice (a) that the period is proportional to the square root of the length l of the pendulum, (b) that it is inversely proportional to the square root of the acceleration of gravity g, and (c) that it does not depend upon the mass of the pendulum.

Galileo's discovery, that the period of a pendulum was constant, was quickly exploited by physicians, who began to use pendulums to measure the pulse rates of their patients. The doctor suspended a ball from a cord, set it into motion, and counted the number of vibrations it made during a chosen number of pulse beats. Soon clocks were invented in which pendulums regulated the rate of ticking. They were so accurate that hour glasses, water clocks, and candles were thrown onto the scrap pile. The pendulum proved useful, also, in determining the value g, the acceleration of gravity. In order to do this, the period of a simple pendulum of known length is measured and the value of g is computed by equation (4).

250. Derivation of the Pendulum Formula. Figure 4 represents a simple pendulum of length l, weight $W = mg$, and mass $m = W/g$. The force W can be replaced by two components, f parallel to the cord and F at right angles to it. The angle θ is assumed to be small so that the triangles ABC and CEG are nearly similar. Hence, approximately,

$$F/W = d/l$$
$$F/d = W/l$$

Now, F is the restoring force and d the displacement, so that

$$F/d \text{ is the force-constant, } K$$

From (2)

$$T = 2\pi\sqrt{m/K} = 2\pi\sqrt{\dfrac{W/g}{W/l}} = 2\pi\sqrt{l/g}$$

When the weight of the pendulum is doubled, the force-constant is also, hence the period is unchanged.

Error arises from the assumption that the triangles are similar but this error is only about 1/50 per cent if the pendulum swings through an angle of 3° from the position of equilibrium. If the angle is 60°, the error is 6 per cent.

SUMMARY

A vibration is the regularly recurring motion of a particle or body.

The restoring force acting on a particle is the external force tending to restore it to its position of equilibrium.

Simple harmonic motion is that type of vibration in which the restoring force is proportional to the displacement.

The period of a vibration is the time required for a complete to-and-fro motion. The frequency is the number of vibrations per unit time.

The period of a simple harmonic vibration is given by

$$T = 2\pi\sqrt{m/(F/d)} = 2\pi\sqrt{\dfrac{W/g}{F/d}}$$

The period of a simple pendulum of length l vibrating through a small angle is given approximately by

$$T = 2\pi\sqrt{l/g}$$

g being the acceleration of gravity.

Simple harmonic motion may be described as the motion of the projection on a straight line of a point moving with constant speed on a circle, the circle and the line being in the same plane.

The phase of a vibration is the angle through which the reference point has moved since the particle left a chosen starting position.

REVIEW QUESTIONS

1. Define vibration, restoring force, force-constant, frequency, period, simple harmonic motion.

2. How does the period of a simple harmonic motion depend upon (a) the force-constant and (b) the mass?

3. State the expression for the period of a simple pendulum, and derive it.

4. Develop the equation for the period of a simple harmonic motion.

5. Define "phase of a vibration."

6. How does the period of vibration of an automobile vary when an additional passenger enters it?

PROBLEMS

1. When a spring is mounted with its lower end in a vise, a force of 2,000 gwt. is required to pull the upper end 2.0 cm. away from its normal position. What is the force-constant?

2′. A child's 200-gram "return ball" is suspended from a long rubber band. If an additional force of 2.04 gwt. would pull it down 10 cm., find the natural period of vibration.

3″. When a 200-gram bird sits on its perch in a cage suspended by a spring, the cage is pulled 0.25 cm. below its level when empty. If the cage weighs 1,000 gwt., find the force-constant and compute the period of vibration of the empty cage.

4′. (a) When a 200-lb. man entered an automobile, the center of gravity descended 1/100 ft. What was the force-constant of the springs? (b) The man and car body just described weigh 900 lb. What is the period of vibration?

5′. The crank of a grindstone is 1 ft. long. The grindstone turns uniformly, making ½ rev./sec. The shadow cast by the handle on the level ground at noon vibrates with simple harmonic motion. Find (a) the period, (b) the frequency, and (c) the amplitude, of the vibration.

6″. A child's swing has a period of 5.0 sec. and the amplitude is 3.0 ft. Find (a) the speed of the imaginary particle moving in the reference circle for this vibration and (b) the maximum speed of the swing.

7′. The acceleration of gravity on the moon's surface is 1/6 that on the earth. That on the sun is 28 times that on earth. If a pendulum beating seconds on the earth is 25 cm. long, how long a pendulum would beat seconds (a) on the moon and (b) on the sun?

8′. The pendulum of a clock beats seconds at the earth's surface. What would be its period on the moon where g is 1/6 the value on the earth?

9′. A boy sits on a swing, his center of gravity being 8.0 ft. below the beam to which the ropes are tied. Find the approximate period of vibration if $g = 32$ ft./sec.^{2}

10′. What is the length of a simple pendulum which has a period of 2.0 sec. at a point where $g = 32.2$ ft./sec.^{2}?

11′. What is the period of a simple pendulum 109 cm. long at a place where $g = 981$ cm./sec.^{2}?

12′. A simple pendulum of mass 60 grams, 100 cm. long, is pulled sidewise so that its displacement is 4.0 cm. What is the restoring force acting on it?

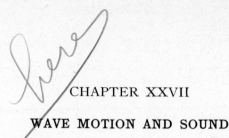

CHAPTER XXVII

WAVE MOTION AND SOUND

What is Wave Motion? Drop a stone into a deep quiet pool and watch the waves which travel out in ever-widening circles. Notice that small twigs and leaves, floating on the surface, are tossed about as the waves pass them. They are not carried forward but vibrate periodically about fixed positions of equilibrium.

Wave motions are periodic disturbances traveling through a medium.

251. Transverse Waves—Wave Length. Tie one end of a long rope to a hook fastened in the ceiling. Hold the other end, and suddenly jerk it sidewise and back. Then a single disturbance or "pulse" will travel up the rope and each particle will move to and fro as the pulse passes (Fig. 1*A*). Jerk the end oppositely and an opposite pulse is produced. Vibrate the end periodically and a series of equally spaced waves travel upward (Fig. 1*C*). Each particle of the rope moves at right angles to the direction of travel, hence the waves are said to be transverse.

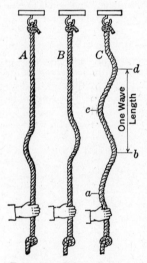

FIG. 1.—Disturbances traveling along a rope.

Wave length is defined as **the distance between adjacent particles which are in the same condition of vibration (or phase).** The distance from *b* and *d* is 1 wave length, for these particles are at their greatest displacement to the right. This distance equals that from *a* to *c*, points of greatest displacement in the opposite direction.

252. Speed, Wave Length, and Frequency. Suppose that the speed of the waves along the rope is 4 ft./sec. Vibrate the end once per second. Then each wave will have traveled 4 ft. when the next one is started, so that this distance is the wave length. Vibrate the rope twice per second, and the wave length will be one-half as great as before. If 10 waves are generated per second, each will travel 4/10 ft. before the next one is started; this is the wave length. In general, if

248

n waves are produced per unit time, and the speed is S, then the wave length λ (lambda) is given by

$$\lambda = S/n$$

so that

$$S = n\lambda.$$

TABLE I

WAVE LENGTHS, SPEED, AND FREQUENCIES

Frequency of Vibration	Speed of Waves	Wave Length
1 per second	20 ft./sec.	20 ft.
2 " "	" " "	10 "
10 " "	" " "	2 "
20 " "	" " "	1 "
n	S	S/n

Example. The wave length of the waves on a lake is 20 ft., and 30 waves per minute pass a floating barrel. What is the speed of the waves?

$$S = n\lambda = \frac{30}{\text{min.}} \times 20 \text{ ft.} = \frac{10 \text{ ft.}}{\text{sec.}}$$

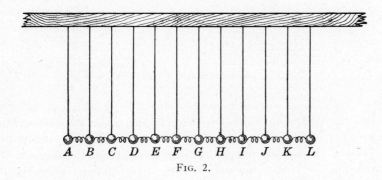

A   B   C   D   E   F   G   H   I   J   K   L

FIG. 2.

253. Compressional Waves. Suspend several balls of equal mass by cords and interconnect them by spiral springs (Fig. 2). Push the ball A toward B, compressing the first spring. Then B will compress the next spring and exert a force on the third ball C, accelerating it to the right and compressing the next spring. This, in turn, will exert a force on the next ball. In this manner the compression passes on from each ball to the next one beyond, and a pulse of compression travels to the right through the system. Pull the first ball to the left, expanding the first spring. Then the second ball is accelerated and the second spring is stretched. Thus the impulse is passed on to the next ball and a pulse of expansion is produced. Vibrate the first ball periodically so as to compress and stretch the first spring alternately, and a series of equally spaced disturbances will travel along the system. In this experiment the wave length is the distance from one point of maximum compression or expansion to the next, that is, the distance between adjacent regions in the same condition of vibration. The balls vibrate in a direction parallel to the line of travel, and the waves are called compressional (or often longitudinal).

254. Sound Waves. To understand the production of sound waves, consider a rubber balloon connected to a cylinder and piston (Fig. 3). Move the piston downward, causing the balloon to expand so that the

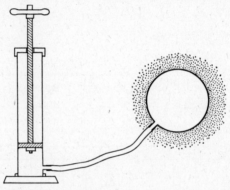

Fig. 3.—The rubber balloon, expanding and contracting periodically, causes compressional waves in the air.

rubber walls move outward, compressing the air near by. Then the air molecules rush outward, crowding against their neighbors. These are accelerated in turn, and a pulse of compression travels out from the balloon. Raise the piston, causing the balloon to contract. The surrounding air rushes inward, forming a rarefaction. Then the disturbance travels outward from the balloon just as the compression did. Move the piston up and down, making the balloon expand and contract periodically, and a train of alternate compressions and rarefactions is set up. The wave length is the distance between successive points of maximum compression.

The prongs of a tuning fork vibrate with simple harmonic motion, creating alternate compressions and rarefactions in the air (Fig. 4). A procession of waves is produced as before, and each air molecule vibrates with simple harmonic motion in a direction parallel to the line of travel. The waves are capable of being heard and are called sound waves.

Sound waves are compressional waves that are capable of being heard.

Sound waves may be produced in water, in iron, or in any medium having volume elasticity. The transmission of sound through wood may be demonstrated by scratching one end of a lecture table with a pencil. The sound will be distinctly heard by a student who listens with his ear close to the other end of the table.

255. The Speed of Sound. The fact that sound travels more slowly than light is well known. The flash of a lightning discharge is seen before the sound of the thunder is heard. The jet of steam from the whistle of a distant locomotive is observed before the sound is perceived. The speed of sound in air may be determined by the following experiment. Two groups of students are provided with rockets and

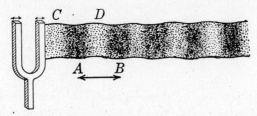

FIG. 4.—The vibrating tuning fork causes sound waves.

stop watches. One group travels a mile or so by automobile along a straight highway, measuring the distance by means of the road-meter of the car. This group discharges a rocket and the first group observes the time elapsing between the seeing of the flash of the exploding rocket and the hearing of the report. The ratio distance divided by time gives the speed of sound. Then the experiment is repeated, but the first group of students fires off the rocket and the second group observes the time. Averaging the two values reduces the error due to the wind, which tends to increase one speed and to decrease the other.

TABLE II

SPEEDS OF SOUND

AT 0°C.

	m./sec.	ft./sec.
Air	332	1,088
Oxygen	317.2	1,041
Hydrogen	1,270	4,165
Water	1,432	4,700
Iron	5,000	16,400

256. Equations for Wave Speed. Two factors determine the speed with which a wave travels through a medium; one the massiveness of the particles that vibrate, the other the elastic forces between them. Suppose that the suspended balls represented in Fig. 2 were replaced by other, more massive balls, keeping the same set of springs. Then the inertia would be increased, a longer time would be required to set each ball in motion, and the speed of the wave would diminish. Suppose, next, that stiffer springs were used. The balls would respond more quickly because the forces exerted on them would be greater, hence the speed of the waves would increase. It can be shown that the speed of sound in a substance of density D is given by

$$S = \sqrt{E/D} \qquad (2)$$

in which E is the elasticity of that substance. This equation might be used to compute the speed of sound in iron, and E would be Young's modulus for that metal. The volume elasticities of gases are proportional to their pressures P. The value for air, hydrogen, oxygen, and nitrogen is approximately,

$$E = 1.41\ P$$

Hence the equation for the speed of sound in these gases is

$$S = \sqrt{1.41\ P/D} = \sqrt{1.41P/(M/V)} = \sqrt{1.41P/(W/g)/V} \qquad (3)$$

Example. At 0°C. and 76 cm.-of-mercury (1,033 gwt./cm.²) the weight-density of air is 0.001293 gwt./cm.³ Compute the speed of sound.

$$S = \sqrt{\frac{1.41 \times 1,033\ \text{gwt./cm.}^2}{0.001293\ (\text{gwt./980 cm./sec.}^2)/\text{cm.}^3}} = 332\ \text{m./sec.}$$

According to equation (3), the speed of sound should be independent of barometric pressure, as, in fact, it is. If the pressure of a gas is doubled, its density is also; therefore the ratio P/D is unchanged. Increase of temperature at constant pressure decreases the density D of the gas and causes the speed of sound to increase. Moreover, the density of the gas is inversely proportional to its Kelvin temperature, and so the rise of temperature causes an increase in the speed of sound.

In more mathematical terms,

$$S \text{ varies as } \frac{1}{\sqrt{D}}$$

$$D \text{ varies as } \frac{1}{T} \qquad \text{(Charles' law)}$$

Therefore $\qquad\qquad S$ varies as $\sqrt{T}$

Hence $\qquad\qquad S_1/S_2 = \sqrt{T_1/T_2}$

ACOUSTICS

The problem of controlling noises is not important to farmers and villagers, but it is very serious to the inhabitants of cities. People living in apartments are very eager to be shielded from the noise of the neighbor's radio and from the clamor of wild night parties. Noise control in factories and offices pays good dividends, for careful studies have shown that the efficiency of workers can be increased by diminishing the clatter of typewriters and of machinery. Another important problem is the control of echoes or reverberations in large halls and auditoriums. The science of acoustics, developed during the last forty years, deals with the control of noises and reverberations.

257. Reverberations. It is much easier for a lecturer to be heard indoors than outdoors because the sounds reflected from the walls reinforce each other. However, trouble arises in large auditoriums because the reflected sounds travel such large distances that the echoes of one syllable may interfere with the next syllable. One remedy is to coat the walls of the room with a kind of plaster which absorbs the sounds more readily so that the echoes die down quickly. The same result is achieved by covering the walls with heavy curtains. Cushions on the backs of chairs are helpful in reducing the echoes in empty auditoriums.

The **period of reverberation** of a room is defined as the time required for a sound to become inaudible. It is desirable that this period, for a large hall, be between 1 and 2 sec. Fortunately, nowadays, the period of reverberation for a hall can be predicted before it is built, and even afterward one can compute just how much wall surface must be modified to reduce the period to a desired value. In making these computations one must know the **absorption coefficients** of the materials used to coat the walls, floors, and ceilings.

TABLE III

A. SOUND ABSORPTION COEFFICIENTS

Open window............................... 100 per cent
Heavy curtains in thick folds.................... 40
Acoustical plaster............................ 20–70
Unvarnished wood.............................   5
Ordinary plaster, varnished woods, glass, linoleum..   3

B. SOME "EQUIVALENT WINDOW AREAS"

Each person in audience........................ 5 ft.²
Each empty, un-upholstered chair................   3

258. Absorption Coefficients. When sound is incident on ordinary plaster wall, only about 3 per cent of the energy is absorbed and about

97 per cent is reflected. Such a surface is a better reflector for sound than a silver mirror is for light. When sound is incident on an open window all of it escapes and none is reflected. Hence we speak of an open window as a "perfect" or "maximum" absorber. The **absorption coefficient** of a surface is defined as **the percentage of the incident sound energy that is absorbed.** The "equivalent window area" of a surface equals **its area times its coefficient of absorption.** Thus 100 ft.^{2} of ordinary plastered wall have an equivalent window area of 3 ft.^{2}

Computing the Reverberation Period of a Room. The reverberation period of a room depends upon its volume V and the equivalent window area of its walls, ceiling, and floor. The following equation has been tested by experiments.

$$T = \frac{0.050 \text{ sec./ft.} \times V \text{ (ft.}^3)}{\text{Equivalent window area (ft.}^2)} \tag{4}$$

Example. (*a*) What is the reverberation period of an empty auditorium the volume of which is 10,000 ft.^{3}? The total area of walls, floor, and ceiling is 3,000 ft.^{2} The absorption coefficient of each surface is 3.0 per cent.

Equivalent window area = 3,000 ft.^{2} $\times$ 0.030 = 90 ft.^{2}

$$T = \frac{0.050 \text{ sec./ft.} \times 10,000 \text{ ft.}^3}{90 \text{ ft.}^2} = 5.56 \text{ sec.}$$

(*b*) What would the reverberation period be if the ceiling (area = 1,000 ft.^{2}) were coated with "acoustical" plaster (coef. = 0.20).

Equivalent window surface

(Ceiling)........ 1,000 ft.^{2} $\times$ 0.20 = 200 ft.^{2}
(Walls, floors)... 2,000 ft.^{2} $\times$ 0.030 = 60 ft.^{2}
_____
Total   260 ft.^{2}

$$\text{Reverb. period} = \frac{0.050 \text{ sec./ft.} \times 10,000 \text{ ft.}^3}{260 \text{ ft.}^2} = 1.92 \text{ sec.}$$

Soundproofing. The important acoustical problem in designing apartment houses is to shut out the noises from the neighbors. One difficulty is that flimsy partitions made of wood and plaster vibrate readily, transmitting sounds like the head of a drum. This cannot be avoided by the use of acoustical plasters. Blocks made of cinders and cement are inexpensive, massive, and rigid, and provide excellent barriers to sound.

259. The Intensity and the Loudness of a Sound. When sound waves enter the ear, they do work in causing the eardrum to vibrate and hence they supply energy. The question arises, at what rate does the sound deliver energy to the ear, or what is the power? The answer is astonishingly small, for the ear can perceive sounds when the power is less than one-million-billionth of a watt! This power would raise a mosquito vertically at a rate of only about 1 ft./yr.! A sound so loud as to be painful is a million million times as intense, yet the power it delivers to the ear would raise the mosquito only 30 ft./sec.!

The **loudness** of a sound measures the amount of sensation that it produces; it depends not only upon the power, or rate at which energy enters the ear, but also upon the frequency of the waves. For example, the sound produced by striking the extreme left key of a piano delivers thousands of times as much energy as that produced when the middle key is struck, though a hearer may judge that the two are equally loud.

In comparing two sounds of the same frequency, the ear judges one to be about twice as loud as the other when its power is 10 times as great. For this reason it is convenient to state the differences in the powers delivered by any two sounds by the **exponent** of 10 which gives the **ratio** of the powers. This exponent is expressed in a unit called the **bel** in honor of Alexander Graham Bell, the inventor of the telephone. It is so large as to be unwieldy, hence the **decibel**, one-tenth as large, is commonly employed.

If sound A delivers 10 times as much power as sound B, of the same frequency, then the difference between their intensities is 1 bel or 10 decibels.

It is customary to assume that a barely audible sound has an intensity of zero decibels, and the amount of power delivered by such a sound is assumed to be 10^{-16} watt/cm.^{2} Thus a sound that delivers ten times as much power has an intensity of 10 decibels or 1 bel. (See Table IV.)

TABLE IV
INTENSITIES OF FAMILIAR SOUNDS

Source of Sound	— Loudness Level —		Relative Intensity	Power/cm. Watts/cm.^{2}
	Decibels	Bels		
Boiler factory (painfully loud).	100	10	10^{10}	10^{-6}
Streetcar..................	80	8	10^8	10^{-8}
Ordinary conversation........	60	6	10^6	10^{-10}
Quiet night in the country....	10	1	10^1	10^{-15}
Faintest perceptible sound....	0	0	10^0	10^{-16}

SUMMARY

A wave motion is a periodic disturbance traveling through a medium.

A transverse wave is one in which the directions of vibration are at right angles to the direction of travel. In a compressional wave the directions of vibration and of travel are parallel.

The wave length is the distance between adjacent particles which are in the same condition of vibration (or phase).

The speed of a wave is given by $S = n\lambda$.

Sound is a compressional wave capable of being heard. The speed of sound in a gas is independent of the pressure and directly proportional to the square root of the Kelvin temperature.

The speed of sound in oxygen, hydrogen, or nitrogen is given by $S = \sqrt{E/D} = \sqrt{1.41\,P/D}$.

The coefficient of absorption of a surface is the percentage of the incident sound that is absorbed. The "equivalent window area" of a surface equals its area times its coefficient of absorption.

The period of reverberation of a room is given in seconds by

$$T = \frac{0.050 \text{ sec./ft.} \times V \text{ (ft.}^3)}{\text{Equivalent window area (ft.}^2)}$$

A *bel* is a unit of loudness. If sound A is 1 bel louder than B, its intensity is 10^1 times as great. One bel = 10 decibels.

REVIEW QUESTIONS

1. Define and discuss the meanings of "wave motion," "wave length," "transverse and compressional waves."

2. Distinguish between "compressional wave" and "sound."

3. Show how to measure the speed of sound experimentally, also how to compute it.

4. Discuss how the speed of sound in a gas is affected by changing (a) the pressure and (b) the temperature of the gas.

5. Define "period of reverberation," "coefficient of sound absorption," "equivalent window area."

6. Show how to decrease the period of reverberation of a large hall. Must all the walls be modified?

7. What is the difference between the intensity of a sound and the loudness? How much does the intensity of a sound change when the loudness is (a) doubled, (b) tripled? Define bel and *decibel*. Discuss the advantage of describing the loudness of music by "pianissimo" and by "15 decibels."

PROBLEMS

1. The speed of sound in oxygen at 0°C. is 1,041 ft./sec.; find the speed in hydrogen at this temperature. Its density is 1/16 that of oxygen.

2. What is the speed of sound in air at normal pressure, (a) at the temperature of boiling nitrogen (−199°C.), (b) at the temperature of boiling helium (−269°C.)?

3″. The velocity of sound in water is about 1,440 m./sec. What is the coefficient of volume elasticity of the water?

4. Thunder was heard 2.0 sec. after a lightning stroke. How far away was the lightning? Temperature = 0°C.

5. A man sets his watch by the noon whistle of a factory 2,200 ft. distant, the temperature being 20°C. How many seconds is his watch slower than the timepiece at the factory? (Speed of sound = 1,100 ft./sec.)

6. An underwater sound is emitted from a steamer, and 2.0 sec. later the echo from the bottom is heard. How deep is the ocean at that point if the speed of sound in the water is 4,800 ft./sec.?

7′. If the speed of sound increases 60 cm./sec. for each centigrade degree rise in temperature, what is the increase in speed per Fahrenheit degree?

8′. The walls, ceiling, and floor of a certain auditorium are of plaster or of wood, each having an absorption coefficient 3 per cent. The reverberation period is 3.0 sec. Find the period if, instead, Sabinite plaster were used for walls and ceiling and a carpet covered the floor, the coefficient of each being 21 per cent.

9′. In foggy weather when the temperature is 0°C. a lighthouse sends sounds simultaneously under water and through the air. A vessel is 1,000 m. from the lighthouse. How much later does one signal arrive than the other?

10″. In an attempt to locate an enemy cannon, three microphones were placed on a straight line at A, at B distant 2,200 ft. from A, and at C distant 4,400 ft. from A. If the explosion reached B ½ sec. and C 1½ sec. after its arrival at A, find the distance of the cannon from A and from B. (Speed of sound = 1,100 ft./sec. Let 1,000 ft. = 1 in. Use a graphical method.)

11′. A sound, the loudness of which is 2 bels, is reflected from a wall which has a coefficient of absorption of 90 per cent. What is the loudness of the reflected sound?

12′. An auditorium has a volume of 100,000 ft.³ The total surface of walls and floor is 20,000 ft.², that of the ceiling is 5,000 ft.² Find (*a*) the equivalent window area and (*b*) the period of reverberation if all the surfaces have coefficients of absorption of 3 per cent.

13′. Deal with the preceding problem, if the ceiling only were coated with acoustical plaster, the coefficient of absorption being 20 per cent.

14′. Find the equivalent window area of a ceiling 20 ft. by 30 ft. if the coefficient of absorption is 3 per cent.

CHAPTER XXVIII

THE PHYSICS OF MUSICAL SOUNDS

Introduction. Almost everyone loves music. The primitive Hottentot in Africa whiles away the night with the sound of the drum, and the patron of the opera is thrilled by the compositions of Wagner and of Mozart. Unfortunately the scientific aspects of music to most people today are as they were to Sir Francis Bacon, "something that is ill-understood, something that may truthfully be reckoned as one of the subtlest pieces of nature." In this chapter, we shall learn some of the simpler facts as to musical sounds.

260. What Is a Musical Sound? Hold a piece of cardboard against the edge of a revolving saw with uniformly spaced teeth. The emitted sound will have a definite pitch and will be musical. If the teeth are spaced unevenly, the sound waves will be irregular and a noise will be heard. In musical sounds, the waves are spaced in a somewhat orderly manner, but in noises regularity is lacking.

261. Standing Waves. One of the most familiar sources of musical sounds is the stretched string. To explain its behavior, let two students hold the opposite ends of a rope and let each student jerk his hand upward, at the same instant, starting two pulses along the rope. These pulses will meet at the midpoint, causing great displacement there. Then let the ends move downward, and two downward pulses will meet at midpoint. Continued vibrations can be timed so that the rope vibrates up and down in one segment (Fig. 1). This is called a "standing wave" because it does not seem to advance. Vibrate the ends of the rope oppositely so that an upward pulse starts from A when a downward one starts from C. Then the two will counteract each other at B, which will be a point of minimum motion. Maximum motions occur in the regions D and D', so that the rope vibrates in two segments. The point B where the transverse motion is least is called a **node**. D and D' where it is maximum are **antinodes**. By vibrating the ends more rapidly, the rope may be made to oscillate in 3, 4, 5, or more segments.

A wire stretched between two posts can be made to oscillate in a similar manner. Pluck it upward at the midpoint, and two upward pulses will travel toward the ends where they are reflected as downward pulses. Then they move to the opposite ends where they are reflected as upward pulses. This process continues, and the wire vibrates in one segment. Hold a feather at the midpoint so that the wire vibrates in two segments with a frequency twice as great as before. By touching it at other places it can be made to vibrate in 3, 4, 5, or more segments, emitting sounds of higher frequencies.

The tone of lowest frequency emitted when the string vibrates in one segment is called the **fundamental**; the others are the **overtones**. Their frequencies are 2, 3, 4, . . . times that of the fundamental tone. The strings of a musical instrument such as a piano or violin vibrate in a complex manner, giving out a blend of different frequencies.

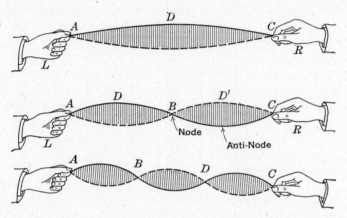

FIG. 1.—A string may vibrate in one or more segments.

262. Vibrating Air Columns. In many musical instruments the sources of sounds are vibrating air columns. Pull the cork out of an empty bottle, and a popping sound is heard which has a definite pitch. Repeat the experiment after partly filling the vessel with water and the pitch is higher than before. Hence the frequency of the sound emitted by an air column depends upon the dimensions of the vessel.

In order to comprehend how an air column can emit a musical sound, suppose that you snap your fingers near the opening in a long narrow tube or pipe which is closed at the other end. The disturbance will cause a compression of the air, and the pulse will travel down to the end, be reflected there, and return to the opening. Here the behavior should be carefully considered. As the pulse escapes, the air expands suddenly, causing a rarefaction behind it. This disturbance travels downward, is reflected, and returns to the opening. As it leaves, the air rushes in, causing a compression. and so on. In this way a single disturbance causes a series of alternate compressions and rarefactions to be emitted, so that a musical sound is heard. The wave length depends upon the time required for a pulse to travel down and back again, being greater for long air columns than for short ones. The sound must progress down and back, a distance twice the length L of the enclosure, during the interval between the emission of a compression and of the next rarefaction. Therefore the waves travel a distance $4L$ during the interval between two successive compressions. It follows that the wave length is approximately 4 times the length of the air column.

The disturbances which we have been describing constitute standing waves, resembling those in strings. When a tube closed at one end

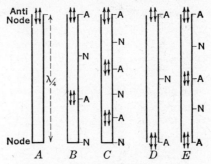

FIG. 2.—Standing waves in tubes.

emits its lowest fundamental tone, there is a node at the far end where the vibrations of the air molecules vibrate least freely. The length of the air column is about equal to the distance from node to antinode or one-fourth of the wave length (Fig. 2A). The same tube can also be made to generate overtones of higher frequency than the fundamental. When the first overtone is emitted, there are two nodes and two antinodes and the wave length is one-third as great as before (Fig. 2B). When the second overtone is sent out there are three pairs of nodes and antinodes and the wave length is one-fifth that of the fundamental (Fig. 2C). In general, the wave lengths of the various overtones are 1/3, 1/5, 1/7, 1/9, etc., that of the fundamental.

A narrow tube open at both ends can also emit sounds. When the fundamental tone is generated, there is a node at the midpoint, and two antinodes are near each end. The length of the enclosure about equals the distance from antinode to antinode or one-half of the wave length (Fig. 2D). The wave length of the first overtone can be found by studying Fig. 2E.

263. Sympathetic Vibrations—Resonance. When one child pushes another one seated in a swing, he finds it advisable to make the frequency of his impulses equal to that of the swing. A man standing on the springboard of a bathing pool can cause great vibrations in the board by jumping up and down with a certain frequency. These are examples of sympathetic vibrations or resonance.

Sympathetic vibrations occur when one body sets another into vibration, the period of the two being the same.

The phenomenon may be demonstrated as follows: Hold a vibrating tuning fork near the open end of a tall, narrow jar and pour water into the vessel. When the length of the air column has a certain value, resonance occurs and the loudness of the sound increases. In this condition the periods of vibration of the fork and of the air column are equal. Push down the pedals of a piano to free the strings and sound a clarinet or other musical instrument near by. Several piano wires will be set into vibration, and they have the same frequencies as the tones that are present in the musical sounds.

264. Forced Vibrations. Hold the handle of a vibrating tuning fork against the top of a table. The intensity of the sound will be greatly increased. The reason is that the table top vibrates with the fork and, having a large area, forces a greater mass of air to vibrate and causes a louder sound. The music from a violin string would be very weak were it not for the thin walls of the wooden box. These walls are caused to vibrate by the string and the sounds are greatly amplified. One reads "tall stories" about the wrecking of suspension bridges caused by the music of violins. Such a happening is impossible because the frictional forces opposing the large vibrations are too great to be overcome by the feeble impulses of the sound waves.

265. A Device for Studying Sounds. Sound waves can be studied by means of the apparatus diagrammed in Fig. 3. A flexible diaphragm is mounted at one end of a tube or horn. A cord, attached to the diaphragm, is wrapped around a horizontal axle and the end of the cord is tied to a spiral spring. A small mirror mounted on the axle reflects a beam of light onto a motion-picture film. When a tuning fork is sounded in front of the diaphragm, the sound waves cause it to vibrate, and the axle oscillates on its pivots. The beam of light, reflected from the mirror, moves up and down. When the photographic film is moved at right angles to the beam, the spot of light traces a wavy line which reveals several characteristics of the sound. The height of the waves is proportional to the amplitudes of the air vibrations, and the number of up-and-down vibrations per second tells the frequency.

The musician distinguishes three characteristics of a musical sound, namely, the **loudness**, **pitch**, and **quality**. Of these the loudness depends upon the energy of the sound and hence upon the amplitude of the vibration. As shown in the preceding chapter, loudness can be expressed in bels or in decibels. The second characteristic is the pitch which is determined by the frequency. When two tuning forks are of the same frequency, the musician judges that the sounds that they emit have the same pitch. (However, in complex blends of frequencies, it is easy to "fool" the ear.) The third characteristic of musical sounds

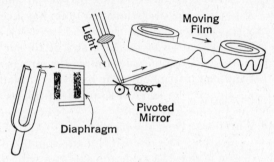

FIG. 3.—Apparatus for studying sound waves.

is quality, which depends upon the frequencies and loudness of the different tones that are blended together.

266. What Is Quality? In purchasing a musical instrument, the musician is concerned not merely that it gives sounds of prescribed pitches, but also that the notes should consist of desirable blendings or combinations of overtones. The need for better quality justifies a musician in purchasing a master violin for ten thousand dollars rather than a fiddle for ten dollars.

When a tuning fork is struck with a wooden stick, a harsh metallic clang is heard which rapidly dies out after which the tone is almost pure; its graphic representation is called a "sine" wave (Fig. 4A and B). The trace of the spot of light tells us that the clang of the fork when it is first struck is due to an overtone of frequency much greater than the fundamental of the fork. A flute sounded strongly yields several overtones that disappear when the sound dies down (Fig. 4C and D). Six strong voices singing the Sextette from "Lucia" produce such a tumult of overtones that it is marvelous that the ear can analyze them sufficiently to distinguish the tenors from the altos (Fig. 4E).

267. Beats. When two tuning forks of slightly different frequencies are sounded together, a rising and falling of sound is heard. At a certain instant, compressions from both forks reach the ear and the resultant sound is very loud. Later, when the two sounds are out of phase, the compressions from one fork counteract the rarefactions from the other. Thus as the forks get into and out of "step" or phase, the sound increases and decreases so that we hear "beats" (Fig. 5).

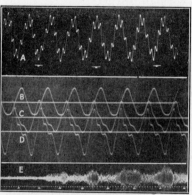

The equation for the number of beats per second can be derived as follows: Suppose that two students walk side by side. One takes 60 steps per minute, the other 59. They will be in step once per minute. If the second man takes 58 steps per minute, he will take 29 steps while the first takes 30 and they will be in step twice per minute. Continuing the argument it will be seen that the number of times per minute that the two men get into step equals the difference between the frequencies of the steps. Consider two tuning forks, of frequencies n_1 and n_2. The frequency of the beats produced when they are sounded together is given by

Fig. 4.—Analysis of sound waves. (A) of a tuning fork recently struck, and (B) after the overtone has died out, (C and D) of a flute sounded strongly and softly, (E) of voices singing the Sextette from "Lucia." (Courtesy of the Macmillan Co., D. C. Miller, "Science of Musical Sounds.")

$$N = n_2 - n_1$$

This equation is useful in tuning pianos. Suppose that a tuning fork of frequency 514 vib./sec. is sounded along with a certain piano wire and that 8 beats per second are heard. Suppose, further, that as the string is tightened the number of beats gradually decreases to 2 per second. In this condition the wire has a frequency $(514 - 2) = 512$ vib./sec.

Fig. 5.—Analysis of sounds from two tuning forks, showing beats.

268. Harmony. When two tones are sounded together and the result is pleasing they are said to be in harmony. The ratio of their frequencies, that is, their **interval**, is found to be expressible by small integers. For example, a note and its octave, of double frequency have an interval 2/1 and are extremely harmonious. The notes *do*, *mi*, *sol*, sounded simultaneously constitute the dominant chord. Their frequencies are proportional to 4, 5, 6, and the ratios of any two of these numbers is expressed in small integers, 4/5, 4/6, 5/6. The notes *mi* and *fa* are less harmonious and their interval 15/16 is not expressible by small integers.

269. The Diatonic Scale. The musical scale most used by Occidental nations is the diatonic scale, "*do, re, mi*," etc., which is produced in the key of C by the white keys of a piano. This scale was developed centuries before sounds were analyzed by physical methods, and so it is interesting to note some of the numerical relationships which hold. For simplicity, beginning with *do* = 24 vib./sec., the scale is as follows:

	do	re	mi	fa	sol	la	ti	do'	re'	mi'
Vib./sec.	24	27	30	32	36	40	45	48	54	60

This scale is advantageous in that the "dominant chord" which is very harmonious can be produced in three ways.

$$
\begin{array}{llll}
\text{do : mi : sol} & 24 : 30 : 36 \\
\text{sol : ti : re'} & 36 : 45 : 54 \\
\text{fa : la : do'} & 32 : 40 : 48
\end{array} \Biggr\} 4 : 5 : 6
$$

270. Tones and Semitones—The Chromatic Scale. The intervals between successive tones of the diatonic scale are three in number, 9/8, 10/9, and 16/15. The first two differ but slightly and are called a **tone**, the latter a **semitone**. The diatonic scale is somewhat like a ladder with unevenly spaced steps (Fig. 6). The **chromatic scale** is formed by introducing five extra notes (represented by the black keys of a piano). The ascent from any note to its octave is made by twelve approximately but not exactly equal semitone steps.

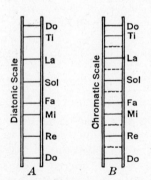

FIG. 6.—The diatonic and the chromatic scales.

271. The Equal Tempered Scale. In the diatonic scale, the semitone intervals are not exactly equal, so that different pianos would be required to play scales beginning with different key notes. To avoid this difficulty, the frequencies of the notes are changed slightly so that one ascends from any note to its octave by twelve exactly equal semitone steps each having an interval approximately 1.06. (This number raised to the twelfth power equals 2, approximately.) In using the "equal-tempered" scale, musical harmony is sacrificed for convenience.

272. Is the Diatonic Scale a "Natural" One? The simple numerical relationships between the notes of the diatonic scale justify the question, "Is this scale a natural one, which is liked by all peoples?" On the contrary, the Chinese use only those notes corresponding to the black keys of the piano. The Japanese, Persians, and Greeks all have used the octave, but all have divided it into different intervals.

273. The Development of Wind Instruments. The first wind instrument probably was invented by some cave man who discovered, as small boys do today, that he could cause a musical sound by blowing across the open end of a piece of hollow reed. Observing that the pitch depended upon the length of the tube, he bound several reeds of different lengths together, producing a set of "pipes" like those represented in statues of the Greek god Pan. In choosing the lengths of the different pipes, this primitive man set up a musical scale. Another improvement came when someone discovered that the different tubes could be replaced by a single tube fitted with holes which might be opened by raising the fingers

	Chromatic Scale	Equal Tempered Scale
512		C 512
480		B 483
461		$A^{\#}$ 456
428		A 430
409		$G^{\#}$ 406
384		G 384
368		$F^{\#}$ 362
341		F 342
320		E 322
307		$D^{\#}$ 304
288		D 287
274		$C^{\#}$ 271.2
$C = 256$		$C = 256$

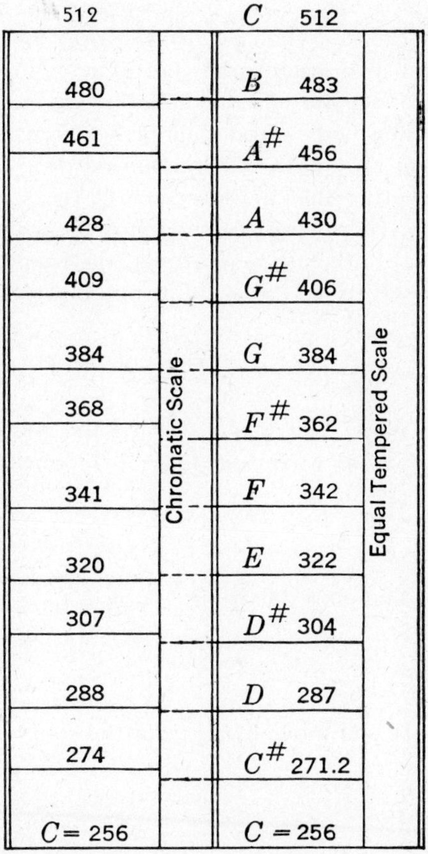

FIG. 7.—The chromatic and the equal-tempered scales.

as in the modern fife. The opening of such a hole, tending to produce an antinode at the point, would change the effective length of the instrument.

In the trombone, the length of the air column is varied by sliding a portion of the tube in and out, and the frequencies of the tone are controlled thus as well as by the tension of the lips. In the bugle the length is constant and the frequency is controlled by the lips of the player. The possible frequencies of this instrument are 3, 4, and 5... times that of the fundamental, since it is open at each end.

274. The Doppler Effect. The pitch of the musical sound that is heard can be changed by traveling toward or away from the source. When one travels toward the source of the sound he goes to meet the waves, as it were, more waves enter the ear per second, and the pitch is raised. When he travels away from the source, fewer waves reach him per second and the pitch is lowered. This phenomenon is called the **Doppler effect.** The following example is familiar to many readers. When your automobile passes another the horn of which is sounding, you may notice a pronounced drop in the pitch of the sound. Before meeting the car, the pitch of the sound was raised; afterward it was lowered, hence the sudden drop in pitch at the instant of passing.

If both cars were at rest, the frequency of the sound you hear would be given by the usual formula

$$\text{Frequency } n = \frac{\text{Wave speed}}{\text{Wave length}} = \frac{S}{\lambda} \tag{1}$$

When you travel toward the source of sound with a speed s, the apparent wave speed is $S + s$, hence the frequency is given by

$$n' = \frac{S + s}{\lambda} \tag{2}$$

Therefore, dividing (2) by (1),

$$\frac{n'}{n} = \frac{S + s}{S} \tag{3}$$

If you move away from the source,

$$\frac{n'}{n} = \frac{S - s}{S} \tag{4}$$

SUMMARY

In musical sounds the successive waves are spaced in an orderly manner.

In standing waves there are nodes or points of minimum motion and antinodes. A stretched string can vibrate in one segment producing its fundamental tone of lowest frequency. It can also vibrate at higher frequencies, emitting various overtones. The frequencies of the overtones emitted by a tube closed at one end are 3, 5, 7 . . . times that of the fundamental tone. Those emitted by a tube open at both ends are 2, 3, 4, 5 . . . times that of the fundamental.

Sympathetic vibrations occur when one body sets another into vibration, the period of the two being the same.

The pitch of a musical tone depends upon the frequency, the loudness upon the amplitude of the sound vibrations, and the quality upon the blend of frequencies that are present.

Two sound sources of different frequencies cause a sound which rises and falls, producing "beats." The number of beats per unit time is given by

$$N = n_2 - n_1$$

When two sounds are in harmony, the ratio of their frequencies— that is, their interval—is expressible by the ratio of two small integers.

When an observer approaches a source of sound at a speed s, the frequency n' of the sound that is heard is given by

$$\frac{n'}{n} = \frac{S + s}{S}$$

REVIEW QUESTIONS

1. Distinguish between musical sounds and noises.

2. Define "standing wave," "node," "antinode," and discuss these terms.

3. Why does a small child have a high-pitched voice?

4. Discuss the vibrations of air columns in tubes closed at one end and also those in tubes open at both ends.

5. Distinguish between "sympathetic vibrations" and "forced vibrations."

6. Discuss "pitch," "loudness," and "quality."

7. What are "beats"?

8. How does *harmony* depend upon *interval*?

9. What are (*a*) the diatonic scale, (*b*) the chromatic scale, and (*c*) the equal-tempered scale?

10. What is the Doppler effect?

PROBLEMS

1. A circular saw has 50 teeth. How many revolutions per minute must it make in order to emit a note of frequency 512 vib./sec. when a card is pressed against its edge?

2'. The speed of the transverse wave in a stretched string is 500 ft./sec. and the length of the string is 1 ft. How many to-and-fro journeys does a wave make per second? What is the frequency of the fundamental tone?

3. The frequency of the tone of lowest pitch that is audible to most people is 30 vib./sec. and that of the highest pitch is 20,000 vib./sec. Find the wave lengths of these sounds in air, the wave speed being 330 m./sec.

4. The frequency of the fundamental tone of a violin string is 256 vib./sec. What are the frequencies of the first and second overtones?

5'. A small empty cartridge shell is 1 cm. deep. (*a*) What is the fundamental frequency of the note which it emits when a person blows across the edge? (*b*) What is that of the first overtone? The temperature is 0°C.

6′. The speed of sound at 27°C. is 350 m./sec. At what centigrade temperature will the speed be twice as great?

7′. In tuning a certain piano string, a fork of frequency 265 vib./sec. is used. As the wire is progressively tightened, the number of beats decreases until the value is 4/sec. What, then, is the frequency of the string?

8. Two tuning forks of frequency 1,000 vib./sec. and 1,500 vib./sec. are sounded together. What is the frequency of the "beat" tone that is heard?

9. The frequency of the fundamental tone of a gong is 500 vib./sec. What is the frequency of the sound that an observer hears (a) if he approaches the source at a speed of 90 ft./sec. (62 mi./hr.) and (b) if he moves away from the source at this speed? (Speed of sound = 1,100 ft./sec.)

10′. If the speed of sound is 1,100 ft./sec., how long must four closed tubes be in order to emit the chord (do, mi, sol, do) of frequencies proportional to 4, 5, 6, and 8 the lowest note having a frequency 256 vib./sec.?

11′. Some pipe organs have pipes closed at one end which give fundamental tones of frequency 16/sec. at 0°C. How long must such a pipe be?

12′. Two organ pipes, each closed at one end, are respectively 2.5 and 2.6 ft. long. Find the frequency of the beats of the two fundamental tones if the speed of sound is 1,100 ft./sec.

13′. What is the wave length in air of (a) the lowest, and (b) the highest notes emitted by a piano, their frequencies being respectively 27.5 and 4,186 vib./sec.? The speed of the sound is 1,100 ft./sec.

LIGHT

CHAPTER XXIX

ILLUMINATION

The problem of the nature of light has always been interesting and is by no means solved. According to one view favored by Sir Isaac Newton three centuries ago, a candle or other luminous body sends out streams of "corpuscles," "light bullets" or "photons." Another view is that light is a form of wave motion. For the present, we shall define it merely as the agency by which we see.

A question often arises over whether or not light exists in the depths of space when no eye is present to observe it. To this question there are two correct and yet contradictory answers, their correctness depending on whether the question is answered by a psychologist or a physicist. Some psychologists define light as a sensation, hence they would say that no light exists where there is no eye to notice it. The physicist on the other hand defines it as the cause of that sensation and therefore he assumes that light can exist independent of an observing eye.

275. The "International Candle," a Standard of Luminous Intensity. The amount of light emitted by a source was formerly specified in terms of the radiation emitted by a candle of carefully specified dimensions made of a certain kind of wax. The present standard, established in 1919, is called the "international candle." A large number of incandescent electric lamps were compared with one another and with a standard candle, thus determining their luminous intensities when operated at prescribed voltages. These lamps are carefully protected like the standard kilogram and meter and they are occasionally used for testing other light sources which are the secondary standards.

276. The Importance of Proper Illumination. A century ago, little reading was done by artificial illumination. For this there were several reasons, among them being the scarcity of books and newspapers, the small amount of leisure, and the lack of adequate light sources. Today the output of printing presses is tremendous, modern machinery replaces labor, providing greater leisure, and the electric lamp affords

illumination which, if wisely used, would be beyond reproach. Unfortunately, the public and even certain architects and engineers are
ignorant of adequate illumination needs. In schools and colleges the
lighting conditions frequently merit severe condemnation. Often a
student seated in some far corner receives too little light. In many
places unshaded lamps near the front of the room or brightly painted
walls reflect light into the eyes and cause "glares" which are very
harmful.

277. The Rectilinear Propagation of Light. In computing the illumination produced by a source, the fact that in free space light travels
in straight lines is highly significant. This truth is well known and is
relied upon by the hunter in aiming his rifle, or the carpenter in sight-
ing along the edge of a board. One of the most striking ways to demonstrate it is to admit sunlight to a darkened room through a small hole
in a window curtain and to observe the straightness of the parallel
beam, made visible by small motes or dust particles suspended in
the air.

278. Illumination and Distance from the Source. In order to study
the variation of illumination with distance from a very small "point"

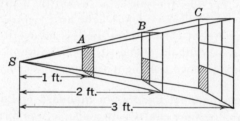

FIG. 1.—The illumination at A is four times that at B and nine times that at C.

source, consider three parallel rectangular frames (Fig. 1) so placed
that all the light passing through A passes through B and C. The distance of the three frames from the point source are 1, 2, and 3 ft.,
and their areas are 1, 4, and 9 ft.^{2}, respectively. The area of the second
frame is 4 times that of the first one, so that each square foot of its
surface receives one-fourth as much energy as an equal area of A.
Similarly, the light received per unit area of C is one-ninth that of A.
Hence the illumination varies inversely as the square of the distance
from the source of light.

$$\text{Illumination} = \frac{\text{Intensity of source}}{\text{Square of its distance}} = E/D^2 \qquad (1)$$

For example, if the distance from a 64-candle lamp to a book is 4 ft.,
the illumination of the book is approximately

$$\frac{64 \text{ candles}}{16 \text{ ft.}^2} = 4.0 \text{ ft-candles}$$

One foot-candle is the illumination of a surface which is 1 ft. from a standard "international candle."

In the metric system, the meter-candle is the illumination of a surface which is 1 m. from a standard international candle.

In this discussion it has been assumed that the light rays strike the surface normally or at right angles. Otherwise the angle of incidence

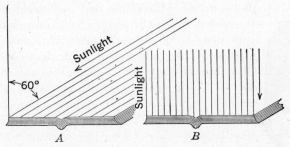

FIG. 2.—The illumination of the surface *A* is less than that of *B*.

of the rays must be taken into account. In Fig. 2*A* the sunlight is incident at an angle of 60°. The light is distributed over twice as large an area and the illumination is one-half as great as when it is incident normally as in Fig. 2*B*.

279. The Photometer. The luminous intensities of two sources may be compared by placing them in such a manner that they produce

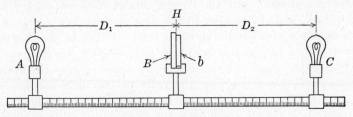

FIG. 3.—A photometer.

equal illuminations at adjoining surfaces. The photometer is a convenient device for this purpose. The Joly type of instrument (Fig. 3) consists essentially of two equal blocks of paraffin *b* and *B* separated by a thin sheet of tinfoil. The purpose of the paraffin is to scatter the light sidewise to the eye of the observer. This unit placed on the line joining the two sources is moved to and fro until the edges of the two blocks appear equally bright. In this condition the illuminations afforded by the two sources are equal. If the luminous intensity of the standard source A is E_1, that of the "test" lamp B is E_2, and the respective distances of the two sources from the paraffin blocks are D_1 and D_2, then

$$\text{Illumination} = E_1/D_1{}^2 = E_2/D_2{}^2 \qquad (2)$$

The intensity of the standard source being known, that of the test lamp may be computed.

280. A Photoelectric Light-Meter. In measuring illuminations the photoelectric light-meter may be employed (Fig. 4). It consists of a photoelectric cell connected to a galvanometer to measure the electric current. As will be explained later, when light is incident on the photoelectric cell, an electric current is established, the needle of the galvanometer is deflected, and the amount of the deflection measures the illumination. The dial of the instrument is calibrated to read foot-candles or meter-candles. This instrument is used by photographers to determine the proper time of exposure. The light-meter is pointed in the same direction as the camera, and the reading of the scale is noted. This may be marked off in foot-candles or it may indicate the required exposure.

FIG. 4.—A photoelectric light meter.

281. Luminous Efficiencies of Light Sources. The development of modern industrial civilization has been marked by rapid improvements in sources of illumination. For thousands of years the principal artificial sources of light were the flaming brand of wood, the wick suspended in oil, and the candle. In the past seventy-five years, candles have been made obsolete by kerosene lamps, which in turn have been largely replaced by electric lamps of progressively greater effectiveness. The effectiveness of a light source is expressed by the **luminous efficiency**, which is defined as the ratio of the light output to the energy input. The output rate may be expressed in terms of the average candlepower (in all directions); the energy input rate is ordinarily stated in watts. Thus the luminous efficiency is expressed in average candles per watt.

Lamps do not emit light equally in all directions, so that the candlepower varies with direction. Engineers prefer to express light outputs in lumens. To understand the relationship between candlepower and lumens, place a standard "point" candle at the center of a hollow sphere of 1-ft. radius with black walls, and let there be an opening in

it 1 ft.² in area (Fig. 5). Then the light passes through the window at
the rate of 1 lumen. Moreover, the area of the entire sphere is 4π
ft.², so that the candle emits light
in all directions at the rate of 4π
lumens. That is:

**A standard "point" candle
emits light at a rate of 4π lumens.**

If a lamp were fitted with a
perfect reflector, the number of
lumens would be unchanged but
the light distribution would be
modified. The mirror of an automobile headlight concentrates
the light into a narrow cone and
increases the apparent candlepower in a certain direction.

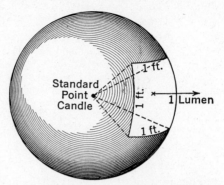

Fig. 5.—A standard "point" candle emits
light at a rate of 4π lumens.

However, it does not increase the number of lumens emitted by the
lamp.

TABLE I

LUMINOUS EFFICIENCIES AND TYPICAL COSTS OF OPERATION
FOR DIFFERENT SOURCES

Light Source	Candles per Watt	Lumens per Watt	Cost in Cents per 100 Candle-Hours
Paraffin candle	0.017	0.21	240.
Kerosene lamp	0.02	0.25	20.
Open electric carbon arc	2.0	25.	1.5
Carbon-filament lamp (40 watts)	0.35	4.4	8.64
Gas-filled tungsten lamp	1.5	19.	2.0
Mercury-vapor lamp (new type)	75.	940.	0.4
Firefly	30.	380.	?

Notice in Table I that the firefly is more than 20 times as efficient
as the tungsten filament lamp and 80 times more than the carbon-
filament lamp. Thus there is plenty of room for improvement. The
reason for the low efficiencies of hot-filament sources is that most of
the radiations are of such wave lengths and frequencies as to be
incapable of causing sight.

282. The Improvement of Illumination. The lighting of offices, factories, and schoolrooms is often faulty because the illumination is insufficient. Researches indicate that the output of workers increases
considerably when the light is increased from the medium to an ample
value. Desirable illuminations for several kinds of work, together with
values for sunlight and moonlight, are shown in Table II.

TABLE II

Illumination Intensities

	Foot-Candles
Noon sunlight	5,000–10,000
Bright moonlight	1/40
Needed for baseball and football	30–50
Needed for street lighting	1/20–1/4
Desirable values for reading	5–10
Desirable values for work requiring close inspection	10–15

SUMMARY

The "international standard candle" is defined as a certain fraction of the luminous intensity of certain incandescent lamps, operated at prescribed voltages.

The illumination received from a small "point" source varies inversely as the square of the distance from the source. The foot-candle is the illumination of a surface which is 1 ft. from a standard international candle; the meter-candle, that received when the distance is 1 m.

The lumen equals the $1/4\pi$ part of the light output—in all directions —of an international "point" candle.

The luminous efficiency of a source equals the ratio of the light output to the total energy input. It is expressed in average candles per watt and in lumens per watt.

REVIEW QUESTIONS

1. Define "light," and give illustrations showing that it travels in straight lines.

2. Criticize this statement. "If there were no eyes to see a burning candle it would not emit light."

3. Define "international candle."

4. Discuss the three factors determining the amount of illumination received at a point on a screen.

5. Prove the inverse square law.

6. Describe a photometer and a photoelectric light-meter.

7. Distinguish between a "foot-candle" and a "lumen." What advantage has the latter? Discuss the effect of a reflector on (a) candlepower and (b) the light output of a lamp.

8. Criticize the illumination of your recitation room. How could it be improved? Could money be saved in so doing?

9. Does the inverse square law apply to the light from (a) a large diffusing globe and (b) an automobile headlight with reflector? Why?

PROBLEMS

Problems 1–6 are mental arithmetic problems. To get full value from these exercises all answers should be listed on a sheet of paper, every problem should be rechecked, and then the answers should be compared with those given below.

1. On a table surface 4 ft. below an 8-candle source the illumination is _____ ft-candle.

2. The intensity of a source which provides illumination of 10 ft-candles at a distance of 5 ft. is _____ candles.

3. When a book is held at a distance of 2 ft. from a lamp, the illumination is 8 ft-candles. At 1 ft. from the lamp, the illumination is _____ ft-candle.

4. If a photographic print can be made in 14 sec. when held 2 ft. from a lamp, the correct exposure when it is held 3 ft. away is _____ sec.

5. A book is adequately illuminated when it is 4 ft. from an 80-candle source; the illumination when it is moved 6 ft. farther away is _____ ft-candles.

6. A 40-watt incandescent lamp is rated at 0.90 candle/watt. Its luminous intensity is therefore _____ candles.

7. What is the luminous intensity of a source which when placed at a distance of 0.50 m. from a point produces at that point illumination equal to that from a 90-candle source at a distance of 3.00 m.?

8. The illumination of noon sunlight in June is about 10,000 ft-candles. What would be the illumination if instead of being at a distance of 96,000,000 miles, the sun were at the distance of the moon, 240,000 miles?

9. How far from a 40-candle source must a book be placed so that the illumination may equal that afforded by the full moon (1/40 ft-candle)?

10′. A standard candle and a 4-candle source are 3.0 ft. apart. How far from the standard candle must a screen be placed to be equally illuminated by each source? (There are two answers. Show why, using a diagram.)

11″. A 100-candle lamp is placed at a distance 1.00 m. from a screen. Afterward a piece of smoked glass is interposed, and to secure the same illumination as before, the lamp must be brought to a distance of 50 cm. from the screen. Find the percentage of the light absorbed by the smoked glass.

12′. If the illumination of a level surface at the equator at noon, when the sun is vertically overhead, is 10,000 ft-candles, find the illumination of such a surface (a) at 30° N latitude, (b) at 60° N latitude, (c) at the north pole. (Assume equal light absorption by the atmosphere in each case.)

Answers to questions 1–6: (1) 0.5 ft-candle, (2) 250 candles, (3) 32 ft-candles, (4) 31.5 sec., (5) 0.8 ft-candle, (6) 36 candles.

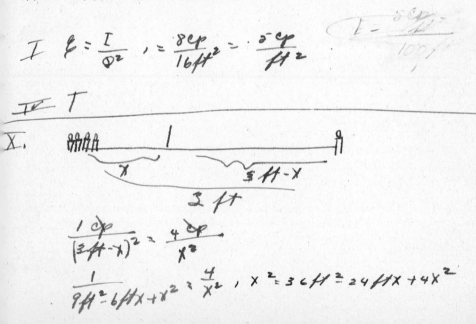

CHAPTER XXX

THE SPEED OF LIGHT

The first recorded attempt to measure the speed of light was made by Galileo, three centuries ago. He stationed two men A and B with lanterns covered with screens on mountain peaks several miles apart. The first observer A removed the screen of his lantern. As soon as possible after receiving the signal, the second person uncovered his lantern in turn, thus sending a signal to A who estimated the time for the signals to make the complete journey. Galileo found that the total time involved was a few tenths of a second. It was, in fact, about equal to the sums of the "psychological reaction times" of the two men. For this reason it did not change appreciably when the distance between the lamps was increased. After repeated trials, Galileo decided that the speed of light was too great to measure by the means at his disposal.

283. Roemer's Method. The first successful attempt to measure the speed of light was that of the Danish astronomer Roemer (1675), who

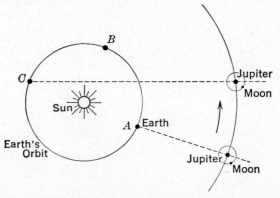

FIG. 1.—More time is required for light from Jupiter to reach the earth at C than at A.

used observations of the eclipses of one of Jupiter's moons. The method will be understood from Fig. 1. This moon has a relatively brief period of $42\frac{1}{2}$ hours. Once during each revolution, it passes into the conical shadow of Jupiter and is eclipsed. It can serve as a kind of "second hand" of a gigantic clock ticking off "seconds" each $42\frac{1}{2}$ hours long.

In Roemer's method, the time elapsing between successive eclipses is noted when the earth is at A and a "time table" or schedule of eclipses is prepared for the entire year. Three months later the earth is at B and the eclipse occurs 8 min. behind schedule. After another three months the earth has moved to C and the eclipse is found to be about 16 min. or 1,000 sec. late. The reason for tardiness is that the light from Jupiter has to travel farther when the earth is at C than when it was at A. The difference in distance equals the diameter of the earth's orbit, about 186,000,000 miles. This distance divided by the time of travel, 1,000 sec., gives the speed of light, 186,000 mi./sec. Thus a beam of light could travel around the earth about $7\frac{1}{2}$ times in 1 sec. It gives some comprehension of the awesome greatness of astronomical distances, if we remember that light traveling at this tremendous speed requires more than four years for the journey from the nearest star and that the light from certain nebulae requires hundreds of millions of years to reach the earth. In measuring huge distances such as these, astronomers use the **light-year**, which is the distance light travels in 1 year or nearly 6 million million (6,000,000,000,000) miles. The distance to the moon is about 2 light-seconds, and that to the sun is about 8 light-minutes.

Laboratory methods for measuring the speed of light were devised by Fizeau in 1849, and by Foucault about 1850. Foucault's method has been improved by other workers, especially Michelson, whose method is most interesting, accurate, and easy to understand.

284. Michelson's Method (1929). In Michelson's method, an eight-sided mirror M (Fig. 2) is mounted on a vertical axis. The mirror is so adjusted that light from an electric arc is reflected from one face c, travels to a mirror about 22 miles away, is reflected by it, and returns to another face a, whence it is reflected to the telescope so that the source is perceived like a distant star. When M is rotated uniformly, a series of flashes of light are sent to the distant fixed mirror. While a given flash is making the 44-mile journey, the mirror turns through some angle so that in general the returning light is not reflected into the telescope. However, if the speed of rotation is carefully adjusted, the mirror will turn exactly one-eighth of a revolution while a flash of light makes the to-and-fro journey. Thus the face b moves to a and is in exactly the right position to reflect the pulse of light into the telescope. Therefore the observer sees the "star" as though the mirror were at rest.

Example. Suppose that, in a determination of the speed of light, an eight-sided mirror turned at a speed of 500.0 rev./sec. Find the speed of light if the distance to the fixed mirror was 23.29 miles.

The time for the light to travel to and fro was

$$\frac{1 \text{ sec.}}{8 \times 500} = 1/4,000 \text{ sec.}$$

Hence the speed of light $= \dfrac{2 \times 23.29 \text{ miles}}{(1/4,000) \text{ sec.}} = \dfrac{186,320 \text{ miles}}{\text{sec.}}$

The most difficult part of the experiment was the measurement of the distance to the fixed mirror. To determine a distance of 22 miles

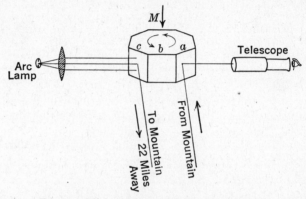

FIG. 2.—Michelson's revolving-mirror method.

over mountainous country with an error of only a few inches was an unequaled achievement in surveying. The work was undertaken by the United States Coast and Geodetic Survey with the hope that later the revolving-mirror method might be employed to measure distances with great accuracy, using Michelson's value of the speed of light. This value is 299,790 km./sec., or 186,400 mi./sec. The probable error of the determination is about 1 part in 75,000.

285. The Speed of Light in Water. The speed of light in water was determined by Foucault in 1850 by placing a tube filled with water between a revolving mirror and a fixed mirror, the distance between them being a few feet instead of 22 miles. He found that light travels more slowly through water than air. Furthermore his work showed that blue light travels a little more slowly (about 1 per cent) than red light. In free space, light of all colors travels with the same speed. If red light traveled faster than blue light, after an eclipse of the sun, the red light would reach the earth first. Thus the sun's disk after it emerged from behind the moon would at first appear red and its hue would gradually change as light of other colors reached the eye.

SUMMARY

Roemer determined the speed of light by measuring the time between successive eclipses of one of Jupiter's moons and from this value predicting the time of successive eclipses for a year. When the earth was most distant from Jupiter the eclipses occurred later than the scheduled time, and he assumed that the difference was the time required for light to travel across the earth's orbit.

In Michelson's method, a beam of light reflected from one face of a revolving mirror traveled to a second fixed mirror and thence returned to the first one. The speed of revolution was so adjusted that the returning beam was reflected into a telescope. The time of travel of the light was measured by noting the speed of revolution of the first mirror.

The speeds of light in all substances are less than that in a vacuum, and the speeds are different for lights of different colors.

REVIEW QUESTIONS

1. Describe Roemer's and Michelson's methods for measuring the speed of light.

2. If in using Michelson's method the distance to the fixed mirror were increased, would the mirror have to turn faster or slower? What is the advantage of using an eight-sided mirror instead of a four-sided one?

PROBLEMS

(Speed of light = 186,000 mi./sec.; 1 light-year = 6×10^{12} mi.)

1'. It takes 4.3 years for the light from the nearest star to reach the earth. How far away is the star?

2. How far would an automobile having a speed of 60 mi./hr. (88 ft./sec.) move while light travels a distance equal to the circumference of the earth (25,000 mi.)?

3. Find the distance in miles of the star Arcturus, the light of which requires 40 years to reach the earth.

4. A pedestrian sets his watch to read 12:00 o'clock when a factory whistle blows. When he hears the 1 o'clock whistle, he notices that his watch reads 10 sec. past one. How far did he walk if the speed of sound is 1,100 ft./sec.?

5'. In a determination of the speed of light by Michelson's method suppose that the eight-sided mirror turned at the rate of 1,000 rev./sec. Find the distance between this revolving mirror and the distant reflector.

6'. In an experiment using Michelson's method, the fixed mirror is 18.6 miles away. How many revolutions per second must the eight-sided mirror make?

CHAPTER XXXI

REFLECTION AND REFRACTION

When sunlight enters a darkened room through a small hole, the narrow beam of light is traced by means of the illuminated dust particles. Let the light be incident on a mirror striking it normally, that is, perpendicularly to the surface. Then the reflected beam will retrace its path, and go out at the same aperture through which it entered. If it is incident at some acute angle, the reflected beam and the incident one make equal angles with the perpendicular (Fig. 1).

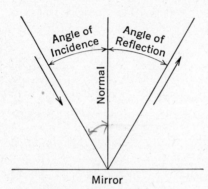

Mirror

Fig. 1.—The angles of reflection and of incidence are equal.

It is very convenient to represent the directions in which light travels by arrows, usually called **rays**.

The **angle of incidence** is the angle between an **incident ray** and the **normal to the surface** at the point where the light is incident. The **angle of reflection** is the angle between the ray of the reflected light and the normal.

286. The Formation of Images. If a piece of unsilvered plate glass is supported in a vertical position and a wooden block is placed in front of it, a dim reflected image or optical counterpart of the block appears back of the mirror. A second block, placed behind the mirror, may be made to coincide with the reflected image. Thus the sizes of the object and its image are exactly equal. Furthermore, the distance from any point on the object to the mirror is equal to the distance from the corresponding image point to it.

287. Proof of the Laws of Reflection. In Fig. 2, light from the point A is reflected by a mirror and seems to come from the point A' behind the mirror. If a pin is placed at A its image is seen at A'; two other pins are placed at B and C so that A', B, and C are on the same straight line. A line is drawn through B normal to the mirror. Then the measurements will show that **the angle of reflection** NBC is equal

280

to the **angle of incidence** ABN. More precise experiments prove that the angle of reflection is always equal to the angle of incidence and that the incident ray, the reflected ray, and the normal to the mirror all lie in the same plane. These laws of reflection have been known since ancient times.

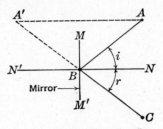

FIG. 2.—The angles of reflection and of incidence are equal.

288. A Perfect Mirror Is Itself Invisible. In one of Aesop's fables a dog saw his mirrored image in a pool and dropped the bone which he was carrying in order to grasp at its image. From the standpoint of physics, the interesting aspect is that the dog did not perceive the mirror surface of the water but only the image behind it. Often, in apartments, large mirrors mounted against the walls deceive the visitor, who thinks that he is looking into another room so that an effect of spaciousness is achieved. Ordinarily, mirrors have imperfections in their surfaces, so that they can be seen, but a perfect reflector would be quite invisible.

289. Diffuse Reflection. When a beam of sunlight is incident on a good mirror in a darkened room, almost all the light is reflected in a single parallel beam with little of it scattered and the mirror is nearly

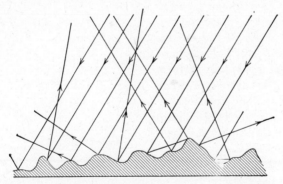

FIG. 3.—Light diffusely reflected from a rough surface.

invisible. When light falls on a piece of paper, diffuse reflection occurs and the paper is visible anywhere in the room. The piece of paper reflects light diffusely in all directions because its surface has a multitude of microscopic hills and valleys (Fig. 3). **Objects viewed by reflected light are visible because they reflect light diffusely.**

290. Refraction. When a beam of sunlight is incident obliquely on a smooth water surface, part of the light is reflected and part enters the

water. The beam entering the water changes direction at the surface
and is said to be **refracted**. A beautiful way to illustrate this phenomenon is to use an aquarium or glass tank partly filled with water to
which a little dye has been added. The air above the water should be

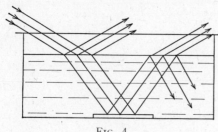

flooded with smoke, and a glass
plate should be used as a cover.
If a beam of light is incident as
in Fig. 4 the beam and the
weakened reflected beam will
be observed in the smoky air
and the refracted beam will be
seen in the water. It will be
noted that as the beam enters
the liquid it is bent toward the

Fig. 4.

normal. At the bottom of the tank the light is reflected by a horizontal mirror and travels backward toward the surface. There, part
is again reflected and part refracted into the air. But the second
refracted beam as it enters the air is bent away from the
normal.

In Fig. 5 let AD be the direction of the beam of light incident on
the water surface, DB the direction of the reflected beam, and DB'
that of the refracted beam in the
water. PP' is a line normal to
the water surface. Simple experiments show that **all these lines
lie in a plane which is perpendicular to the reflecting surface.**

**291. Snell's Law—The Index
of Refraction.** The relationship
between the angle of incidence
of a beam and the angle of refraction may be studied by means of
the device shown in Fig. 6. A

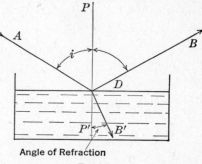

Angle of Refraction

Fig. 5.

narrow parallel beam of light passing through the slit is incident on a
semicircular disk of glass. Part of the light is reflected and part enters
the glass being refracted toward the normal. On leaving the disk the
beam is not deviated. (Why?) The angles of incidence i and of refraction r can be read from the scale, which is graduated in degrees. The
position of the slit is then changed so as to vary the angle of incidence
and the corresponding angle of refraction. Experiments such as this
have established Snell's law, which states that **the ratio of the sine of
the angle of incidence to the sine of the angle of refraction is a con-**

stant for a given substance. (See Appendix.) **This constant is called the index of refraction of the substance.**

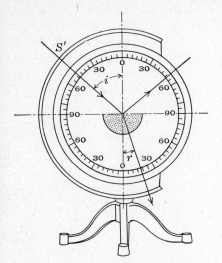

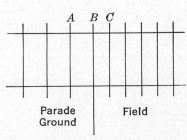

FIG. 7.—The ranks of men do not change direction as they enter the plowed field.

FIG. 6.—Apparatus for measuring angles of incidence and refraction.

292. Refraction and Wave Speed. Before considering the refraction of light further, it will be helpful to discuss the change of direction of a company of soldiers who march in close formation from a parade

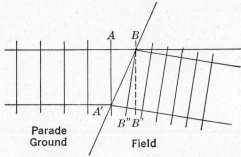

FIG. 8.—The line of march deviates toward the normal when the ranks enter the field.

ground onto a plowed field (Fig. 7). Assume that on the parade ground each soldier has a speed of 3 ft./sec., but in the field his speed is only 2 ft./sec. While one rank of soldiers marches from A to B, each soldier in the preceding rank will move a shorter distance from B to C, and the line of march will not change. Next, suppose that the soldiers cross the boundary obliquely as in Fig. 8 and that each man travels at right angles to the rank. Then while the soldier at A marches to B, the one at A' will move only two-thirds as far, arriving at B'' instead of B'. Hence the line of march deviates to the right. The slower the speed on the plowed ground, the greater will be the deviation of the line of march.

Now assume that Fig. 7 represents a train of water waves approaching the shore of a lake and that at B the waves pass over a ledge and the water becomes more shallow. Because of this the speed will diminish, and the waves will crowd together. In this illustration the "rays" or lines of advance of the waves are not deviated. However, when the waves cross the ledge obliquely (Fig. 8), the end B will be retarded and the waves will be deviated to the right. The greater the change of speed, the greater will be the change of direction.

293. Snell's Law and the Wave Theory of Light. A later chapter on the new physics will show that the problem of the nature of light is not yet solved. There is

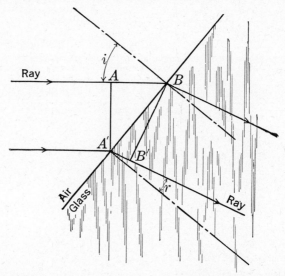

Fig. 9.—The beam of light entering the glass is deviated toward the normal.

much experimental evidence to justify the view that a light source emits waves and that the wave lengths are a few hundred-thousandths of an inch. We shall now see how this hypothesis explains the refraction of light. Assume that a parallel beam of light is incident on a block of glass (Fig. 9), and let AA' represent a wave front. While the part of the wave at A advances to B, A', traveling in the glass, advances a smaller distance to B'. Then the ratio $AB/A'B'$ equals the ratio of the wave speed in air to that in the glass.

$$\frac{\text{Speed of light in air}}{\text{Speed of light in glass}} = \frac{AB}{A'B'}$$

Divide both the numerator and denominator by $A'B$

$$\frac{AB/A'B}{A'B'/A'B} = \frac{\sin\, AA'B}{\sin\, A'BB'}$$

But $AA'B$ equals i, the angle of incidence, and $A'BB'$ equals the angle of refraction r, hence

$$\frac{\text{Speed in air}}{\text{Speed in glass}} = \frac{\sin\, i}{\sin\, r} = n,\ \text{the index of refraction}$$

The ratio of the speeds is a constant for the glass, so that Snell's law is explained.

294. The Absolute and Relative Indices of Refraction. The ratio of the speed of light in a vacuum to that in a substance is defined as the **absolute index of refraction** of that substance. For example, the absolute index of water for light from a sodium flame is 1.333, and so the speed in a vacuum is 1.333 times that in water.

The **relative** index of refraction for two substances is the ratio of the speeds of light in the two mediums. The speed of light in air differs very slightly from the speed in a vacuum, and hence the absolute indices of substances differ little from their relative indices with respect to air.

TABLE I

ABSOLUTE INDICES OF REFRACTION FOR THE YELLOW LIGHT
FROM A SODIUM BURNER

Air............	1.00029	Alcohol, ethyl........	1.36
Diamond......	2.47	Canada balsam.......	1.53
Crown glass....	1.51–1.52	Carbon disulfide......	1.64
Flint glass.....	1.57–1.89	Olive oil.............	1.48
		Cottonseed oil.......	1.47
		Turpentine..........	1.57

295. Index of Refraction Dependent upon Color. When Foucault measured the speed of light in water, using a revolving-mirror method, he found that red light traveled at a slightly higher speed than blue light, and this statement applies to all substances. It follows that the index of refraction of a substance is different for light of different colors. In glass the differences are less than 2 per cent.

296. Total Internal Reflection and the Critical Angle. Thus far this chapter has dealt principally with situations in which light is incident from a less dense medium in which the speed is greater to more dense mediums in which it is less. An interesting case occurs when light passes in the opposite direction. In Fig. 10 light rays diverge from a lamp at the bottom of an aquarium. At the water surface, reflection and refraction occur. The ray OF deserves close attention, for the refracted ray is parallel to the water surface. In other words, the angle of refraction for this particular ray is *90°*. Light incident at any point *G* at the right of *F* does not emerge from the water but is totally reflected. The angle θ for which the angle of refraction is 90° is called the critical angle.

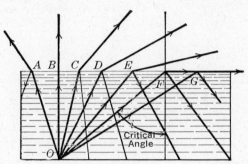

Fig. 10.—All rays incident at angles greater than the critical angle are totally reflected.

The critical angle of a substance is the angle of incidence of light, in the medium of slower speed, for which the angle of refraction is 90°.

Notice that light is totally reflected only when it is incident in the "denser" medium. A demonstration of this fact may be made as

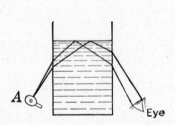

Fig. 11.—The light beam from *A* is totally reflected at the water surface.

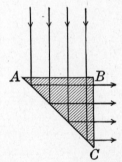

Fig. 12.—A totally reflecting prism.

follows. Hold an electric lamp above a tumbler of water; little light is reflected at the surface since most of it enters the water and is refracted. If the lamp is below the level of the surface (Fig. 11) light will be totally reflected as from a well-silvered mirror.

An important application of total reflection is the reflecting prism (Fig. 12). Light incident on the face *AC* is totally reflected, and so the prism acts like a mirror. Such prisms are often used in field glasses and in the periscopes of submarines because there is no metallic film which may be corroded.

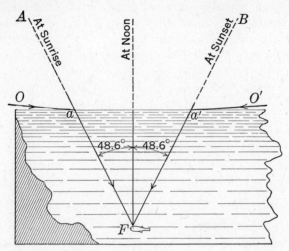

FIG. 13.—The fish sees the image of the sun along AF.

297. As a Fish Views the World. Few fishermen realize that to the finny tribe the world above water seems quite different from that which we see. For example, consider how an intelligent fish might tell the time of day from the elevation of the sun above the horizon. In

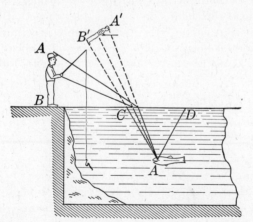

FIG. 14.—The fisherman seems to be "up in the air."

Fig. 13 let OO' represent the smooth, unruffled, surface of a pond. At sunrise the light incident at a is refracted downward toward the normal, and reaches the eye of the fish to which the sun seems to be high in the heavens. As the sun travels across the sky, its apparent motion is through the smaller angle AFB.

Consider, also, the appearance of a fisherman as viewed by the fish (Fig. 14). Though he stands by the water's edge, the man's image seems to be high up in the air at $A'B'$.

298. Atmospheric Refraction—Looming and Mirage. When the sun is near the horizon, the light beams are refracted downward as they pass through the atmosphere so that the sun seems to be higher in the

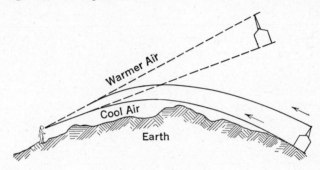

FIG. 15.—Looming.

sky than it really is. For this reason the sun is completely visible when, geometrically considered, it is slightly below the horizon. Because of this the time from sunrise to sunset is lengthened several minutes. The deviation of the light rays just described usually is rather small. When the air near the earth's surface is colder than that higher up, the deviation is more pronounced so that the observers can see images of objects beyond the horizon. This phenomenon, called "looming," is most often observed at sea or over great plains. In 1906, Peary, the

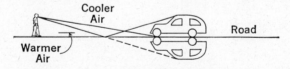

FIG. 16.—A mirage.

discoverer of the North Pole, reported the existence of Crocker Island in the Arctic. More recent expeditions have failed to find it; apparently Peary saw in the skies an image of some more distant region.

The explanation of the looming will be made clear by a study of Fig. 15. The light from the lower part of the building travels through denser air than that from the upper part, hence the lower part of the beam is retarded so that the light is deviated and the image is seen in the sky.

On still, summer days the layer of air above a concrete highway becomes strongly heated and less dense than the air farther up. Light from the sky is refracted upward near the roadway so that the surface seems to be covered with a reflecting layer of water. Under favorable conditions images of approaching vehicles may be seen reflected in this manner (Fig. 16). Often mirages are observed just as an automobile reaches the summit of a hill where there is an accumulation of heated air which flows up from the valley. The image of the sky can be seen reflected at the roadway.

SUMMARY

A ray is a line indicating the direction of travel of waves.

The angle of incidence of light at a surface is the angle between an incident ray and the normal to the surface; the angle of reflection is the angle between the reflected ray and the normal. The angles of incidence and reflection are equal. The incident ray, the reflected ray, and the normal to the surface are in the same plane.

The image of an object formed by a plane mirror is equal in size to the object. The object distance and image distance are also equal.

A perfect reflector would be invisible, and non-luminous objects are seen solely by diffused, reflected light.

When light passes obliquely from one medium to another, refraction occurs. The ratio of the sine of the angle of incidence to that of the angle of refraction is a constant called the refractive index of the substances. It equals the ratio of the speeds of light in the two substances.

The absolute refractive index of a substance equals the ratio of the speed of light in the free space to that in the substance.

The critical angle of a substance is the angle of incidence of light, the angle of refraction being 90°.

"Looming" and "mirage" are caused by atmospheric refraction.

REVIEW QUESTIONS

1. Define "angle of incidence," "angle of refraction."

2. State the laws of reflection and refraction. Also show how they may be tested in the laboratory.

3. Show that a perfect mirror must be invisible.

4. Define index of refraction, and prove that it equals the ratio of the speeds of light in the two mediums. Also distinguish between "absolute" and "relative" indices of refraction.

PROBLEMS

1. To see his complete image, a man 6 ft. tall must use a mirror at least _____ ft. high.

2. To see an object most distinctly a person with normal eyes holds the object at a distance of about 1 ft. When looking at his own image in a plane mirror he should hold the mirror at least _____ ft. from his face.

3. If a man of such height that his eyes are 5 ft. above the floor is able to view his shoes in a small vertical mirror, the top of the mirror must be at least _____ ft. above the floor.

4. If a man walks toward a plane mirror with a speed of 3 ft./sec. he approaches his image with a speed of _____ ft./sec.

5. A man who wishes to spear a fish seen obliquely through the surface of the water should aim _____ the apparent position of the fish.

6. Light passing from air into water is bent less than when it is incident at the same angle on a surface of carbon disulfide. Hence the index of refraction of carbon disulfide is _____ than that of water.

7. The absolute index of refraction of a substance, for which the critical angle is 30°, is _____ .

8. Two plane mirrors are placed at an angle of 60° with each other. What is the angle between an incident ray on the first mirror and its reflected ray from the second one?

9. The speed of light in free space is 300,000 km./sec. What is its speed in water?

10′. Two mirrors face each other, being parallel. A candle is placed between them at a point 1 ft. from mirror A and 2 ft. from mirror B. How far back of B is the second reflected image of the candle?

CHAPTER XXXII

LENSES AND CURVED MIRRORS

Introduction. Most optical devices such as cameras, telescopes, and microscopes are combinations of lenses and, less frequently, of curved mirrors. It is essential before studying these instruments to understand the elements of which they are composed.

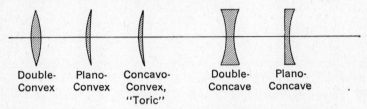

Double-   Plano-   Concavo-   Double-   Plano-
Convex   Convex   Convex,   Concave   Concave
                               "Toric"

FIG. 1.—Convex and Concave Lenses.

A lens is a piece of glass or other transparent material, having two polished surfaces at least one of which is curved (Fig. 1). Lenses are divided into two classes, convex or converging and concave or diverging. Convex lenses are thickest at the center, and concave lenses are thinnest there.

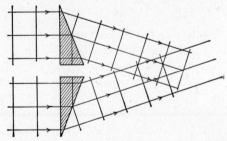

FIG. 2.—The two prisms deviate the light beams.

The **principal axis** of a lens is the straight line through the centers of its two polished surfaces.

In explaining the effect of lenses on light, first consider two prisms placed as in Fig. 2. Light waves from a distant source are incident on the two prisms. The portions of the waves passing through the thicker

291

parts of the prisms are more retarded than those through the thinner parts, for light travels more slowly in glass than in air. It follows that the outer portions of the waves get ahead and the beams are deviated

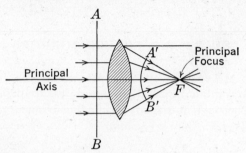

FIG. 3.—The convex lens converges the beam, forming a point image of a star.

toward each other. The effect of a convex lens is similar, but its surface is curved so that the outer rays are bent more than the others and all the light is converged at a point (Fig. 3).

299. Images formed by Convex Lenses. Hold a reading glass, or other large convex lens, so that sunlight, passing through it, falls on

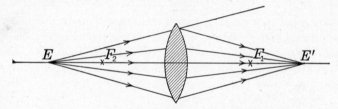

FIG. 4.—E′ is the image at E.

a piece of paper. Move the paper to and fro until an image of the sun is formed on the paper. All the light passing through the lens converges to form this image. The point where rays parallel to the principal axis intersect after being deviated is called the **principal focus** of the lens.

When the source of light is moved from a far-away location toward the principal focus, the image moves away from the lens. Thus if the source is at E (Fig. 4) the rays intersect at E′ beyond the principal focus. Move the source up to the principal focus and the rays from the lens are parallel,

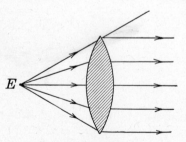

FIG. 5.—When the source is at the principal focus, the rays are rendered parallel.

forming an image at an infinite distance (Fig. 5). Lastly, when the source

is between the principal focus and the lens, the rays do not converge
beyond the lens but they diverge from a point behind it (Fig. 6).

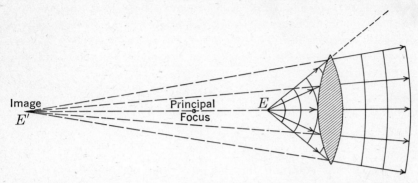

Fig. 6.—When the source is between the principal focus and the lens, the image is
virtual.

300. Real and Virtual Images. When the light converges beyond
the lens, it forms a **real image.** A thermometer placed at the image
would be heated and photographic paper would be "blackened." The
image can be projected on a screen. When rays diverge from a point
behind the lens, the image is **virtual** and it cannot be projected on a
screen. **A real image is one formed by a converging beam, which can
be projected on a screen. A virtual image cannot be so projected.**

301. Location of Images by a Graphical Method. In locating the
image of an extended object such as a candle, it is convenient to draw

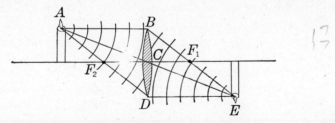

Fig. 7.—Locating the image of a candle.

three rays from some point on the object (Fig. 7). One of these, AB,
parallel to the principal axis, is deviated by the lens so as to pass
through the principal focus, F_1. Another ray AD through the other
principal focus F_2 is rendered parallel and the two intersect at E.
The third ray AC through the center of the lens is not appreciably
bent because the two faces of the lens are nearly parallel at the points
where the ray enters and leaves. The point E where the three rays
intersect is the image of A.

The image of any other point on the candle can be found in the same way.

302. The Image-Equation. Images can be located by the graphical method, which we have discussed, but often it is more convenient to do so by computation. The relation between the distance D_o of the object from the lens, the distance D_i of the image, and the focal length F is given by:

$$\frac{1}{\text{Object distance}} + \frac{1}{\text{Image distance}} = \frac{1}{\text{Focal length}}$$

$$\frac{1}{D_o} + \frac{1}{D_i} = \frac{1}{F}$$

In using this equation the distance from the object is taken as positive. The image distance of a real image is also positive, but that of a virtual image is negative.

Example. (*a*) A candle is placed at a distance of 36 cm. from a converging spectacle lens of focal length 12 cm. What is the image distance, and what kind of image is formed?

$$\frac{1}{36 \text{ cm.}} + \frac{1}{D_i} = \frac{1}{12 \text{ cm.}}; \; D_i = +18 \text{ cm. (real image)}$$

(*b*) If the candle were 8.0 cm. from the lens, where would the image be?

$$\frac{1}{8.0 \text{ cm.}} + \frac{1}{D_i} = \frac{1}{12 \text{ cm.}}$$

$$D_i = -24 \text{ cm. (virtual image)}$$

303. Derivation of the Image Equation. In Fig. 8, the image is located by the graphical method.

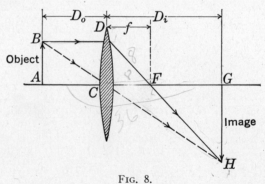

FIG. 8.

The triangles ABC and GCH are similar, hence

$$\frac{GH}{AB} = \frac{CG}{CA} = \frac{D_i}{D_o} \tag{1}$$

The triangles CDF and GFH are also similar, therefore

$$\frac{GH}{CD} = \frac{GF}{CF} = \frac{D_i - F}{F}$$ (2)

$AB = CD$, hence the left-hand terms of (1) and (2) are equal.

$$\frac{D_i}{D_o} = \frac{D_i - F}{F} = \frac{D_i}{F} - 1$$

$$\frac{1}{D_o} + \frac{1}{D_i} = \frac{1}{F}$$

304. Magnification. The size of the image formed by a lens or mirror may be larger than, smaller than, or equal to the size of the object. The **magnification** is defined as the ratio of image length to object length.

$$\text{Magnification} = \frac{\text{Image length}}{\text{Object length}}$$

In Fig. 8, the triangles ABC and GHC are similar, hence their corresponding sides are proportional:

$$\frac{GH}{AB} = \frac{GC}{AC} = \frac{D_i}{D_o} = \text{Magnification}$$

This equation holds for all kinds of lenses and mirrors. **The magnification produced by a lens or mirror equals the ratio of the image distance to the object distance.**

305. Images Formed by Concave Lenses. When a beam of light

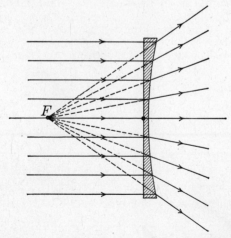

FIG. 9.—A concave lens produces a virtual image.

passes through a concave lens, the central part of the beam gets ahead because it traverses a smaller thickness of glass than the outer part.

In Fig. 9 the incident beam, parallel to the principal axis, is diverged and the light leaving the lens seems to come from the point F which is a principal focus of the lens. The image at F is virtual and it cannot be projected on a screen.

The image of an extended object is located by the same method as that used for convex lenses. Two rays are drawn from the point A of

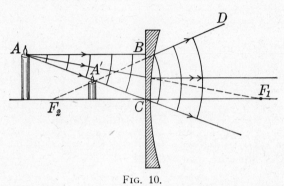

FIG. 10.

the object (Fig. 10). One of these, AB, parallel to the principal axis, is deviated upward so that the light travels along BD directed away from the principal focus F_2. The second ray AC, through the center of the lens, is not deviated appreciably. To an eye beyond the lens, the candle flame seems to be at A', which is the virtual image of A.

The image formula is used for concave lenses, but the focal length is considered to be negative.

Example. A candle is placed at a point 4.0 cm. away from a concave lens of focal length $F = -12$ cm. (a) What is the image distance? (b) What is the magnification?

(a)
$$\frac{1}{4.0 \text{ cm.}} + \frac{1}{D_i} = \frac{1}{-12 \text{ cm.}}$$
$$D_i = -3.0 \text{ cm. (image virtual)}$$

(b)
$$\text{Magnification} = \frac{D_i}{D_o} = \frac{3.0 \text{ cm.}}{4.0 \text{ cm.}} = 0.75$$

306. Thick Lenses—Spherical Aberration. The graphical methods which have been described and the associated formula are fairly satisfactory for thin lenses such as those in spectacles, but they fail when used for thick lenses like the one represented in Fig. 11. Parallel light, incident on a thick lens, is not brought to a single point focus, and therefore sharp images cannot be produced. This defect is called **spherical aberration**.

The image formed by a lens may be made sharper and better defined by interposing an opaque diaphragm or "stop" so as to cut off the outer parts of the beam. In aplanatic lenses the surfaces near the outer edges are ground off so as to decrease their curvatures, making them more nearly flat. Therefore the outer beams are less deviated than before, and they intersect at the same region as those passing through the central portion of the lens.

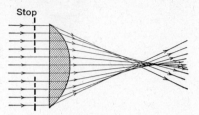

307. Curved Mirrors. Mirrors with curved surfaces are used like lenses to render light beams either more con-vergent or more divergent. The most familiar examples of these mirrors are the reflectors of automobile head-

FIG. 11.—A thick lens does not focus a parallel beam of light at a single point.

lights and the rear-view mirrors sometimes mounted on the fenders of automobiles and trucks. As curved mirrors are less used than lenses they will be dealt with more briefly.

The laws of image formation with curved mirrors closely resemble those for lenses. The following points should be kept in mind.

1. A **spherical mirror** is one of which the surface is part of a sphere and its **radius of curvature** equals that of the sphere (Fig. 12).

2. The **principal axis** is a line drawn through the center of curva-ture C and the center of the mirror.

3. The **focal length** of a spherical mirror is one-half of the radius of curvature (Fig. 13).

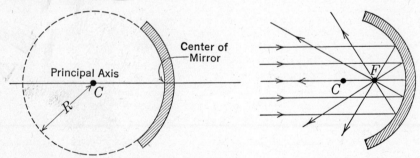

FIG. 12.—The principal axis of a mirror passes through the center of curvature and the center of the mirror.

FIG. 13.

308. Graphical Construction to Locate the Image. The method of image location for concave mirrors is like that used for convex lenses. In Fig. 14 the ray AG is drawn parallel to the principal axis, and the reflected ray GE, therefore, passes through the principal focus F.

A second ray AH passes through the center of curvature C of the mirror, is incident, normally at H, and is therefore reflected along itself.

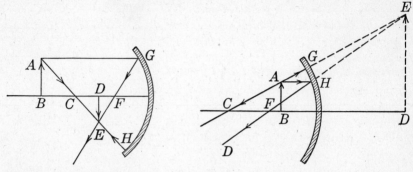

FIG. 14.—Locating the image of an extended object.

FIG. 15.—Virtual image, formed by a concave mirror.

The two rays intersect at E, which is the image of the point A. The image DE may be formed on a screen, hence it is real.

309. Virtual Images Formed by a Concave Mirror. When the object distance is less than the focal length of the mirror (Fig. 15), the image is formed behind the mirror. The two reflected rays diverge and must be produced backward to find the point of intersection. The reflected light does not come from the image, which therefore is virtual.

310. Convex Mirrors Cause Divergence. When a beam of light is incident on a convex mirror parallel to the principal axis, the reflected

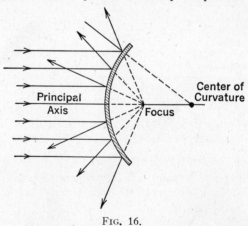

FIG. 16.

beam diverges from the principal focus which is behind the mirror (Fig. 16). The image of an object is located, as in concave mirrors, by drawing a ray AB (Fig. 17) parallel to the principal axis and another one AG normal to the mirror. The two reflected rays diverge from a point E, which is the image of A. The images produced by convex mirrors, like those formed by concave lenses, are always virtual.

Convex mirrors are often mounted on the left front fenders of trucks to afford a view of the roadway behind. Because of the convexity, the image is reduced in size. The driver can see a wide field in the mirror whereas in a plane mirror the view would be narrowly restricted.

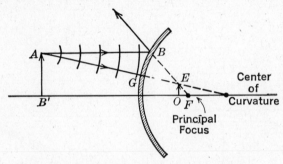

FIG. 17.—Image formation by a convex mirror.

311. The Image Equation. The formula interrelating object distance, image distance, and focal length is the same for mirrors as for lenses, i.e.,

$$\frac{1}{D_o} + \frac{1}{D_i} = \frac{1}{F}$$

The rules for signs are identical with those for lenses and are applied in the same manner.

Example. A spherical, concave, shaving mirror of radius of curvature 24 in. and focal length 12 in. is held at a distance of 6.0 in. from the face. Find the position of the image, and the magnification.

$$\frac{1}{6.0 \text{ in.}} + \frac{1}{D_i} = \frac{1}{12 \text{ in.}}, D_i = -12 \text{ in. (virtual image)}$$

Magnification = 12 in./6.0 in. = 2.0

312. Spherical Aberration. In the discussion of lenses it was pointed out that the image equation and the graphical method for locating images may be applicable for thin lenses with spherical surfaces but fail for thick lenses. Similarly the equations and graphical methods are valid for shallow mirrors, but they fail when applied to deep mirrors. As shown in Fig. 18, the rays incident near the edge of a deep mirror do not converge at or near the principal focus. To avoid "spherical aberration," a parabolic mirror is used (Fig. 19). The most familiar example is the reflector of an automobile headlight. The filament of the lamp bulb is mounted near the principal focus of the parabolic mirror, and the reflected beam is nearly parallel. In searchlights for military purposes, the parabolic mirrors are so well designed that the

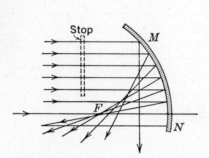

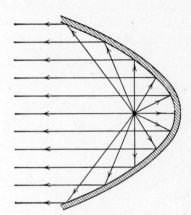

FIG. 18.—A deep, concave, spherical mirror does not converge parallel rays at a point.

FIG. 19.—A parabolic mirror.

illumination of a distant object may be many thousands of times greater than it would be if the bare source were used.

SUMMARY

A lens is a piece of transparent substance bounded by curved surfaces. A converging lens is thicker at the center than at the edge.

The principal axis of a lens is a line through the centers of its two faces. The principal focus of a lens is a point where a beam of light, incident parallel to the principal axis, converges. The focal length of a thin lens is the distance from a principal focus to the lens.

A real image can be projected on a screen.

The image of the head of an arrow may be located by drawing two rays from it, one parallel to the principal axis, the other passing through the center of the lens. The second ray is not deviated by the lens, but the first one is bent so as to pass through the principal focus. These rays intersect at the image of the point.

When the object distance is greater than the focal length of a converging lens, the image is real. When it is less, the image is virtual.

The image of an object produced by a diverging lens is always virtual.

Magnification is defined as the ratio of image length to object length:

(image length)/(object length) = (image distance)/(object distance). The image equation is:

$$\frac{1}{D_o} + \frac{1}{D_i} = \frac{1}{F}$$

The object distance is positive. The image distance is positive for real images and negative for virtual ones. The focal length is positive for converging lenses or mirrors and negative for diverging ones.

Spherical aberration is the failure of a lens or mirror to bring parallel rays to a point focus.

The radius of curvature of a spherical mirror is the radius of the sphere of which the mirror surface is a part. The focal length of a spherical mirror is one-half of its radius. The laws of image formation for lenses and mirrors are closely analogous.

REVIEW QUESTIONS

1. For a thin lens define "principal axis," "principal focus," and "optical center."

2. Explain the effect of a convex lens on plane light waves.

3. Under what condition, if ever, is the image of an object formed by a convex lens (a) smaller and inverted, (b) smaller and erect?

4. In what direction will the image move when an object moves from a distant point toward (a) a convex lens, and (b) a concave lens?

5. What is the difference between a real and a virtual image?

6. By graphical construction locate the images of arrows placed at the following distances from a convex lens of focal length 2 in.: (a) 6 in., (b) 3 in., (c) 1.5 in., (d) 1 in.

7. Deal with question 6 for a concave lens.

8. Deal with question 6 for a concave mirror.

9. Define "magnification," and show that it equals the ratio image distance/object distance.

10. What is spherical aberration, and how may it be eliminated?

PROBLEMS

A. OBJECTIVE PROBLEMS

1. An image of the sun is formed by a silvered glass sphere 1 ft. in diameter. The distance from the surface of the sphere to the image is   in.

2. A reading glass has a focal length of 6 in. The least distance at which it can be held from an object to form a real image is   in.

3. A person looking into a mirror sees a small erect image of his face. Therefore, the mirror must be   .

4. As seen in a convex mirror, the image of a man's nose is relatively   than that of an ear.

5. When a convex lens is submerged in water, the focal length is   .

6. The real image formed by a convex lens of focal length 1.0 cm. is the same size as the object. The object distance is 2 cm.

B. Non-Objective Problems

7. A candle is placed 6.0 in. in front of a concave lens of focal length −6.0 in. Where is the image formed? Make a graphical construction.

8′. A piece of paper 8 in. by 10 in. is placed at a distance of 20 in. from a convex lens of focal length 10 in. What are the dimensions of the image?

9″. Assuming the sun's diameter to be a million miles and its distance to be 100 million miles, find the size of the sun's real image formed by a convex lens, the focal length being 50 ft.

10″. (*a*) A lens has a focal length of 6.0 in. How far from it must an object be placed in order that the real image may be as large as the object? (*b*) How far if the real image is twice as large as the object?

11″. A lamp and screen are 3.0 ft. apart. At what distances from the screen must a convex lens of focal length 8.0 in. be placed to form an image of the lamp on the screen? Show that there are two solutions, and find the magnification in each case.

12″. A lens when placed 4.0 in. from an object forms a virtual image one-half as large as the object. What is the focal length of the lens?

13″. An electric lamp is placed at a distance of 2.0 ft. from a plane mirror suspended against the east wall of a hall 6.0 ft. wide. Light emitted by the lamp is reflected by the mirror to a lens placed beside the lamp. What is the focal length of the lens if a real image of the lamp is formed on the west wall?

14. The image of the setting sun seen in a convex fender mirror of a car seems to be 4.0 ft. behind the mirror. What is the focal length of the mirror?

15. By computation, find the position of the image of a candle placed at a distance of 5.0 cm. from a concave mirror of radius 20 cm.

16′. A shaving mirror held at a distance of 6.0 in. from a man's face produces twofold magnification. Find the focal length of the mirror. (The image is virtual.)

17′. An object is placed 5.0 cm. from a concave mirror, and the image is formed 10 cm. behind the mirror. Find its focal length.

18″. A dentist holds a concave mirror of radius of curvature 5.0 cm. at a distance of 2.0 cm. from a filling in a tooth. Where is the image formed, and what is the magnification?

Answers to problems 1–6: (1) 3 in., (2) 6 in., (3) convex, (4) larger, (5) increased, (6) 2 cm.

CHAPTER XXXIII

OPTICAL INSTRUMENTS

"I will make such telescopes and see such things."
—WM. HERSCHEL.

The Importance of Optical Instruments in Affecting Modern Thought.
If, as a well-known proverb states, seeing is believing, whatever affects
the vision of men will also affect their beliefs. The first artificial aids
to vision were mirrors, which were used in the days of the pharaohs in
Egypt. Spectacles were invented 4,500 years later, in the thirteenth
century. The great scientific awakening in the time of Galileo gave the
microscope and the telescope, but the camera and the motion-picture
projector are recent innovations. As the years go by, new improvements will come giving greater magnifications, greater light-gathering
ability, and greater refinements to these instruments.

313. The Camera. A photographic camera (from the Latin word
camera, room) consists of a system of lenses or, in cheap cameras, of a
single lens, mounted at one side of an opaque enclosure and producing
on a light-sensitive film a real and inverted image of the object to be
photographed. Usually the sides of the camera box are extensible so
that the distance from the lens to the film may be varied until the
image is sharply focused. To aid in this adjustment, in some instruments the film is replaced temporarily by a ground-glass screen on
which the image is viewed while the focusing is accomplished. In others
a scale indicates the proper lens setting for an object at a known distance.

The shutter of the camera is a diaphragm, covering the lens, which
is removed during the exposure of the film. A second diaphragm called
the "stop" has a variable aperture. When the stop is wide open, the
illumination is greater than when it is small, and the time of exposure
is reduced. When the aperture is nearly closed, a longer exposure is
required, but advantage is gained since the spherical aberration is
diminished, the images are more sharply defined, and less careful
focusing is required.

314. The Process of Development. The light-sensitive coating of
the photographic film consists, in part, of silver salt (usually silver

bromide) embedded in gelatin. Light incident on this salt affects the silver bromide molecules in some little-understood way. When the exposed plate is later immersed in a suitable "developer," the silver bromide molecules affected by light are separated into bromine and silver atoms. A second immersion in a "fixing solution" dissolves away the silver bromide, but the silver which was separated remains as a black deposit. The plate thus formed is called a "negative" because the brighter parts of the view photographed appear as darker parts of the image. To make a positive print, the negative is laid on a piece of sensitized paper and placed in a beam of light. The more dense parts of the negative absorb more light than the less dense parts, and hence the silver salts will be more affected under the lighter parts of the negative than under the darker regions. The exposed sensitized paper is developed and fixed in the same manner as the film. It is called a "positive" because the brighter parts of the scene photographed appear as the brighter parts of the image.

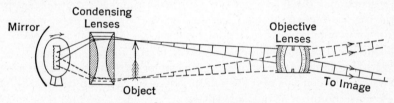

FIG. 1.—A projection lantern.

315. The Motion–Picture Camera and Projector. The motion-picture camera differs from an ordinary camera in that a series of pictures are taken at equal, short, time intervals on a long, narrow film. Usually 16 or more pictures are taken per second. The shutter and film shifter operate automatically. After each exposure, during the short interval while the shutter is closed, a new section of film is shifted into position.

The motion-picture projector is a very compact projection lantern (Fig. 1). It consists of a light source fitted with a reflector, a "condensing lens" system which converges the light onto the film or lantern slide, thus brilliantly illuminating it, and, lastly, an "objective" lens system which produces on the distant screen a real, enlarged image of the film. The motion-picture projector, like the camera, is provided with an automatically operated shutter and film shifter. The successive film images are usually projected at a rate of 16 per second. The eye does not distinguish the individual images, hence an illusion of motion is produced because of the persistence of vision.

316. The Human Eye. The human eye (Fig. 2) closely resembles a photographic camera. The eyelids correspond to the shutter. The iris diaphragm, corresponding to the stop, is an opaque screen with an aperture or "pupil" which widens in dim light and narrows when the illumination is intense. Instead of a photographic film the eye has a retina in which there are thousands of nerve endings that send signals to the brain when light is incident upon them.

When a person first goes from a sunny street into a darkened motion-picture theater, he cannot perceive surrounding objects, but later his

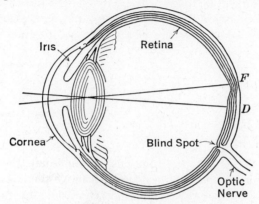

FIG. 2.—The structure of a human eye.

vision improves so that he has little difficulty. This improvement in vision comes in part from the dilation of the pupil of the eye and in part, it is believed, from the accumulation in the retina of certain dyes or pigments which increase the sensitivity of the nerves. When the

FIG. 3.—To locate the blind spot.

illumination is intense these dyes are bleached by the light and the amount present is relatively small. In a dimly lighted room, the rate of bleaching decreases, the pigment accumulates, and the sensitivity of the retina gradually rises. Every one who drives a car at night has experienced discomfort when a stab of light from an approaching automobile partially blinds him. The reason is that the light falling on the retina quickly bleaches out most of the pigment, greatly diminishing the sensitiveness of the eyes. Afterward several minutes are required for the pigment to accumulate again.

The blind spot, a small region of the retina where the optic nerve enters the eyeball, is insensitive to light. The existence of the blind spot is easily demonstrated by holding this book at arm's length, and closing the left eye and looking at the X in Fig. 3. In this position the circle at B and the square at C are both visible. Move the page closer to the eye. At a certain distance, C disappears because its image is formed on the insensitive blind spot. Move the page still closer, and another position will be found when B disappears but C is visible.

317. Accommodation, Nearsightedness, and Farsightedness. When a photographer takes a picture of a landscape, he shifts the lens to a

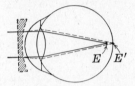

FIG. 4.—The near-sighted eye forms images of distant objects in front of the retina.

point such that the distance from lens to film equals the focal length. In photographing a nearer object, he must move the lens farther away from the film. The eyes of fishes are focused in the same manner. In the human eye the distance from lens to retina is fixed. The focusing is accomplished by changing the curvature of the lens. When a healthy eye is resting, the lens forms the images of distant objects on the retina. When a person reads, sews, or examines objects closely, the eyes are focused for close vision. The muscles exert forces so that the curved surface of the lens bulges, forming the image on the retina.

For some people, especially children, the lenses of the eyes are too convex, so that distant objects cannot be seen distinctly. These people, in reading, hold the book or newspaper closer to the eyes than normal, hence the defect is called "nearsightedness." The defect arises because the lens system converges the light to form images in front of the retina. The remedy is to use spectacles with concave lenses (Fig. 4).

When a person passes the age of fifty, he usually encounters trouble in reading because the lenses of the eyes harden so that they will not bulge sufficiently to focus the light for near vision. Spectacles with convex lenses are prescribed which increase the convergence of the light. Sometimes bifocal eyeglasses are used. The upper part of the lens, less curved than the lower part, is employed for distant vision, and the lower, more converging, part for reading.

318. Astigmatism. One of the most common defects of vision is **astigmatism**, which arises because the cornea is not of uniform curvature. In the normal eye the cornea is uniformly part of the surface of a sphere, somewhat like the top of an egg, but in the astigmatic eye the surface is more like that of the side of the egg, being more curved in one plane than in another at right angles to it. Because of the defect the lens system forms the image of a horizontal line at one position and of a vertical line at another one.

Astigmatism can be detected by means of the charts shown in Fig. 5. With normal eyes the sets of parallel lines will be seen with equal distinctness at all distances from the eyes. If there is astigmatism, however, at a certain distance the vertical lines will be sharply defined, while the horizontal lines seem blurred. At another distance the horizontal lines are clearly seen while the others are indistinct. Rotating the page about the line of sight as an axis will cause first one set of lines, then another, to be clearly focused.

FIG. 5.—Astigmatism chart. (Courtesy of the Central Scientific Company.)

319. Deceiving the Eyes. Though "seeing is believing," it is comparatively easy to "fool the eye." Every one knows that when the moon is high in the heavens it seems smaller than when it is near the horizon, though in fact the angle which it subtends at the eye is about the same in each case. The reason for this illusion is as follows. When the moon is high it seems small compared with the clouds, or the vastness of space, but when it is near the horizon it subtends a greater angle than distant objects which we know to be large. In Fig. 6, the baseball seems larger than the pitcher's head; being nearer to the camera, it subtended a larger angle.

As other illustrations of the ease with which the eye is deceived, notice that the line A in Fig. 7 seems to be shorter than B though actually both are of equal length. The two long lines of C are parallel though they seem to approach each other.

320. The Eyepiece or Simple Magnifying Glass. Examine a page of this book, bringing it as close as possible to the eyes so that each printed letter subtends a large angle. As the picture is moved nearer, the lens of the eye bulges more so that the image may be focused on the retina. When the page is a few inches from the eye, the lens is distorted as much as possible and the object cannot be moved closer if sharp vision is to be attained. This nearest distance is called **the distance of distinct vision**. It varies for different persons, the average

FIG. 6.—Jim Weaver pitching a "fast" ball. (Courtesy of the Pittsburgh Press.)

value being 25 cm. or 10 in. Now put a convex lens or eyepiece to the eye; the book may be moved nearer and the letters will seem to

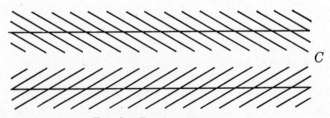

FIG. 7.—Deceiving the eyes.

be larger because they subtend larger angles.

The magnification M produced by an eyepiece of focal length F is:

$$M = \frac{D}{F} + 1$$

D being the distance of distinct vision.

Example. A jeweler uses a lens of focal length 2.5 cm. to examine the hair spring of a watch. What is the magnification? Distance of distinct vision = 25 cm.

$$M = \frac{25 \text{ cm.}}{2.5 \text{ cm.}} + 1 = 11$$

321. Derivation of the Eyepiece Magnification Formula. When an object is viewed through an eyepiece, it is held at a point just inside the principal focus of the lens

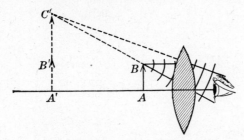

FIG. 8.—Image formed by a simple magnifying glass.

so that an enlarged, virtual image is seen at the distance of most distinct vision (Fig. 8). The image is virtual, hence its distance is considered to be negative and

$$D_i = -25 \text{ cm. or } -10 \text{ in.}$$

Thus

$$\frac{1}{D_o} - \frac{1}{25 \text{ cm.}} = \frac{1}{F}$$

$$\frac{1}{D_o} = \frac{1}{F} + \frac{1}{25 \text{ cm.}}$$

$$\frac{25 \text{ cm.}}{D_o} = \frac{25 \text{ cm.}}{F} + 1$$

But 25 cm./D_o is the ratio of image distance to object distance, and equals the magnification M

$$M = \frac{25 \text{ cm.}}{F} + 1 = \frac{10 \text{ in.}}{F} + 1$$

322. The Compound Microscope. The compound microscope has two lens systems, which produce two magnifications. The object is placed just beyond the principal focus of the objective lens L_1 (Fig. 9) which produces a real, enlarged image I_1. The magnification caused by this lens is given by

$$M_1 = D_i/D_o$$

This image is further magnified by an eyepiece L_2 which produces a virtual image at the distance of distinct vision. Its magnification is

$$M_2 = \frac{25 \text{ cm.}}{F} + 1$$

The total magnification equals the product of the two.

Example. A compound microscope has an objective lens of focal length 2.0 cm. and an eyepiece of focal length 5.0 cm. Find the total magnification it produces if the distance from the objective to the real image is 20 cm. (Assume that the distance of distinct vision is 25 cm.)

For the objective,

$$1/D_o + 1/20 \text{ cm.} = 1/2.0 \text{ cm.}$$
$$D_o = 2.22 \text{ cm.}$$
$$M_1 = 20 \text{ cm.}/2.22 \text{ cm.} = 9.0$$

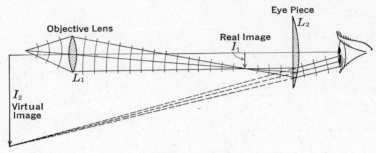

FIG. 9.—A compound microscope.

The magnification produced by the eyepiece is given by

$$M_2 = \frac{25 \text{ cm.}}{5.0 \text{ cm.}} + 1 = 6.0$$

Total magnification = $9.0 \times 6.0 = 54$.

323. The Astronomical Telescope. The astronomical telescope, like the compound microscope, has two lens systems, the objective and the

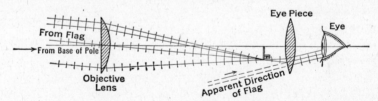

FIG. 10.—An astronomical telescope.

eyepiece. The important difference is that the object is far away. The real image, formed at the principal focus of the lens, is smaller than the object. In Fig. 10, two beams of light, incident on the objective lens, are shown. The slanting beam comes from the top of a distant flagstaff; the horizontal beam from the base. The objective lens converges these beams, forming a real, inverted image of the flagstaff at the principal focus of the lens. This image is viewed by the eyepiece, so adjusted that the image and the object are at the same distance D_o.

The total magnification is given by

$$M = \frac{\text{Focal length of objective}}{\text{Focal length of eyepiece}} = \frac{F}{f}$$

324. Derivation of Magnification Formula. Let the distance of the object be D_o. The object is far away, hence the image distance equals F, and

$$M_1 = F/D_o$$

The distance from the real image to the eyepiece equals the focal length f of the eyepiece (Why?). The virtual image is at a distance D_o, hence

$$M_2 = D_o/f$$

Total magnification $= M_1 \times M_2 = F/D_o \times D_o/f = F/f$.

325. Reflecting Telescopes. Some telescopes have objective lenses more than a yard in diameter, weighing more than a ton. These lens

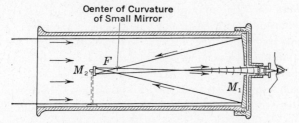

FIG. 11.—A reflecting astronomical telescope.

systems are very expensive because as will be explained presently the objective consists of two lenses, one convex, the other concave. Giant astronomical telescopes constructed in recent years have parabolic mirrors instead of objective lenses. The essential parts of one type of reflector telescope are shown in Fig. 11. Light from a star is incident on the parabolic mirror which converges it at F. A smaller mirror M_2 reflects the beam downward. It is viewed through an eyepiece in the usual manner. The new telescope at Mount Palomar, California, has an objective mirror 17 feet in diameter, as large in area as the floor of a living room. The mirror, made of Pyrex glass, weighs 18 tons, and the completed telescope will cost $6,000,000. The cost of operating it, including interest and depreciation, will exceed $100 per hour. It will be used principally in studying great clusters of stars called nebulae, like our "Milky Way," some of which are at distances of hundreds of millions of light-years. The light received from the stars will tell nothing as to their present conditions, but it will yield information as to their positions, sizes, temperatures, and velocities as they were when the light was emitted eons ago. The methods of securing some of this information will be described in the next chapter.

SUMMARY

Important parts of the eye are the cornea, the iris, the lens, the retina, and the optic nerve.

When near-by objects are viewed, the lens of the eye bulges so that its converging power increases. In nearsightedness the lens causes too great convergence and the image of a distant object is formed in front of the retina. This defect is remedied by spectacles with concave lenses. In farsightedness the eye lens causes too little convergence and convex spectacle lenses are required.

The distance of distinct vision is the smallest distance at which an object can be held, a real image being produced on the retina.

The simple magnifying glass is a lens which enables one to bring an object closer than the distance of distinct vision, thus increasing the apparent size. The magnification is given by $D/F + 1$.

In the compound microscope a real image of the object is produced by the objective, and this image is further magnified by an eyepiece used as a simple magnifying glass, forming a virtual image at the distance of distinct vision.

In the telescope a real image is produced near the focus of the objective. The eyepiece is so located that the virtual image is produced at the same distance as the object. The magnifying power equals the ratio of the focal length of the objective to that of the eyepiece.

REVIEW QUESTIONS

1. Make a sketch showing the essential parts of a camera.

2. Describe the various steps in producing a photograph from an exposed plate.

3. Make a sketch showing the important parts of a projection lantern.

4. Make a sketch showing the cross section of the human eye, labeling the important parts.

5. State ways in which the eye and the camera are similar and several in which they differ.

6. What is the purpose of the iris of the eye?

7. The images on the retina are inverted. Why does not the world seem "upside down"?

8. Explain why a swimmer with eyes adjusted for distant vision cannot see distant objects clearly when he is submerged. Does a diver with a helmet have equal difficulty?

9. Discuss "accommodation."

10. What are nearsightedness and farsightedness, and how can they be corrected by spectacles?

11. In a projection lantern, where is the lantern slide placed with reference to the principal focus of the objective lens?

12. What happens to the eye lens as a book is brought nearer to the eye? Is there a limit to this process?

13. What is the distance of distinct vision? Why does a simple magnifying glass make objects seem larger?

14. Develop the formula for the magnification of a simple magnifying glass.

15. Make sketches showing image formation by a simple magnifier and by a compound microscope.

16. Make a sketch showing the image formation by an astronomical telescope. Also derive the magnification formula.

17. In telescopes the magnification increases with increasing focal length of the objective lens. In compound microscopes the opposite is true. Explain.

PROBLEMS

1. In a cheap camera the distance from lens to film is 10.0 cm. In order to form the sharpest image, the objects photographed must be 300 cm. from the lens. What is its focal length?

2. What is the size of the image of a 6-ft. man who stands at a distance of 300 cm. from the camera described above?

3'. The focal length of a camera lens system is 12 in. At what distance from the lens must a man be if he is 6.0 ft. tall and his image on the negative is 6.0 in. long?

4'. The lens of a camera has a focal length of 6.0 in. How far must the lens be shifted to change the focus from infinity to that for an object 5.0 ft. away?

5. On a motion-picture film, the image of the nose of an actor is 1.0 mm. long. The distance from the film to the center of the lens system of the projector is 4.0 in. What is the size of the image formed on a screen which is 120 ft. from the lens?

6'. A nearsighted person cannot see clearly an object which is more than 2.00 m. distant. What is the focal length of the spectacle lenses required in order that he may see very distant objects? (Parallel light rays after passing through the spectacle lens must diverge from a point 2.00 m. distant; i.e., $D_o = \infty$, $D_i = -200$ cm.)

7'. A farsighted person must hold a book at a distance of 50 cm. from the eyes. What is the focal length of the required spectacle lenses so that he may hold the book at a distance of 25 cm.? (With this object distance, the virtual image distance is -50 cm.)

8. A jeweler uses a simple magnifying glass of focal length 2.5 cm. to examine a gem. (*a*) At what distance from the lens must the object be placed in order to produce a virtual image at a distance of 25 cm.? (*b*) What is the magnification?

9'. In a compound microscope the focal lengths of the objective and eyepiece are respectively 0.50 cm. and 1.00 cm. The real image is formed by the objective at a point 20 cm. from it, and the virtual image distance is -25 cm.; find (*a*) the distance of the object from the objective lens, (*b*) the two magnifications, and (*c*) the total magnification.

10. The distance of the moon is 240,000 miles. At what distance would it have to be for its mountains to seem as large as they do when seen through the Lick Observatory telescope? The objective and eyepiece focal lengths are respectively 1,500 cm. and 3.0 cm.

11. In an astronomical telescope the focal lengths of the objective and eyepiece are 36 in. and 0.50 in., respectively. At what distance apart should the lenses be to view the moon, and what is the magnification?

12. The focal lengths of the lenses of an astronomical telescope are 36 in. and 0.50 in., respectively. What should be the distance between them in order to form a real image of the moon on a screen 6.0 in. behind the eyepiece?

CHAPTER XXXIV

THE SPECTROSCOPE, A MASTER DETECTIVE

Newton

Could Rembrandt but have painted him, in those hours
Making his first analysis of light
Alone, there, in his darkened Cambridge room
At Trinity! . . .
     He caught
The sunbeam striking through that bullet-hole
In his closet shutter—a round white spot of light
Upon a small dark screen.
     He interposed
A prism of glass. He saw the sunbeam break
And spread upon the screen its rainbow band
Of disentangled colours, all in scale
Like notes in music; first, the violet ray,
Then indigo, trembling softly into blue;
Then green and yellow, quivering side by side;
Then orange, mellowing richly into red.
    ALFRED NOYES: *"Watchers of the Sky"*
     Courtesy of Frederick A. Stokes Co.

Most optical instruments are used to produce magnified images of objects, to locate their positions, or to photograph them. The **spectroscope** has quite different purposes. It yields information as to the different colors of the light from a body, the physical and chemical nature of its surface, its temperature, and its velocity.

326. Newton and the Spectrum. The first careful study of color phenomena was made by Sir Isaac Newton when he was a student at Cambridge University. He placed a triangular glass prism in a narrow beam of sunlight and observed that the prism dispersed the light, spreading the beam out fanwise, forming a wide image of rainbow hues on the opposite wall of the room (Fig. 1). Such an image, in which radiations of different hues and wave lengths occupy different positions, is called a spectrum. Next Newton placed another, reversed, prism beyond the first one, and brought the beams together again, producing white light. Thus the young student by two very simple experiments showed that white light may be dispersed into rainbow hues and that radiations of different colors can be combined to produce white light.

327. The Rainbow. From ancient times, the beauty of the rainbow, rarely seen after a storm, has produced a striking impression on ob-servers. A rainbow is caused by the re-fraction and reflection of light from multitudes of water droplets in a cloud. In Fig. 2A a narrow ray of sunlight is incident on a water drop. The refracted beam enters the drop, is dispersed into rainbow colors, and is partly reflected

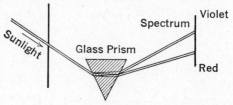

Fig. 1A   Fig. 1B

Fig. 1A.—Newton produces a spectrum. (Fig. 1B) Using a prism to disperse a beam of light.

at *D*. After emerging, the light travels out as a wedge-shaped beam. The rainbow which an observer sees in the sky is formed by the action

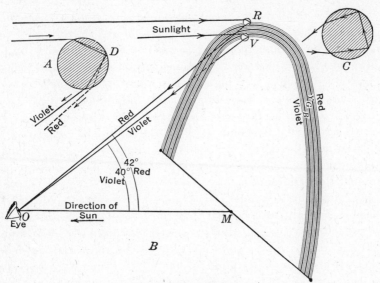

Fig. 2.—The rainbow.

of myriads of droplets. In Fig. 2B the horizontal rays of the setting sun are reflected from droplets along *RV*. The eye receives red light from R, violet light from V, other spectral colors from intermediate points. All the rays of red light make angles of about 42° with OM, hence the rainbow is seen as a circular arc across the sky.

Sometimes a larger "secondary" rainbow is also visible. In this case the light enters near the bottom of the droplet, and it is *twice* reflected (Fig. 2C). The order of the colors is reversed, and the upper part of the bow is blue.

328. Chromatic Aberration. The reader will recall that Galileo, who died the same year that Newton was born, constructed a crude telescope by means of which he discovered the moons of the planet Jupiter. After his study of the spectrum, Newton constructed telescopes with

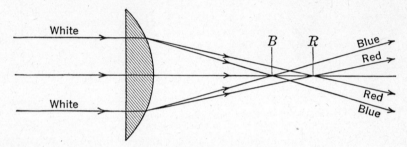

FIG. 3.—Chromatic aberration.

larger lenses than those of Galileo. These telescopes were ineffective because the images were blurred. The reason was that the lenses deviated the light of different wave lengths by different amounts. In Fig. 3 white light from a distant lamp is incident on a convex lens. The blue light converges at B, forming an image there. The red light, less deviated than the blue, is focused at R, and radiations of other colors at intermediate points. If a screen is placed at R, the red, central image will be surrounded by bands of color, the outer edge being blue. If it is placed at B the center will be blue and the outer edge red. This failure to converge light of different hues at the same point is called **chromatic aberration**.

329. Achromatic Lenses. After considerable effort, Newton abandoned the attempt to construct large refracting telescopes and invented the reflecting telescope, which is free from chromatic aberration, for light radiations of all colors are reflected at the same angle. Later other workers discovered that chromatic aberration may be corrected by using combinations of lenses **made of different kinds of glass**. In explaining how this is done, let us assume that a convex lens of "crown" glass (common glass) (Fig. 4) refracts the ray AB of blue light inward, towards the principal axis, through an angle of 16° and the red light through 15°. The average deviation is 15½°, and the dispersion or angular separation of the blue and red is 1°. The diverging lens made of "flint" glass, containing a large proportion of lead, refracts the ray

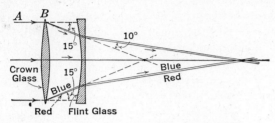

FIG. 4.—An achromatic lens combination.

of blue light outward 10°, the red light 9°. The average deviation is 9½°, and the dispersion is 1° outward. The two lenses together produce an average refraction of 15½ − 9½ or 6° inward, and the dispersion is 0°; so that all the light converges at the same point. Usually the two lenses are placed in contact with each other and the combination is termed achromatic (Greek, "without color"). In spectacle lenses and in those of cheap cameras, no attempt is made to eliminate chromatic aberration, but in many optical devices expensive combinations of lenses eliminate the dispersion.

330. The Spectroscope Produces a "Pure" Spectrum. The spectrum formed by a prism is said to be "impure" because there is considerable overlapping of light of different colors and wave lengths. The spectroscope (Fig. 5) is used to produce an approximately pure spectrum. The

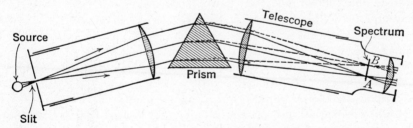

FIG. 5.—A spectroscope.

light entering through a narrow slit is made parallel by a lens. Then the light is dispersed by a prism and enters the objective lens of a telescope. The lens converges the beams, forming a spectrum at AB. This spectrum is viewed through the eyepiece, or it may be photographed on a film.

331. Incandescent Gases and Vapors Produce Bright-Line Spectra.

The light from an ordinary incandescent lamp-filament, or any other hot, glowing solid, forms a continuous spectrum of the rainbow hues, violet, indigo, blue, green, yellow, orange, and red. The spectrum of an incandescent gas is strikingly different. It consists of bright lines, with dark spaces between them. Dip a platinum wire into a solution of sodium chloride and then insert it in the flame of a bunsen burner. The salt is vaporized and the sodium atoms emit a yellow light. Its visible spectrum is two yellow lines, very close together. Strontium and potassium chlorides, treated in this manner, give spectra consisting of several lines. Metals vaporized in an electric arc yield more complicated spectra (Fig. 6). Gases are studied by enclosing them in glass or

FIG. 6.—The bright-line spectrum of magnesium. (Permission of Dr. F. A. Saunders.)

quartz tubes through which electrical discharges are sent. They also produce bright-line spectra.

332. Absorption Spectra.

Place an incandescent lamp in front of the slit of a spectroscope and, looking through the eyepiece, observe the continuous spectrum of the light emitted by the filament. Then interpose a glass bottle containing a dilute solution of a black dye. The various parts of the spectrum will be dimmed about equally. Replace the bottle with one containing blood in water. A dark band will be seen in the yellow and green part of the spectrum. Bubble ordinary manufactured illuminating gas through the solution and the carbon monoxide in the gas will combine with the blood, producing a chemical change. Now two dark bands will be seen instead of one. The spectroscope is often used in this manner to detect chemical transformations. Colored glass, jewels, and many other solids produce the same type of spectra as colored liquids.

Light absorption also occurs in gases and vapors. To demonstrate this effect, place two or three bunsen burners between the slit of a spectroscope and an incandescent lamp so that the light from the lamp must pass through the flames. Dip small pieces of asbestos into a sodium chloride solution, place them on the top of the burners, and the vaporized sodium will cause the flames to be yellow. A dark line will be seen in the yellow part of the spectrum. It occupies precisely the same position as the yellow line (or pair of lines close together) seen when one views a sodium flame alone.

This is an example of **sympathetic vibrations** or of **resonance** in light. The sodium atoms absorb radiations of the same frequency as the light which the sodium emits. The photograph of an absorption spectrum due to passage of light through hydrogen is reproduced in Fig. 7.

FIG. 7.—The absorption spectrum of hydrogen. (After Curtis.) (From p. 100, "Pittsburgh Atomic Physics.")

Before studying the practical uses of the spectroscope, we summarize a few facts as to types of spectra.

TABLE I

TYPES OF SPECTRA		SOURCE OF LIGHT
Emission	{ Bright-line	Gas or vapor
	Continuous	Solid or liquid
		ABSORBER
Absorption	{ Band	Liquid or solid
	Line	Gas or vapor

333. The Spectroscope—A Master Detective. The spectroscope is of great utility when only a small amount of the substance to be detected is present in a mixture. For example, the presence of one part of sodium in a million may be readily detected. Suppose that one wishes to determine the amount of tin and lead (undesirable constituents) in a casting made of aluminum and copper. Then he places a chip of the metal in a hole in a carbon rod and causes an electric discharge to flow between this rod and another, forming an electric arc. The metal is vaporized by the intense heat, and the spectrum shows the characteristic lines of each substance that is present (Fig. 8). Industry is rapidly adopting the spectroscope for chemical analysis. Great interest is aroused by its use in securing evidence against "hit and run" drivers and criminals. In one case a motorist was accused of colliding with another. A few chips of glass were found near the ruined car. The glass was compared with that taken from a shattered headlight lens of the accused's automobile. The spectroscope's evidence helped to bring a conviction. In a murder case, the defense claimed that the fatal shot was fired from outside of the room, and presented as evidence a piece of window screen in which there was a hole. The spectroscope showed that there was no trace of lead around the edges of the opening, so that it could not have been made by the lead bullet.

Not only does the spectroscope detect the presence of chemical elements in a mixture, but in some instances it yields information on **how much** of an element is present. If a block of silver contains no copper, its spectrum will show none of the characteristic lines of that element. If a trace of the impurity is present, certain of the stronger lines only will be seen, and, as the amount of copper increases, other spectrum lines of copper appear. Thus by means of the spectroscope

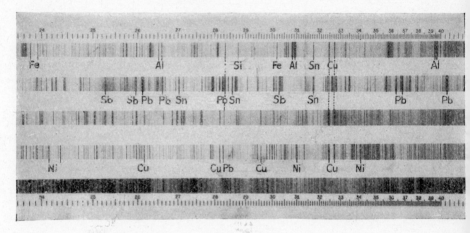

Fig. 8.—The spectroscope detects impurities in aluminum castings. (Courtesy of Bausch and Lomb.)

the observer can learn whether the metal contains more nearly 0.01 per cent or 0.1 per cent of copper.

334. The Spectroscope and Astrophysics. Until the middle of the nineteenth century, the astronomer was merely a surveyor of the heavens, busying himself with studying the motions of the planets and those of a few score of the nearer "fixed" stars. The invention of the spectroscope opened new vistas. The astronomer gave place to the astrophysicist, who measures the sizes and distances and velocities of stars as well as their surface temperatures. He does not limit his attention to the stars of our own little cluster, the "Milky Way," but peers far out into space, studying other clusters or "island universes" hundreds of millions of light-years distant.

335. The Fraunhofer Lines in the Sun's Spectrum. The spectrum of light from the sun tells an interesting story as to the condition of its surface. The spectrum is not continuous, but is crossed by hundreds of dark lines; it is a *dark-line* spectrum. This fact proves that the light must have passed through vapors or gases which absorbed radiations of certain frequencies. Two of these lines correspond exactly with the yellow lines of sodium. Hence we know that sodium exists in the sun's atmosphere. Other lines reveal the existence of calcium, magnesium, iron, copper, and numerous other elements. The most interesting of these is helium. About seventy years ago, a dark line was observed near the sodium "yellow" lines which could not be produced by any previously known substance. It was attributed to a new element which was named helium from the Greek word *helios* meaning "sun." Later, minute traces of helium were detected in radium ores, and after that large quantities were found in the natural gas from wells in the southwestern states. Today it is used in balloons and dirigibles.

The spectra of some stars have dark lines like the sun's. These stars have hot solid cores surrounded by gases and vapors. Other stars are known to be gaseous, for their spectra show bright lines only. Others having continuous spectra are hot bodies without atmospheres.

336. The Velocities of Stars are Measured by the Doppler Effect. The Doppler effect was described in the section on sound. It was pointed out that when an observer approaches a source of sound, he observes that the apparent pitch is higher than when the velocity of approach is zero. The frequency n of the sound emitted, and the frequency n' of the sound that is heard, are interrelated by

$$\frac{n'}{n} = \frac{S + s}{S}$$

S being the velocity of the sound and s that at which the car approaches the observer. When a star is approaching the earth, the frequencies of the light waves are increased in a similar way. Therefore the positions of all the spectral lines are shifted toward the blue end of the spectrum. If the star is moving away from the earth, its spectral lines are shifted oppositely toward the red end of the spectrum. The velocity of the star, along the line of sight, may be determined by measuring the amount of this shift.

337. The Milky Way. At the beginning of the twentieth century the distances of only about one hundred of the nearer stars were known. During the last forty years, the telescope, spectroscope, and other devices have been perfected so much that stars can be studied that are millions of light-years away. The new knowledge thus achieved staggers the imagination. Copernicus and Galileo showed that the earth is merely one of several tiny planets circling around the sun. We now know that the sun itself is a rather mediocre member of a stellar cluster which we call the Milky Way. In this cluster more than a billion stars are dispersed through a disk shaped somewhat like a watch. The disk is many thousand light-years wide and perhaps one-tenth as thick. If one looks at the Milky Way, his line of sight is in the plane of the disk. A vast number of stars are seen, most of them too distant to be distinguished separately. Shifting the line of sight 90°, relatively few stars are seen because one is looking through the narrow part of the disk.

338. "Beyond the Milky Way." Most of the stars appear as mere single points of light even through the most powerful telescope, but some cloudlike objects called nebulae are seen which prove to be star clusters. The nearest of these outside our own system is Andromeda, which is visible to the naked eye and is about one million light-years distant. From the evidence secured by huge modern telescopes, thousands and even millions of nebulae are known to exist. Some of them are globular, some disk shaped, and some, like Andromeda, are gigantic spiral pinwheels revolving in space. Our own Milky Way is one of these clusters and may be a spiral nebula.

SUMMARY

The light from an incandescent solid is dispersed by a prism into a continuous spectrum of rainbow hues. That from a luminous gas forms a bright-line spectrum. A gas or vapor strongly absorbs light of the same frequencies that the gas or vapor would emit. A liquid or solid absorbs light of a wide range of frequencies, hence the transmitted light forms a dark-band spectrum.

Chromatic aberration is the failure of a lens to converge, at a point, light of different colors. Chromatic aberration is avoided by using a combination of lenses made of glasses having different dispersive powers.

A "pure" spectrum is one in which radiations of different wave lengths do not overlap.

Fraunhofer lines are dark lines in the sun's spectrum caused by absorption in the sun's atmosphere.

REVIEW QUESTIONS

1. Describe Newton's experiments with the prism.
2. Explain the production of the rainbow.
3. Devise an arrangement of mirrors by which the light of the spectrum could be concentrated at one part of a screen. What would be the color of the image thus produced?

4. What is chromatic aberration? How can it be avoided?

5. Make a sketch of a spectroscope and explain the purpose of each part.

6. State the conditions under which (*a*) a continuous spectrum, (*b*) a bright-line spectrum, (*c*) a dark-line spectrum, (*d*) a dark-band spectrum are produced.

7. A star gives out a bright-line spectrum. What is the physical state of its surface?

8. If you were given some calcium and a mixture of chemicals, how could you find out: (*a*) Whether or not calcium is present in the mixture? (*b*) How much is present?

9. A glove was found at the scene of a murder. It was claimed that this glove belonged to a worker in a lead mill. How could the spectroscope help to decide the question?

10. What information do the Fraunhofer lines yield as to the sun? Describe the discovery of helium.

11. Discuss the service of the spectroscope to astronomy.

CHAPTER XXXV

COLOR, DIFFRACTION, AND INTERFERENCE

Newton's famous experiment showed that sunlight can be dispersed into rainbow hues and that these recombine to give white light. The hues of the spectrum can be combined in various proportions to yield not only white light, but also all others, such as cerise, magenta, heliotrope, and lavender. Moreover, the sensation of white may be caused by mixing lights of two colors only. Such pairs are termed **complementary**. For example, blue and red are complementary, also, green and purple. The three hues red, green, and violet—the so-called primary hues—are especially important because they can be combined to give any color.

339. Maxwell's Color Triangle. The triangle represented in Fig. 1 is highly convenient in discussing the blending of colored lights.

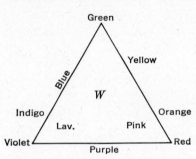

FIG. 1.—Maxwell's color triangle.

Notice that the hues of the spectrum are arranged in their proper order along the two upper sides of the triangle, the three primary hues being at the corners. Any color listed along the sides of the figure can be produced by mixing lights of the colors which are adjacent. Thus green and orange give yellow; red and violet, purple; indigo and green, blue. White light, resulting from a mixture of the others, is represented by the W at the center of the triangle.

By the mixture of white light with colored light, the various **tints** are developed. Thus, in the triangle we see that white and red give pink. White and violet yield the tint called lavender.

340. Colors by Subtraction. What causes the change of color produced when sunlight passes through a piece of red glass? The answer to this question is found by interposing the glass in a beam of sunlight which is dispersed into a spectrum by means of a prism. Then the yellow, green, and blue will fade out from the spectrum and only the red remains. Thus it is shown that the reddening of the beam is caused by the **absorption** of the light of other hues. Similarly, a piece of green glass absorbs the red, yellow, and blue light.

The colors of objects depend upon the hues of the light which they send to the eye. A white rose reflects all the colors of sunlight about equally. Place it in the red part of the spectrum and it seems red, but in the blue part it seems blue. A red rose reflects red light, but it absorbs the green and blue. Hence it shows its natural color in the red part of the spectrum, but in the other regions it seems black. Evidently, then, the apparent color of a body depends upon the illumination. A person buying a necktie or scarf needs to keep this fact in mind, for the light from an ordinary tungsten lamp is more yellow than daylight and the appearance of the cloth may alter greatly when taken out of doors. Sometimes "daylight" tungsten lamps with slightly blue bulbs are used for illumination. The glass absorbs part of the yellow and red and the transmitted radiations have about the same relative intensities as sunlight.

341. Mixing Dyes and Pigments. When white clothes are washed, they become yellow because of iron and other impurities. The laundress adds to the water a trace of blue dye some of which is deposited in the cloth. This dye absorbs some of the yellow and red light, so that the cloth appears more nearly white. Artists are highly skilled in mixing pigments so as to achieve desired colors. For example, a blue paint absorbs most of the incident light except the **green**, blue, and violet. Yellow paint absorbs all but the **green**, yellow, and red. The mixed pigments appear green, for this is the only hue that is reflected.

Shades are produced by mixing black pigment with others of different colors. Thus black and white give gray; blue and black, navy-blue; yellow and gray, brown; red and brown, maroon. The sensation of black cannot be produced by light, so that it is impossible to get shades by mixing lights of different hues.

So much light is absorbed by mixed pigments that the pictures are dull. More vivid effects are achieved in the "pointilism" system of painting in which the pigments are not mingled. Instead, small dots of paint are placed so close together without overlapping that the eye cannot distinguish them but sees the blended resultant color. For instance, blue pigment reflects violet, blue, and green light; yellow pigment, green, yellow, and red. When the two pigments are applied in small dots close together, the green predominates in the reflected light. The combination of other hues produces the sensation of white. Paintings so executed seem more luminous than those in which the pigments are mixed.

342. Motion Pictures in Color. The following method is commonly used for the production of commercial motion pictures in color. A device placed behind the lens of the camera produces three separate images, side by side, on three motion-picture films. Light absorbing "filters" are interposed in the three beams so that the films are "blackened" by lights of different hues. One film is then immersed in a blue dye, another in a yellow dye, and the third in a purple dye. In each bath the dye adheres to the film only at the regions that were exposed to the light. Then the three films are used, one after the other, to transfer the three colors onto a fourth film, which is employed for projecting the pictures. The part of the film that should be blue will receive blue dye only, parts that should be yellow will receive yellow, and purple will be purple. Regions that are to be white receive no dye at all, and the black parts will receive all three colors. A green surface will be coated with both blue and yellow dye, for, as explained in the preceding section, one dye transmits violet and green, the other green and red. The combination therefore transmits green only. The reader can figure out what dyes must be superimposed to reproduce the several colors listed in the preceding section.

DIFFRACTION

343. What is Diffraction? When waves pass near the edge of an obstacle, they deviate into the shadow of the obstacle. This bending

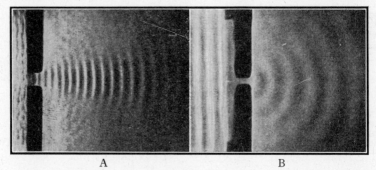

A   B

Fig. 2.—Diffraction of ripples by slits. The diffraction is pronounced when the aperture is small compared with the wave length.

or deviation is called **diffraction**. Its most familiar examples are in sound. When the music from a distant band enters the open window of a room, the sound does not travel straight forward in a well-defined beam, but is diffracted and spreads out sidewise. Try to shut off the noise of a radio by holding a book between your ear and the source. You will find that it causes little decrease in the loudness of the sound for the waves pass around the book quite readily. The amount of deviation or diffraction produced at an opening depends upon the wideness of the aperture. This may be demonstrated by causing ripples on the surface of a pool of water to pass through a slit. In Fig. 2A the aperture is wide and the waves travel forward, spreading out but slightly at the edges. In 2B the opening is narrower, and the diffraction very great. **In all kinds of wave motion diffraction effects are considerable when the aperture is small compared with the wave length.**

We shall see presently that the wave lengths of light are but a few hundred-thousandths of an inch, hence the diffraction of light at most apertures is negligibly small. To demonstrate the diffraction of light look between two fingers at a distant, small source such as an electric arc. Then gradually move them toward each other until the opening is closed. Just before the light is cut off, you will notice that the source seems to broaden out. This is because the narrow beam spreads out sidewise in passing through the narrow slit.

344. The Resolution of Images by a Lens. When an automobile is a mile or more away, its two headlights are seen as one; but when it is closer, the two are seen separately and the images are said to be resolved. If the observer looks through a telescope or field glass he can see the separate images when the car is much farther away because the aperture of the telescope lens is larger than that of the eye. Suppose that a beam of light from a distant star is incident on a lens which converges the light to form an image. The light will be diffracted at the edge of the lens, and part of it will be deviated outward but the circular image is so small that it seems to be a mere point. Now place a screen with a circular opening before the lens. The diffraction will be greater than before, there will be more bending of the light, and the image will occupy a considerable area.

Many of the stars which we see with the naked eye are double. They appear to be single because their images overlap on the retina. Giant astronomical telescopes having objective lenses with great apertures can separate the images of these stars. The great 17-ft. telescope at Mount Palomar, California, could produce separate images of two candles, 1 ft., apart, at a distance of several thousand miles.

345. Resolution and the Microscope. When a biologist uses a microscope to study cells, he wishes to see the minute details of their structures and so he needs an instrument which has high "resolving power." To this end, the aperture of the objective lens should be large as compared with the focal length. Moreover, he finds it advisable to use blue light for illumination rather than red. The blue light, being of shorter wave length, is less diffracted at the edges of the lens. Hence the diffraction patterns are smaller and better resolution is obtained.

346. The Scattering of Light. A beam of sunlight admitted to a darkened room reveals small motes or dust particles which scatter the light sidewise. Blow some smoke into the air, increasing the number of particles, and the amount of scattered light will increase. The characteristics of the scattered light depend upon the size of the particles.

When they are very large, compared with the wave length, light of all colors is scattered equally, but when they are small the blue light is scattered more than the red. The smoke from a cigarette seems blue because the particles are very small and do not scatter red light. Cigarette smoke which has been inhaled and then expelled is white because the particles have grown larger by the deposition of water vapor, so that they scatter light of all colors about equally.

The scattering of light accounts for many striking atmospheric phenomena. Great cumulus clouds seen on a summer's day are white because the water droplets are large enough to scatter all colors equally.

Fig. 3.—Downtown Pittsburgh on a foggy day. At left, photographed by infra-red, at right, by light. (Courtesy of Pittsburgh Press.)

The sky is blue because the air molecules and other particles are extremely small so that they scatter blue light much more than red. Red sunsets are seen because the clouds through which the sunlight passes scatter the blue light sideways and transmit red light to the observer. Camera films have been devised which are sensitive to the long-wave, infra-red radiations. These radiations are transmitted readily through fog and smoke of moderate density (Fig. 3).

INTERFERENCE

347. What is Interference? When two groups of waves are incident at a point, they are said to **interfere** and the resulting waves may have greater or less amplitude than either. To demonstrate interference, tie two ropes to a third one as represented in Fig. 4 and vibrate the two ends E and E' in unison. Then the waves traveling upward along the ropes will arrive at F in step or in phase and they will cause large waves in the single rope. Vibrate the ropes oppositely as in B and the waves will counteract each other at F so that no motion is produced in the single rope.

To illustrate interference of water waves, drop stones into a quiet pool at A and B (Fig. 5) so as to cause a series of circular waves. Consider the effects of these waves in causing erosion at the shore of the pool. The point C is equidistant from A and B so that crests will always arrive there in step. The resulting waves will be relatively high, and they cause considerable erosion. The point D is one-half wave length farther from one source than from the other. Therefore when a crest arrives from A, a trough will arrive from B. The two will counteract each other. Notice next the point E which is **one wave length** farther from one center than the other. Here again crests from the two sources arrive simultaneously and the resultant waves are higher than at D. By similar reasoning, it will be seen that there are other regions of maximum erosion and other regions where it is minimum.

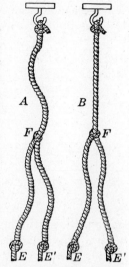

Fig. 4.—Interference. In A the two waves combine to cause waves of greater amplitude beyond F. In B, the two waves annul each other beyond F.

348. Interference of Light. The following experiment was performed by an English physician, Dr. Thomas Young, early in the nineteenth century. Its result strongly favored the theory that light is a form of wave motion.

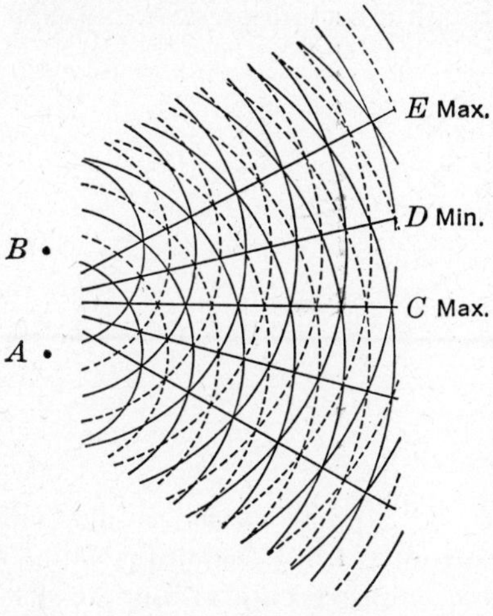

Let a beam of red light be incident on a slit in a screen. The light passing through this aperture is diffracted and illuminates a visiting card in which there are two slits very close together (Fig. 6). The light from these two openings falls on a third screen, producing interference. The explanation is similar to that given for the water waves. The point D is equidistant from each slit so that the two beams reinforce each other, causing a maximum of illumination. F is one wave length

Fig. 5.—Interference of water waves.

farther from one slit than the other, and the beams are in phase, producing a second maximum. Between these two points there is a region where the waves are out of phase and hence there is a minimum illumi-

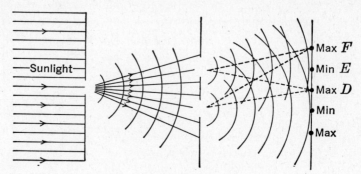

FIG. 6.—Interference of light.

nation. By continuing this reasoning, the reader will see why there are several bright and dark bands.

349. The Diffraction Grating. The wave lengths of light can be measured by means of a **diffraction grating**. One form is essentially an opaque screen in which there are numerous equidistant slits (Fig. 7). Let a beam of light of wave length λ be incident normally on this screen. The light passing through these narrow slits is diffracted, hence the name of the grating. Consider that part of the radiation from these slits which is diffracted through a certain angle θ. Suppose

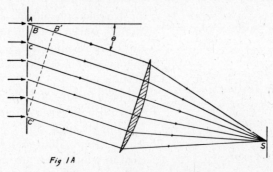

Fig 1A

FIG. 7.—A diffraction grating.

that the angle is so chosen that the distance from the upper slit to the lens of a telescope is just one wave length greater than the distance of the next slit. Then each wave from the slit C will reach the lens at the same instant as the preceding wave that left A. Hence the two will be in phase. Similarly, waves from the second slit will be in phase with those from the third one. In fact, the waves from all the slits will reach the lens in phase so that they will produce a great effect at S and a bright image will be seen through the eyepiece. If the telescope is set at some slightly smaller or larger angle the different waves will be out of phase when they reach the lens, and will counteract each other, producing no disturbance at the point where they converge.

The relationship between the wave length λ, the distance d between adjacent slits, and the angle of diffraction θ is given by

$$\frac{\lambda}{d} = \sin \theta$$

Example. The distance between adjacent slits of a grating is 0.000090 cm. The angle of diffraction θ is found to be 30°. What is the wave length of the light?

$$\sin \theta = \lambda/d$$
$$0.50 = \lambda/0.000090 \text{ cm.}$$
$$\lambda = 0.000045 \text{ cm.}$$

350. Derivation of the Diffraction Grating Formula. In Fig. 8 let the path from A to the lens be one wave length λ greater than that from C, and let d be the distance between the two slits. In the triangle ABC,

$$AB/AC = \lambda/d = \sin ACB$$

But ACB equals θ, the angle of diffraction. Hence

$$\sin \theta = \lambda/d$$

Fig. 8.

The student can show that there is another, larger angle of diffraction θ_2 for which the difference in path for adjacent beams is 2λ and there will be a maximum reinforcement if

$$\sin \theta_2 = 2\lambda/d$$

In general, a bright image is formed if the difference in path is $n\lambda$, where $n = 1, 2, 3. \ldots$ The number n is called the "order" of the interference band or line.

TABLE I

WAVE LENGTHS OF SPECTRAL LINES

(1 Micron = 10,000 Angstroms = 10^{-4} cm.)

	Centimeters	Microns
Fraunhofer red line A............................	0.00007594	0.7594
Red cadmium line (in vacuum) as determined by Michelson....................................	.000064384702	
Yellow, sodium D lines		
D_1..	.00005896	.5896
D_2..	.00005890	.5890
Yellow mercury lines........................... {	.00005791	.5791
	.00005770	.5770
Green mercury lines............................	.00005461	.5461
Fraunhofer K line in extreme violet.............	.00003934	.3934

351. Colors by Interference. Strange to relate, the colors of the peacock's feathers, of soap bubbles, and the iridescence of the pearl are not due to pigments or other coloring matter. The effects are produced by thin, nearly transparent, films on the surfaces. Part of the incident light is reflected at the first surface, the remainder going through and being reflected at the second one. The eye receives two reflected beams which have traveled different distances and may therefore either reinforce or oppose each other. After a rain, pools of oil are often spread out into thin films over the highway. Such surfaces display gorgeous colors. Suppose that red light of a certain wave length incident on the film is partly reflected at the upper surface of the film and partly at the lower one. The light from the second surface is retarded so that the two reflected wave trains may either reinforce or oppose each other. If they are exactly in phase, the surface seems red; if they are opposite it seems black; hence alternate bands of red and black are observed. When the surface is illuminated with white light, the colors of the rainbow are seen, for the radiations of different wave lengths are selectively reflected at different regions.

352. Light Waves—The Physicist's Foot Rule. The bright interference bands formed by two reflecting surfaces are often used in measuring small distances. Fig. 9 represents a beam of light of a certain wave length incident on two adjacent surfaces. Part of the light is reflected at the upper surface and part at the lower one. Suppose that the pairs of reflected rays are in phase at A, B, C, and D so that bright bands are seen there. The distance to the upper plate at B is one-half wave length smaller than at C. If the lower plate is moved downward, away from the upper one, the bright band at C must move to the left, for the distance of separation where this bright line is seen must always be constant. If the plate is lowered through a distance equal to one-half wave length, C will move to the position formerly occupied by B (Why?) As the motion is continued, other bands move to the left past this point, and by counting them the total displacement in wave lengths of light can be measured. Distances as small as one millionth of an inch can be determined in this manner. Little wonder that light waves are often called "the physicist's foot rule."

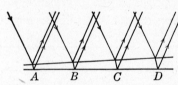
FIG. 9.—Formation of Interference Bands.

353. Invisible Radiations. The word light is properly applied only to those radiations which are capable of causing vision. There are others which do not affect the retina. Among these are radio waves, infra-red radiation, ultra-violet rays, and X-rays. Radio waves and X-rays will be discussed later.

354. Infra-Red Radiations. Produce a spectrum of sunlight by means of a prism, and place the blackened bulb of a thermometer in the band of color. Some of the radiations will be absorbed and the temperature will rise. Move a bulb into the region just beyond the red and the heating will be quite evident. This demonstrates the existence of an **infra-red** spectrum of invisible radiations. Their wave lengths can be measured by means of a diffraction grating. When a fire is kindled in a stove, at first there is but little radiation and one does not notice it. The metal becomes hotter and the bystanders move farther away so as to diminish the amount of radiation which they receive. Later the metal may become red hot so that light is emitted in addition to the invisible rays. If the temperature were increased far enough, the metal would become white hot and the total radiations, visible and invisible, would be very great.

355. The Ultra-Violet Spectrum. When a thermometer bulb is shifted from the visible part of the sun's spectrum to a region just beyond the violet, the heating decreases greatly, but it is still appreciable. This proves that the sun emits "ultra-violet" radiations. The ultra-violet rays are more effective than light in causing chemical changes. A piece of sensitized photographic paper placed in the ultra-violet part of the spectrum is blackened more than when placed in the visible region. The invisible radiations cause some substances to "fluoresce" or emit visible light without being appreciably heated. For example, a picture drawn with vaseline as "paint" is invisible under ordinary illumination, but it stands out vividly when "black light" or ultra-violet radiations are incident upon it.

356. Applications of Ultra-Violet Radiations. Light is effective in killing some germs, but ultra-violet rays are much more potent. They are used in sterilizing water and milk. Their effect on animals may be beneficial or harmful. On the one hand, they may produce excessive sunburn and cause serious illness; on the other, they develop a protective coating of tan. One extremely important function is to prevent rickets by aiding nature in putting lime into the bones. For this reason some farmers use mercury-arc lamps in winter to supply the "health rays" to rapidly growing pigs and chickens. Children need ultra-violet radiations, and much of the window glass made nowadays transmits the health rays of sunlight. However, in most cities, the smoke and dust in the atmosphere absorb them, and many cases of rickets occur because of a deficiency of vitamins. Fortunately, a substance, ergosterol, which is a source of the vitamins, is found in cod-liver oil and in some foods which are recommended for children. The amount of vitamins from these substances may be greatly increased by exposing them to ultra-violet radiations.

SUMMARY

Lights of three "primary" hues, violet, green, and red, can be mixed in varying proportions so as to produce all other colors. The colors of objects seen by reflected light depend upon the nature of the illumination and also upon the radiations which are absorbed.

When waves pass near an obstacle, they are *diffracted* and some of the wave energy travels into the "shadow" of the obstacle. Waves passing through an aperture are diffracted, the amount depending on their wave length and the size of the opening. Diffraction is very great when the aperture is smaller than the wave length.

When the images of two objects do not overlap, the two are said to be "resolved." The ability of a lens to resolve two point sources depends upon the aperture and upon the wave length of the light.

Small particles reflect or "scatter" light sidewise. Particles which are small compared with the wave length scatter blue light more than red. Larger particles scatter all the light about equally.

When waves which have traveled different distances arrive at a point they "interfere" and the resultant effect may be greater or less than that produced by either train of waves alone.

The diffraction grating is a series of equidistant apertures in a screen. When light waves pass through it and are focused by a lens they produce maximum illumination (a) along the direction of the incident beam and (b) if diffracted through an angle θ such that $\sin \theta$ equals λ/d, λ being the wave length and d the distance between adjacent slits.

Interference of light may be produced by a partially reflecting film near a surface. Part of the incident light is reflected at the film and part at the surface. Two reflected beams interfere. If they are in phase maximum illumination results. When white light is incident on the surfaces, rainbow colors appear.

Radio waves, infra-red radiations, ultra-violet, X-rays, and gamma rays are of the same nature as light but of different wave lengths. They do not affect the retina to cause sight.

REVIEW QUESTIONS

1. Discuss color mixing and the colors of objects seen by reflected light.

2. An artist uses red, green, violet, white, and black paints, placing the dots close together. How can he produce the following colors: (a) yellow, (b) purple, (c) pink, (d) brown?

3. Explain the blue color of water in a lake, and that of the sky; also the red of the sunset, and the white of snowflakes.

4. Discuss diffraction.

5. Explain why the two lights of a distant automobile are seen as one. Why does a telescope enable the observer to see them separately?

6. What is interference?

7. Show how wave lengths of light are measured by the diffraction grating. How does the grating utilize (a) diffraction and (b) interference?

8. Explain the colored bands seen on oil film.

PROBLEMS

1. An observer looks at a distant source of green light (λ = 0.00005 cm.) through a silk handkerchief and sees a bright diffracted beam near the central beam. The sine of the angle between the two beams is 1/500. (a) What is the distance between the adjacent apertures in the cloth? (b) How many apertures are there per centimeter?

2′. In a diffraction grating the distance between adjacent apertures is 1/10,000 cm. At what angle would light of wave length 0.000050 cm. be diffracted and form an image if the difference of path for beams from adjacent slits were one wave length?

3″. A flat plate glass is placed on another, horizontal plate, the two being not exactly parallel. The system is illuminated by a vertical beam of yellow light of wave length 0.00006 cm. Twelve of the diffraction bands extend over a space 1 cm. wide. (a) How much farther apart are the plates at one end of the space than at the other end? (b) How many bands would occupy the space if water (index of refraction 4/3) filled the gap between the plates? (c) If red light of longer wave length were used, would there be more or fewer bands per centimeter?

CHAPTER XXXVI

POLARIZED LIGHT

Diffraction and interference give evidence in favor of the wave theory of light, but they give no hint as to whether the waves are transverse like those in a stretched rope or compressional like sound waves. The answer to this question is found in the phenomena of **polarization** which will now be described.

357. What are Polarized Waves? Vibrate one end of a long horizontal rope in a vertical direction so that waves travel along it. Each

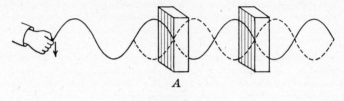

A

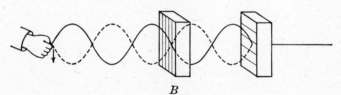

B

FIG. 1.—Polarized transverse waves in a rope pass through the slots when they are parallel to the line of vibration.

particle of the rope is caused to oscillate up and down on a straight line. All these lines lie in the same vertical plane, and the waves are said to be **plane polarized.** Now vibrate the rope up and down and sideways, at all possible angles. Each particle will also move in a random manner and the waves are unpolarized.

Polarized waves are transverse waves in which the particles vibrate repeatedly on the same line or path.

Polarized waves in the rope can also be produced by passing it through a slot in a grating. Vibrate the end up and down and sidewise in random directions as before, causing unpolarized waves. The slot prevents the sideways motion but permits vertical vibrations to pass through. Hence plane polarized waves only are transmitted through the opening.

Pass the rope through a second slot, beyond the first one, the two being parallel (Fig. 1A). The vertical vibrations will pass through both slots freely. Turn the second slot to a horizontal position and it will stop the waves (Fig. 1B). Then perform a similar experiment replacing the cord by a long spiral spring, but set up compressional waves in it. In this experiment the waves will pass through freely whether the slots are vertical or horizontal. Hence an arrangement of slots can cut off transverse waves, but not those that are compressional.

358. Light Waves are Transverse. The following experiment leads to the belief that light waves are transverse. Look through two tour-

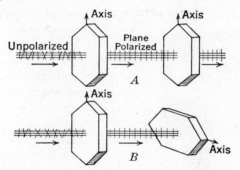

Fig. 2.—Two tourmaline crystals, are transparent when their axes are parallel but opaque when they are at right angles to each other.

maline crystals at a lamp, the two having their longer sides parallel (Fig. 2). Then a good deal of light is transmitted. Rotate the second crystal 90° about the beam as an axis, and the light is cut off.

The light incident on the first crystal is unpolarized, its vibrations being up and down and sidewise in random directions. The tourmaline crystal has the remarkable property of absorbing all the sidewise components of the vibrations and transmitting only plane-polarized light. This passes through the second crystal when it is vertical, but it is absorbed when the crystal is rotated 90°. If the waves were compressional, like sound, they would pass through equally freely in both cases.

359. Double Refraction. When a beam of light is incident obliquely on a block of glass, part of the light is refracted in a single beam. However, when incident on a crystal of Iceland spar (calcium carbonate), it is **doubly refracted** so that two beams enter the crystal (Fig. 3). Look through the crystal at an illuminated pinhole, and you will see two images. Examine their light through a tourmaline and turn it about the beams as an axis. When the tourmaline is vertical the beam E is extinguished and when it is horizontal the other one disappears and only E is seen. This proves that the two are polarized and that their planes of vibration are at right angles to each other.

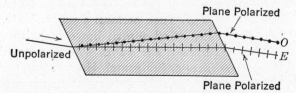

FIG. 3.—The incident beam is doubly refracted by the crystal.

360. The Doubly Refracted Beams Travel at Different Speeds. The fact that the beams are refracted at different angles proves that they

FIG. 4.—Double refraction. (Courtesy of Central Scientific Company)

travel at two speeds for they have two indices of refraction. An analogy will aid in explaining why the speeds are unequal. A piece of wood can be cut more easily parallel to the grain than across the grain. It can be compressed more easily in one direction than the other. If it were transparent, like glass, we should expect light waves vibrating parallel to the grain to travel at a different speed from that of the waves vibrating at right angles to it. Now a piece of Iceland spar resembles a piece of wood in that it splits readily along certain "cleavage planes." It is not surprising, therefore that light waves vibrating in one direction have a different speed from those vibrating in a direction at right angles to it.

361. The Polaroid. Tourmaline, a semi-precious gem, is too expensive for wide use in producing and detecting polarized light. The recently invented polaroid consists of a transparent film mounted between two glass plates. In this film millions of needle-like microscopic crystals are embedded, all their axes being parallel to each other. Each tiny crystal acts like a tourmaline, so that the polaroid transmits plane-polarized light. Two polaroids are transparent when their axes are

FIG. 5.—The two "crossed" polaroids are opaque.

parallel, but they are opaque when the axes are "crossed" at right angles (Fig. 5).

362. The Nicol Prism. The Nicol prism, named for its inventor, is often used for producing and detecting polarized light, but it will probably be displaced by the polaroid. It is constructed by sawing a crystal of Iceland spar into two wedge-shaped pieces which are glued together with a cement called Canada balsam. Ordinary unpolarized light, incident on the crystal, is doubly refracted, and the two beams strike the Canada balsam film at slightly different angles. The lower beam, vibrating in the plane of the paper, is mostly transmitted. The upper one, vibrating at right angles to the plane of paper, is incident on the film at an angle greater than the critical angle for the crystal-balsam surface. Hence it is tòtally reflected.

363. Polarization by Reflection. Polarized light can also be produced by reflection. Illuminate a glass plate or a water surface, and using a

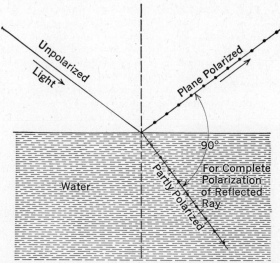

Fig. 6.—The beam reflected at a certain angle is plane polarized. The refracted beam is partly polarized.

polaroid, examine the light reflected at an oblique angle (Fig. 6). Rotating the polaroid will cause the intensity of the transmitted beam to vary, hence it must be partly polarized. Change the angle of reflection, until the reflected beam can be cut off entirely by adjusting the polaroid. In this condition the reflected light is plane polarized. The refracted beam is partly polarized in a plane at right angles to that of the reflected light.

364. Applications of Polarized Light. One of the most important uses of polarized light is the measurement of the concentration of sugar in solutions. This substance, like quinine, quartz, and others, has the property of rotating the plane of vibration of light. Suppose that two polaroids are crossed so that they cut off the light from a sodium flame. Interpose between them a flask containing a solution of ordinary cane sugar, and the illumination is restored. The sugar molecules have rotated the plane of vibration of the light through some angle, say 30°. The second polaroid may be turned through this angle, again cutting off the light. Now suppose that the flask is replaced by another, equal one containing a less concentrated solution which rotates the plane of vibration through only 15°. Then the concentration of sugar is known to be half as great as before.

Another application is the testing of glass for internal strains. Before describing the method, we must understand that a piece of doubly refracting material, inserted between crossed polaroids, will restore the illumination. Place a polaroid in a vertical plane in front of an illuminated pinhole, so that the transmitted light vibrations are in a vertical plane. Then lay a block of Iceland spar against the polaroid, and adjust it so that two light beams are seen. The waves in one beam vibrate upward to the left, but those in the other one vibrate upward toward the right. Another polaroid with its axis horizontal will transmit part of the light in each beam because each has a component of motion in a horizontal direction.

Ordinary glass will not restore the illumination when placed between polaroids crossed in this manner because it has the same properties in all directions. Com-

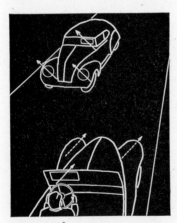

pressed between the jaws of a vise, the molecules are crowded together along one axis and the glass is strained so as to become doubly refracting. When hot glass cools slowly, it is "annealed" so that there is little strain, but if cooled faster, strains are present. A poorly annealed glass goblet is likely to burst into thousands of fragments. Therefore newly manufactured glassware is tested by placing it between crossed polaroids to see if the illumination is restored. If the glass is found to be doubly refracting, and to restore illumination, it is sent back to the ovens to be reheated.

365. Polaroids to Prevent Headlight Glare. It is probable that some day polaroids will be used to eliminate the blinding glare of the headlights of approaching automobiles. Assume that the headlights of the car are equipped with polaroids set at

Fig. 7.—The use of polaroids to prevent headlight glare.

an angle of 45° with the vertical, directed upward to the driver's right. The second driver looks through a screen, which can be pushed aside when not needed. Being set at the same angle, directed upward toward his right, it is at right angles to the direction of the polaroids in the headlights of the other car (Fig. 7). Hence all the light is cut off. Incidentally, the screen will permit the driver to see the light of his own headlights reflected from the roadway, for the plane of its polarization will be parallel to the axis of the polaroid in his screen.

Automobile drivers find polaroid goggles helpful in absorbing sunlight reflected from pavements (Fig. 8).

FIG. 8.—The left-hand picture shows the driver's view without polaroids, the right-hand picture when he wears polaroid goggles.

SUMMARY

A plane-polarized wave is a transverse wave train in which all the vibrations are in a single plane.

In ordinary light the vibrations are in random directions in a plane at right angles to the beam, but in plane-polarized light they are in a single plane parallel to the beam.

Plane-polarized light may be produced by passing ordinary light through a tourmaline crystal or a polaroid.

If light from a tourmaline crystal is incident on a second one the beam can be cut off by setting the second tourmaline with its axis at right angles to the first. This shows that such a crystal transmits light vibrating in one plane only and that light waves are transverse.

A beam of light incident on the surface of a crystal may be doubly refracted, the two beams traveling at different speeds.

A sheet of doubly refracting substance placed between crossed polaroids may restore the illumination.

Light may also be polarized by oblique reflection, in which case the refracted beam is partly polarized.

REVIEW QUESTIONS

1. Define "polarized waves," and describe two ways of producing them in a rope.
2. State evidence indicating that light waves are transverse.
3. What is double refraction, and how is it produced?
4. Describe the action of a tourmaline crystal, of a polaroid, and of a Nicol prism.
5. How can polarized light be produced and detected?
6. How can polarized light be used to detect strains in glass?

ELECTRICITY

CHAPTER XXXVII

ELECTRIC CHARGES

"In Nature's infinite book of secrecy a little I can read."
—SHAKESPEARE.

Introduction. The first record of an experiment in electricity was made by the Greek philosopher Thales (Tháy leez) about 2,600 years ago. He stated that a piece of amber rubbed with fur attracted light objects such as feathers and bits of straw. Thales like the other Greeks loved to speculate, but he made no effort to extend his knowledge of electricity by experimenting. Twenty-two centuries elapsed, empires rose and fell, before there was any progress. Then in the days of Shakespeare and of Galileo came the great scientific awakening. Sir William Gilbert, physician to Queen Elizabeth, began to use the scientific method advocated by Galileo. He showed that many other substances behave as amber does after they are rubbed. Gilbert described this condition by saying that substances are **electrified,** from the Greek word *elektron* for amber. Later, it was found that any two dissimilar substances become electrified or acquire electric charges when they are touched together and then separated. Rubbing is not essential; it merely ensures that large areas of the two substances are brought into contact with each other.

366. Positive and Negative Electricity. Rub two pieces of sealing wax with flannel and suspend one of them by a cord. Bring the other piece close to the first one and the two repel each other. Bring a glass rod which has been rubbed with silk near to the suspended piece of wax and the two attract each other. These experiments demonstrate that there are *two kinds* of electricity. The kind appearing on the glass is arbitrarily called *positive*; that on the wax is called *negative*. Thus **a positively charged body is one that behaves like glass which has been rubbed with silk, and a negatively charged body is one that behaves like wax rubbed with flannel. Like charges repel each other, but unlike charges attract.**

When the charges in a body do not move in any particular direction, they are termed electrostatic; when moving along a wire or other conductor, they constitute an electric current.

367. The Process of Electrification. In discussing what takes place when a body is electrified, keep in mind that, according to present views, an atom is a tiny solar system, the nucleus or "sun" being composed of particles about as massive as the hydrogen atom. Some of these particles in the nucleus are positively charged and are called protons. Others, uncharged, are the neutrons. The planets of the atomic solar system, the electrons, are negatively charged and are about 1/1,840 as massive as a hydrogen atom. An uncharged atom contains equal numbers of protons and electrons.

When a piece of wax is rubbed with flannel, trillions of electrons are transferred from the cloth to the wax, which therefore becomes charged negatively. The flannel, having lost the electrons, has trillions of excess protons. The two are equally but oppositely charged. Notice that the process of electrification does not create electricity, but merely separates electrons from protons.

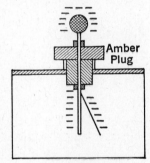

Fig. 1.—A gold leaf electroscope.

368. The Electroscope. A charged wax rod suspended by a cord may be used to test the existence of charges on other bodies. If the charge on the rod is negative and a negatively charged body is brought near, the two repel each other, but the approach of a positively charged object causes attraction. A more sensitive device called an electroscope is made by fastening a thin strip of metal foil to a rod mounted in an amber plug at the top of a box with glass ends (Fig. 1). Rub a wax rod with flannel, charging it negatively. Then rub some of the excess electrons from the wax onto the insulated metal rod. These electrons will distribute themselves over the rod and the gold leaf, causing it to diverge. The angle at which it stands depends upon the amount of electric charge imparted to the electroscope.

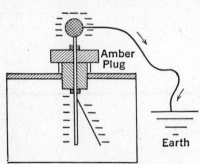

Fig. 2.—Electrons conducted through a wire.

369. Conductors and Non-Conductors. Charge an electroscope negatively and touch its knob with a copper wire which is connected to the earth or to a waterpipe (Fig. 2).

The gold leaf will move downward quickly, showing that the electrons have been carried from the electroscope along the wire to the earth. Electric charges are transferred readily through metals, which are said to be good conductors. Repeat the experiment, replacing the wire by a silk thread, and no motion will be detected. Most substances, like silk, afford great resistance to the passage of charges and are classified as non-conductors or insulators.

370. Why Do Metals Conduct Electricity Readily? In metals some of the electrons are loosely attached to the atoms, and they break loose from time to time, wandering among the "neighbors." When the electroscope was charged negatively, some of the excess free electrons on it, being repelled by those near by, moved over onto the wire. Those invaders repelled other electrons, driving them along the wire. These, in turn, acted on others beyond, so that finally, in the twinkling of an eye, the electroscope was discharged. The reader can see for himself what would happen if the vessel had been charged positively (for example, by contact with a glass rod which had been rubbed with silk).

371. Charging a Body by Induction. A body may be electrified either by rubbing it with silk or flannel or by bringing it into contact with

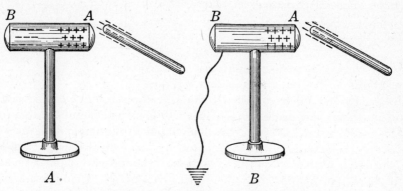

Fig. 3.—Charging an insulated cylinder by induction.

some other charged body. A third important method is by induction. Hold a negatively charged rod near one end of the cylinder (Fig. 3) at a distance of an inch or so. Then the free electrons of the metal will be repelled and will crowd toward the far end of the cylinder. This end is therefore negatively charged and the near end positively. Test the nature of the charges as follows: Touch the cylinder at B with a metal ball mounted on a glass rod for insulation. Then bring the ball into contact with a negatively charged electroscope and the divergence of the gold leaf will increase. This proves that the charge at B is negative.

Touch the ball at A and some of its electrons will move over onto the cylinder so that the ball will be positive. When it is touched against the knob of the electroscope, the gold leaf moves down. After testing the nature of the two charges in this manner, touch the cylinder with a wire connected to earth and electrons will escape. Disconnect the wire, and then remove the wax rod. The charges will be distributed symmetrically over the cylinder. In thus charging the body by induction, no electricity escaped from the wax rod.

372. The Electrophorus. The electrophorus, a convenient device for generating electrostatic charges, gives an illustration of induction. It consists of a flat plate made of sulfur, wax, or some other insulator, and a metal plate with an insulating handle. Rubbing the sulfur with flannel causes its surface to be peppered over with excess electrons

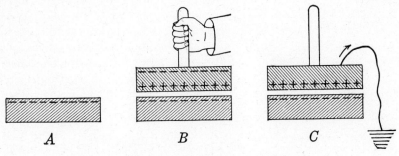

A   B   C

FIG. 4.—Charging an electrophorus by induction.

(Fig. 4). Suppose that the metal plate is placed on the sulfur. Because the surfaces are rough, the two make contact at only a few points, so that only a little of the charge escapes. The remaining excess electrons repel others in the metal, driving them to the upper surface, whence they escape when the metal is touched with a wire connected to earth. Remove the plate and it will cause a large spark when one's hand is moved near to it. The process of charging and discharging may be repeated indefinitely without appreciably diminishing the amount of electricity on the lower plate.

373. Excess Charges Reside on the Outside of a Conductor. Charge an insulated, hollow, metal vessel negatively, and touch a metal ball, suspended by a silk cord, against the outer surface (Fig. 5). The ball will be charged by conduction. Its charge may be tested by means of the electroscope and will be found to be negative. Next lower the ball inside the vessel so as to touch the bottom. Remove it and bring it into contact with the knob of an uncharged electroscope. The leaf will not diverge, hence the ball is uncharged. Repeat the experiment as often as you wish, and the result will always be the same. Electrons will not remain on the ball when it touches the inside surface of the metal. This result might have been predicted, for all the excess electrons on the ball repel one another and they distribute themselves so as to get as far apart as possible, hence they move to the outside of the vessel. Experiments like this prove that **electrostatic charges reside only on the outside of a conductor.**

374. Charges are Most Dense Where the Surface is Most Curved. When an insulated sphere is charged, the electricity is distributed

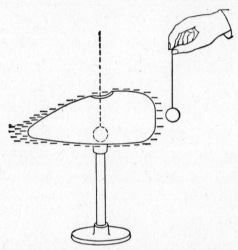

FIG. 5.—Electrostatic charges reside on the outer surface of a conductor and are most numerous at the regions of greatest curvature.

uniformly over the surface but the charges on an egg-shaped conductor (Fig. 5) crowd together at the regions where the surface is most curved. The distribution of the charges can be tested by means of a small metal plate such as a silver dime supported by a silk thread for insulation. Hold the plate first against the flat side of the vessel, then against the knob of an electroscope, noting the deflection of the gold leaf. Repeat the experiment, touching the plate against the curved end of the vessel. More of the electricity is transferred to the plate and the divergence of the gold leaf is greater than before.

375. Charges Escape Readily from Sharp Points. Since charges accumulate more at curved portions of a conducting surface than at flat regions, it follows that the accumulation at a needle point will be very great indeed. In fact, a needle fastened to the surface of a strongly charged body may permit the electricity to escape. This is because the charges at the needle point dislodge electrons from nearby air molecules, and some of these charged particles called "ions" are drawn to the needle, neutralizing its charge. To demonstrate this effect, attach a sewing needle to the knob of an electroscope and charge it so that the leaf stands out nearly at right angles. Hold your finger at a small distance from the needle point, and the gold leaf will move down showing that the charge is escaping.

376. The Van de Graaff Generator. The Van de Graaff generator serves the same purpose as the electrophorus but it is much more

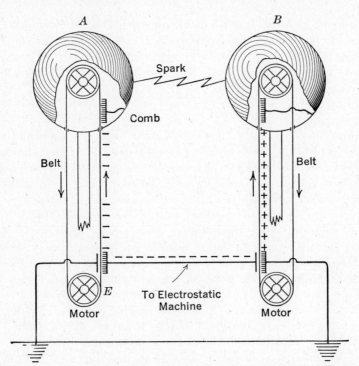

FIG. 6.—A Van de Graaf Electrostatic Generator. (Simplified diagram.)

elaborate. Two hollow metal spheres are supported on insulating columns (Fig. 6). In each column there is a paper or silk belt passing over an upper pulley in the sphere and a lower one which is driven by an electric motor. Let us limit our attention, for the time being, to the left system A. The metal comb E, supported near the belt, is charged negatively by an electrophorus or by other more practical means to be described later. Electric charges escape from the sharp needle points of the comb and are sprayed over onto the belt which carries them upward into the sphere. Within the sphere, the charges escape from the belt to a second comb and are conducted to the outer surface where they accumulate until a miniature lightning discharge occurs to the neighboring sphere.

Now consider the action of the second system B. The lower comb is connected to earth, and the flat plate opposite it is charged negatively. This plate causes electrons to escape from the paper to the comb, and the upward-moving belt carries positive charges upward into the sphere where they attract electrons from the upper comb so that the sphere is charged positively.

The great Van de Graaf machine owned by the Massachusetts Institute of Technology has spheres 15 ft. in diameter, mounted on supports 30 ft. high. It can cause "lightning strokes" 10 ft. long. This machine is to be used in experiments on the disintegration of atoms which are described in the section of new physics.

377. Lightning. During violent storms, the clouds become highly charged with electricity, and gigantic sparks or lightning strokes jump from one cloud to another or to the earth. These sparks heat the air through which they pass, causing it to expand suddenly, producing thunder. The reason for the charging of the clouds is not well understood. It is known that when water drops are broken up by a blast of air the smaller ones are positive, and the larger ones negative. One theory of thunderstorms assumes that raindrops are broken up by violent gusts of wind; the smaller, positively charged drops being carried upward, while the larger negatively charged ones are left behind. In this way, the higher clouds acquire positive charges.

378. Franklin Flew a Kite. When Benjamin Franklin was forty years old, he retired from business and became a gentleman of leisure. For several years he amused himself by making electrical experiments. Using a few pieces of cloth and needles from the sewing room, some pans and bits of wax from the kitchen, he made a discovery and an invention that released men from fear so that Franklin became the Edison of his day. He discovered that electric charges escape more readily from sharp points than from blunt ones, and invented the lightning rod. At that time there was considerable doubt as to the nature of lightning. Franklin suggested that if, as some supposed, it was an electrical phenomenon, the charges might be collected from the clouds by means of a long, pointed rod erected on the roof of a tall building. He sent this suggestion to a friend in England, who presented it to the Royal Society of London. The British scientists gave little heed to the message from the wilds of America, and so Franklin's friend sent it on to Paris where it was warmly received. Soon the exper-

iment was tried and it was conclusively proved that lightning is merely
an electric spark. Meanwhile, Franklin, in far-off Pennsylvania, weary
of waiting, decided to experiment himself. There were no high buildings
in Quaker Philadelphia, and so he made a silk kite which he flew during
a thunderstorm. The lower end of the kite string was attached to a silk
ribbon held by Franklin, who stood in a dry place, so that the electrical
charges could not escape. Soon he was delighted to see that the loose
fibers of the kite string bristled out like the hairs of an angry cat.
When he touched the wet string, he received a painful shock. Later it
was proved that electric charges brought down from the clouds by the
kite string had the same properties as those generated by friction or by
induction. The identity of lightning and the electric spark was
established.

379. Protection from Lightning. Though Franklin performed the
experiments solely to satisfy his curiosity, they quickly proved to have
a practical value. He suggested that houses might be protected from
lightning by mounting on their roofs metal rods connected to earth.
Soon these lightning rods appeared on buildings all over Europe. Formerly the lightning stroke had been regarded as a means of punishment
by an offended deity; thereafter it was considered as a natural phenomenon, like rain or hail, which might be guarded against by well-
understood means.

A building can be perfectly shielded from lightning by surrounding
it on all sides with walls of metal screen. Excellent protection is secured more simply by mounting metal rods, 3 ft. high, connected to
earth, at intervals of 15 ft. or less along the highest parts of a building.
The protective effect of such rods may be demonstrated by placing a
bunsen burner inside a toy house with the top of the burner sticking
out like a chimney through a hole in the roof. Support a metal plate,
connected to a Van de Graaf or other generator, above the roof, and
a spark will jump to the burner, igniting the gas. Now erect a lightning rod, connected to a water faucet, at the other end of the roof,
and the "lightning" will jump to it instead of to the burner.

The efficacy of lightning rods is proved by the fact that steeples,
factory chimneys, and skyscrapers are struck scores of times without
being damaged. During a storm in 1933, the Empire State Building
in New York City was struck 15 times in 15 minutes.

People who fear lightning should remember that a building fitted
with lightning rods gives complete protection, at the street level, at a
distance about two and one-half times its height. For this reason there
is little danger from lightning in large cities. In the open country, keep
away from trees and small sheds, for they are likely to "draw" the

lightning. If you are in an open field, it is advisable to stoop down and be drenched rather than to stand up and be "burned."

380. Dangers from Static Electricity. In cotton mills and paper mills electrical charges are generated when the cloth or paper passes over metal rolls. Sometimes sparks occur which cause disastrous fires. This danger is avoided by humidifying the air so that water films conduct away the electricity from the surfaces. The friction of gasoline flowing through a hose at a filling station may electrify the metal nozzle so that a spark is produced when the nozzle is touched against the gasoline tank of a car. The danger is greatly decreased if the nozzle is "grounded" or connected to earth by a wire. The splashing of gasoline, transported by motor truck, may generate a charge so that the gasoline vapors are ignited when someone starts to open a valve. Often a metal chain is attached to the truck. One end, dangling against the ground, carries away the electrostatic charges. It is very dangerous to rub clothing with a gasoline-soaked cloth, for the friction may generate an electrical charge and cause a spark which ignites the vapor.

SUMMARY

Two dissimilar substances become electrified by contact with each other. Positive charges appear on glass rubbed with silk, and negative charges on wax rubbed with fur.

Like charges repel and unlike charges attract each other.

An atom of ordinary hydrogen is composed of one positively charged proton as a heavy nucleus and one negatively charged electron. The proton is about 1,840 times more massive than the electron. Heavier atoms are believed to be built up of protons, neutrons, and electrons. When a body is negatively charged, it has excess electrons; if positively charged, there is a deficiency of electrons.

In metallic conductors many of the electrons are free to travel about among the atoms like molecules of a gas.

When electric charges are "static" they do not progress in any definite direction. Excess electrostatic charges reside on the outer surface of a conductor, their density being greatest at regions of greatest curvature.

In charging a body A negatively by induction, another positively charged body B is brought near to it and electrons travel from the earth to the body A, if the body is grounded. Meanwhile the charge of B does not change.

An ion is a charged particle. The molecules of a gas can be ionized by means of an intense electric field which detaches electrons from certain molecules.

REVIEW QUESTIONS

1. Define "positive" and "negative" electric charge. Describe three ways of charging a body.

2. Why do metals conduct electricity better than non-metals?

3. Why do electric charges tend to escape from sharp points more readily than from blunt ones?

4. Describe the operation of the Van de Graaff generator.

5. What were the contributions of Benjamin Franklin to electrical science?

CHAPTER XXXVIII

AMPERES, COULOMBS, AND OHMS

In the preceding chapter some of the properties of "static" electricity were presented. Now we shall deal with electric currents consisting of charges traveling through a conductor. The electrostatic machine represented in Fig. 1 may be used to generate an electric

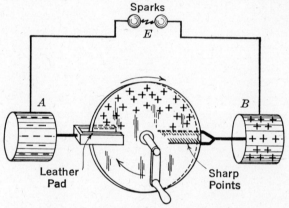

FIG. 1.—A simple electrostatic generator.

current. A leather pad pushes against one face of a circular glass plate which is turned by means of a crank. Electrons are transferred from the plate to the leather pad and thence to the cylinder A, charging it negatively. The excess protons on the glass are forced around to B where there is a metal comb with needle-point teeth. From the sharp needle points the protons attract electrons which jump the air gap, so that the cylinder, having lost electrons, is charged positively. As the rotation continues, the opposite charges accumulate until a spark jumps across the gap at E. Then the charges increase again and other sparks occur. Interconnect the two knobs with a wire, and there will be a constant flow of electricity, that is, a constant electric current.

It is more convenient to produce a current by means of a dry cell (Fig. 2A). Its central electrode, made of carbon, is charged positively, and the outer, zinc, electrode is negative. Connect the two electrodes by means of a wire and electrons will flow from zinc to carbon. The

352

action of the cell in causing a flow of electrons is like that of a pump which produces a flow of water in a pipe (Fig. 2B). The pump does not create the water, but merely causes it to move. Similarly, the dry cell does not create the electrons, but merely forces them to travel through the wire.

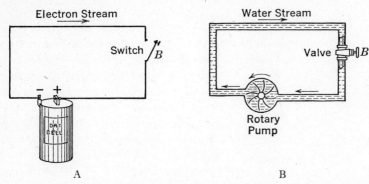

Electron Stream   Water Stream

Switch   Valve

Rotary
Pump

A   B

Fig. 2.—(A) A dry cell forces electric charges to travel around a circuit. (B) A pump causes water to circulate.

When the electrodes of the cell are interconnected by a wire and electricity flows, we say that the circuit is closed, but when there is a break in the wire so that the current is zero, the circuit is open. The switch B in Fig. 2A, used to open the circuit, serves the same purpose as a valve in a waterpipe (Fig. 2B).

381. Measuring Electric Currents—What is an Ampere? Electric currents may be measured by several effects which they produce. One

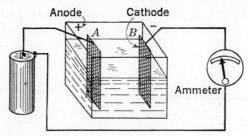

Anode   Cathode

Ammeter

Fig. 3.—The strength of an electric current may be measured by its electroplating effect.

of these is the "electrolytic" or electroplating effect. Connect the electrodes of a dry cell to two silver plates which are immersed in a water solution of silver nitrate (Fig. 3). Then silver atoms will dissolve from the positive plate A and silver atoms will be deposited on the negative plate B. The amount of silver that is deposited at B is proportional to the strength of the current and to the time. This fact is used in defining the unit of current called the international ampere.

The international ampere is that constant current which in 1 sec. liberates 0.001118 gram of silver from a silver nitrate solution. Thus:

1 amp. in   1 sec. liberates 0.001118 gram of silver.
1 amp. in 1,000 sec. liberates 1.118   grams of silver.

The electroplating method is too inconvenient for ordinary service in measuring electric currents. The silver plate must be weighed twice, once before and again after the circuit is

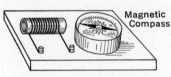

FIG. 4.—A simple ammeter.

closed. Then, too, the time of flow must be determined. Currents are usually measured by means of ammeters. Most ammeters use the magnetizing effect of a current, which will be more fully discussed presently. A crude ammeter is made by wrapping a piece of insulated wire into a spiral coil which is placed with one end near a magnetic compass (Fig. 4). A current through the wire magnetizes the coil and causes it to attract one pole of the compass needle. The greater the current, the greater will be the deflection of the needle, so that the current is measured by the angle through which the needle turns. Other more practical ammeters will be described later.

382. The Coulomb—a Unit of Quantity. The amount of electricity transferred past a point on a wire depends upon two factors, the strength of the current, and the time of flow. A current of 1 amp. transfers just as much electrical charge in 10 sec. as a current of 10 amp. in 1 sec. **The amount of charge transferred by 1 amp. in 1 sec. is called a coulomb.**

$$\text{Thus, Quantity} = \text{Current} \times \text{Time}$$
$$Q = I \times t$$
$$1 \text{ coulomb} = 1 \text{ amp-sec.}$$
$$\text{Current} = \text{Quantity/Time}$$
$$I = Q/t$$
$$1 \text{ amp.} = 1 \text{ coulomb/sec.}$$

Later it will be shown that 1 coulomb of negative charge consists of 6.25 billion billion electrons, so that a current of 1 amp. transfers this enormous number of electrons each second past any section in a wire.

Example. An automobile storage battery delivers a current of 8.0 amp. for 10 hr. What quantity of electricity is transferred?

$Q = I \times t$
  $= 8$ amp. $\times$ 10 hr.
  $= 8.0$ amp. $\times$ 36,000 sec. $= 288,000$ coulombs

383. Electrical Resistance. There are instructive resemblances between the flow of liquids through pipes and of electricity through wires. Connect a long horizontal pipe packed with cotton to an opening near the bottom of a vessel filled with water and measure the amount of water that is delivered per second. Then replace the pipe by one of the same diameter but twice as long and the flow rate will be about one-half as great. Replace the pipe by another of the same length but twice as large in cross section and the flow rate will be doubled. The resistance to the flow of water afforded by the pipe is proportional to its length and inversely proportional to its cross-sectional area.

Connect 20 ft. of No. 30 copper wire to a dry cell, measuring the current by means of an ammeter. Then replace the wire by one of the same diameter but twice as long. The current will be half as great as before. Replace the wire by one of equal length, but twice as large in cross section and the current will be doubled. **The resistance of a wire to the flow of electricity is proportional to its length and inversely proportional to its cross section.**

The resistance R of a conductor of length L and cross section A is given by

$$R = KL/A$$

in which K is the **resistivity** of the substance. It is numerically equal to the resistance of a wire made of the substance, 1 cm. long and 1 cm.^{2} in cross section. Values for several materials are given in Table I.

TABLE I

Resistivities at 20°C. in Millionths of an Ohm-Centimeter

Substance	Millionths of an Ohm-Centimeter	Substance	Millionths of an Ohm-Centimeter
Silver....................	1.47	Nichrome alloy...........	100.
Aluminum..............	2.8	Tungsten................	5.5
Copper.................	1.70	Fused quartz (an excellent	
Iron....................	10.	insulator)	5×10^{24}
Mercury...............	95.783	5% sodium chloride water	
Carbon (lamp filament)...	5000.	solution..............	15
		Slate....................	2×10^{14}
		Plate glass..............	9×10^{19}

384. The International Ohm. In setting up a standard resistance, it is necessary to specify the length of the conductor, its cross-sectional area, the temperature, and the substance of which it is composed. The unit of resistance is the international ohm which is defined as **the resistance at 0°C. of a column of mercury 106.300 cm. long and 1 mm.[2] in cross-sectional area.** Fig. 5 represents the structure of a standard resistance of the dimensions given above. The glass tube, with a capillary bore 1 mm.[2] in cross section, is 106.3 cm. long. Its ends are inserted into large bulbs filled with mercury to make contact with the wires through which the electricity flows.

It is convenient to remember that the resistance of a copper wire 1,000 ft. long and 1/10 in. in diameter is about 1 ohm. Then the resistances of other copper wires can be found by proportion. For example, the resistance of a copper wire 4000 ft. long and 2/10 in. in diameter would also be 1 ohm.

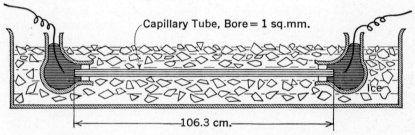

Capillary Tube, Bore = 1 sq.mm.

106.3 cm.

FIG. 5.—A standard mercury column of one-ohm resistance.

385. Resistance and Temperature. The resistance of a conductor depends not only upon its length and cross section, but also upon the temperature. In order to demonstrate this, wrap several feet of thin iron wire onto a piece of asbestos and connect the wire, through an ammeter, to a dry cell. Heat the coil in the flame of a bunsen burner and the current through the wire will diminish because the resistance increases. The resistances of all metallic conductors increase with temperature, but that of most forms of carbon diminishes.

The variation of the resistance of a pure metal with temperature resembles that of the pressure of a gas with temperature (Charles' law). This suggests that the free electrons in a metal behave like a gaseous atmosphere. When the temperature rises, the atomic nuclei vibrate with greater amplitudes. Hence the forward motion of the electrons is impeded, they drift along the wire more slowly, and the resistance increases.

386. Standard Resistances. Coils of wire of known resistance are useful in making electrical measurements. The wires are made of an alloy the resistivity of which varies but little with temperature. Several of the resistance coils are mounted in a "resistance box," so that different coils may be connected into a circuit (Fig. 6). The ends of the wires are soldered into brass blocks mounted side by side. Tapered plugs are inserted between adjacent blocks. When all of them are in place, the electrons flow through the massive bar and the resistance is practically zero. Removing any plug forces the current to traverse one

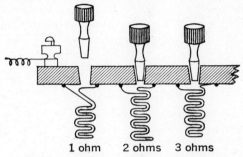

1 ohm   2 ohms   3 ohms

FIG. 6.—Standard resistance coils.

of the coils. For example, if the 1-ohm plug and the 2-ohm plugs are out, the resistance is 3 ohms.

387. The Slide-Wire Rheostat. The current in a circuit may be varied by changing the amount of resistance in the circuit. One way to do this is by means of a slide-wire rheostat. It consists of a spiral coil of wire wound around a tube made of porcelain or some other insulating material (Fig. 7). The electricity enters the coil at one end and leaves it at the movable contact or slider, whence it travels along

FIG. 7.—A slide-wire rheostat. (Courtesy of Chicago Apparatus Company.)

the massive bar and leaves the rheostat. When the slider is at the midpoint as shown, the electricity flows through part of the coil only. When the slider is pushed to the right as far as possible, the current must traverse the entire coil; the resistance is great and the current small. When the slider is at the extreme left, the current does not enter the coil but goes directly along the massive bar. The resistance will therefore be very small and the current large.

SUMMARY

The international ampere is defined as that constant current which deposits 0.001118 gram of silver per second from a silver nitrate solution.

The international ohm is the resistance of a uniform column of mercury 106.300 cm. long and 1 mm.^{2} in cross section, at 0°C.

The resistance R of a conductor of length L and cross section A is given by $R = KL/A$. The "resistivity" K is numerically equal to the resistance of a section of the substance 1 cm. long and 1 cm.^{2} in cross section.

The resistances of most conductors increase with temperature.

REVIEW QUESTIONS

1. Define "international ampere," "international ohm," "international coulomb."

2. Show the resemblances between the production of a water stream by a pump and of an electric current by a dry cell.

3. Show how to measure a current by its electroplating effect.

4. Describe a slide-wire rheostat and a resistance box.

5. Define "resistivity," and show how to compute the resistance of a wire of known length and cross section.

PROBLEMS

1′. A piece of uniform wire 10.0 m. long and 1.00 mm. in diameter has a resistance of 1.00 ohm. Find the resistance of a wire of this material 50 m. long and 0.50 mm. in diameter.

2′. A copper wire of resistance 20 ohms is drawn out so that its length is doubled and its cross section is reduced one-half. What is its resistance afterward?

3′. What is the resistance of a carbon lamp filament 20 cm. long and 1/1,000 cm.^{2} in cross section?

4′. What time would be required for a current of 10 amp. to electroplate a mass of silver equal to that of a dime (2.50 grams) onto a platter?

5. In problem 4, how many coulombs and how many electrons are transferred past a point in the wire?

6′. A trolley wire made of copper is 1,000 m. long and 1.00 cm. in diameter. What is its resistance?

7. The filament of a lamp is 15.7 cm. long and 0.020 cm. in diameter. Its resistance is 12 ohms. What is the resistivity of the material?

CHAPTER XXXIX

POTENTIAL DIFFERENCES

Having discussed some properties of electric currents and resistances, we shall now consider a third very important topic in electricity, potential difference. It is helpful to begin with an analogy between the

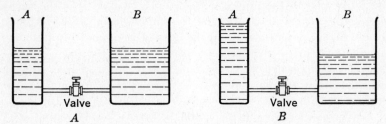

FIG. 1.—Water tends to flow from points of greater elevation to those of lower elevation.

flow of electricity and that of liquids. Suppose that two reservoirs A and B (Fig. 1A) are filled with water to the same level. Then the pressure is the same at the ends of the horizontal pipe which joins them and there is no flow of water. From an energy standpoint, we see that a pound of water in A has just as much potential energy as a pound of water in B. Make the level in A higher than that in B, and water will flow through the pipe from the end where the pressure is higher to the end where it is lower. The water flows in the horizontal pipe from a region of higher pressure to one of lower pressure. Also it flows from a region of higher to one of lower potential.

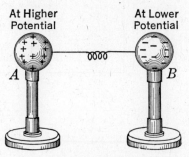

FIG. 2.—Positive electric charges tend to flow from points of greater electrical potential to those of smaller potential.

Now think of a similar situation as to the flow of electricity. Two insulated spheres A and B (Fig. 2) are charged, one positively, the other negatively. Then positive electricity tends to flow from A to B just as the water tended to flow from one vessel to the other. Moreover, a positive charge on A has more elec-

359

trical potential energy than it would have on B. Thus **positive electricity tends to flow from regions of higher to those of lower electrical
potentials.**

In gravitational problems frequently it is assumed that a body at
sea level has zero potential energy, and all other elevations are measured from this level. Usually in electrical theory the electrical potential of the earth is taken as zero, and the potentials of all bodies are
measured with reference to the earth.

The analogy between the flow of water and that of electricity is
faulty in that the positive charges in a wire cannot flow because they
are tightly tied in the nuclei of the atoms. In fact, it is the negative
charges that travel in a wire, and they move from points of lower to
those of higher potentials. From the days of Benjamin Franklin, it has
been the custom to say that the current is directed from positive to
negative, as the positive charges would flow if they were free. Nowadays
we believe that the current in a wire consists solely of a swarm of
electrons drifting along from negative to positive. We still keep the
old convention because little would be gained by changing it. **The
actual electron current in a wire is opposite to the conventional,
assumed, positive current.**

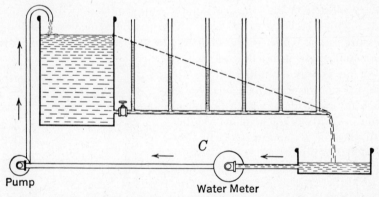

Fig. 3.—The strength of the water current through a narrow tube is proportional to
the pressure difference between its ends.

388. The Laws of Liquid Flow. Before studying the laws of electric
currents, let us consider some more facts as to the flow of liquids. In
Fig. 3, water flows from a reservoir through the horizontal pipe into a
basin whence it is pumped back into the reservoir, so that a continuous current is maintained in the circuit. The pressures at several points
along the pipe are indicated by the water levels in the vertical tubes.
The flow rate (for example, in gallons per hour) may be measured by

means of the flow meter C and the fall of pressure by the water levels in the vertical tubes. Partly close the valve until the pressure drop is half as great as before, and the flow rate decreases one-half.

Replace the horizontal pipe by one twice as long, offering twice as great "resistance" to the flow. Then, if the pressure drop is constant, the flow rate will decrease to one-half of its previous value.

The flow of water through the pipe is proportional to the fall of pressure and inversely proportional to the resistance.

The laws of the flow of electricity can be studied experimentally, using the circuit represented in Fig. 4. It consists of a storage battery D, a slide-wire rheostat, an ammeter C, and a voltmeter V, together with interconnecting wires. The battery "pumps" the electrons around the circuit; the rheostat acts like a valve to regulate the amount of

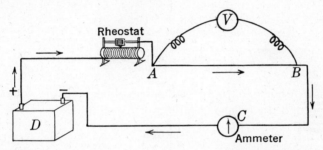

FIG. 4.—The strength of the electric current in a wire is proportional to the difference of potential between its ends and inversely proportional to its resistance.

current; the ammeter measures the current, and the voltmeter indicates the difference of potential between the ends of the wire AB. First adjust the slide-wire rheostat so that the current has a desired value such as 0.1 amp., and note the voltmeter reading (for example, 2 volts). Then change the rheostat to make the current one-half as great as before, and the voltmeter reading will also decrease to one-half its previous value.

The current through a conductor the resistance of which is constant is directly proportional to the potential difference between its ends.

Now make the length of the wire AB twice as great. The resistance is double its previous value, and, if the potential difference is the same as before, the current will be one half as great. That is, **the current varies inversely as the resistance if the potential difference is constant.**

These two rules can be combined, giving Ohm's law, as follows:

The current I through a conductor is directly proportional to the potential difference V between its ends and inversely proportional to the resistance R of the conductor.

What is a volt? Ohm's law is used to define the unit of potential difference, the volt, in terms of the ampere and the ohm, as follows:

The international volt is the potential difference between the ends of a conductor having a resistance of 1 international ohm, when the steady current through it is 1 international ampere.

If the potential difference across a conductor is V and the resistance is R, the current I is given by

$$I \text{ (amperes)} = \frac{V \text{ (volts)}}{R \text{ (ohms)}}$$

$$\text{Amperes} = \text{Volts/Ohms}$$

also,

$$V \text{ (volts)} = I \text{ (amperes)} \times R \text{ (ohms)}$$

Example. The potential difference (voltage) across the terminals of an electric iron is 110 V. The resistance of the coils is 20 Ω (20 ohms). What is the current?

$$I = V/R = \frac{110 \text{ V}}{20 \text{ ohms}} = 5.5 \text{ amp.}$$

Students who have trouble in distinguishing amperes, coulombs, and volts will find the following table worthy of study.

TABLE I

	In Electricity, Expressed in	In Liquid Flow, Expressed in
Current......................	Amperes	Gallons per second
Quantity of charge............	Coulombs	Gallons
Potential difference............	Volts	Pound-weights per square inch

389. Potential Difference and Electromotive Force. We have seen that the potential difference V between the ends of a resistance is proportional to the current I and the resistance R so that $V = IR$. There is another important term, electromotive force (e.m.f.), that is often confused with voltage. It equals **the sum of all the IR potential differences in all parts of the circuit traversed by any charge.**

Suppose that a battery is connected in series with two wires of resistances 1 ohm and 2 ohms, respectively, and let the current be 2 amp. Assume that the resistance inside the battery itself is negligibly small. Then the potential differences across the two wires are 2 volts and 4 volts. The sum of the IR potential differences is 6 volts, which is the electromotive force of the battery.

$$\text{e.m.f.} = IR_1 + IR_2$$

Suppose that the resistance r of the battery equals 1 ohm. Then the total resistance of the circuit is 4 ohms and the current is 1.5 amp.

$$\text{Current} = \frac{\text{e.m.f.}}{\text{Internal resistance} + \text{External resistance}}$$

390. The Voltage Across the Terminals of a Battery. When a cell or battery is on "open circuit," and the current through it is zero, the potential difference across its terminals equals the e.m.f. of the battery. When the battery is producing a current, the potential difference across its terminals is less than the e.m.f. This is because of the loss of voltage due to resistance and current inside the battery itself. For instance, an automobile storage battery has an e.m.f. of 6 volts and the internal resistance is 1/50 ohm. On open circuit the reading across its terminals is 6 volts. When the battery causes a current of 50 amp. in driving the starting motor, there is a fall of potential inside the battery and the terminal voltage is smaller. Thus

e.m.f. − Loss of potential in battery = Terminal voltage
E $- Ir = V$ (Discharging battery.)
6 volts − 50 amp. $\times$ 1/50 Ω = 5 volts

When a battery is being charged the current is opposed by the e.m.f. of the battery and also by the resistance, so that the terminal voltage must be greater than the e.m.f.,

$$E + Ir = V \text{ (Charging battery)}$$

Example. What is the terminal voltage when the battery described above is being charged, the current being 10 amp.?

$$6 \text{ V.} + 10 \text{ amp.} \times 1/50 \ \Omega = 6.2 \text{ V.}$$

SUMMARY

Positive electricity tends to move from points of higher potential to those of lower potential; negative electricity tends to move oppositely.

The international volt is the potential difference between the ends of a conductor, having a resistance of 1 international ohm, when the steady current through it is 1 international ampere.

$$\text{Amperes} = \text{Volts/Ohms}$$

The electromotive force in a circuit equals the sum of the IR potential differences in all parts of the circuit. The voltage across the terminals of a battery on open circuit equals the e.m.f. of the battery.

The terminal voltage V of a battery of resistance r carrying a current I is given by

$$V = \text{e.m.f.} \pm Ir$$

REVIEW QUESTIONS

1. What is analogous to electrical potential difference in (a) the flow of fluids, (b) gravitation, (c) the flow of heat?

2. Discuss the resemblances between the laws of flow of fluids in pipes and those of electricity in conductors.

3. Define the international volt, and state Ohm's law.

4. Distinguish between potential difference and electromotive force.

PROBLEMS

1. The voltage across a certain incandescent lamp is 115 V. and the current through it is 0.50 amp. What is the resistance of the lamp?

2. An electric iron of resistance 20.0 Ω is connected to a 115-V. line. What is the current through the iron?

3'. What will be the resistance which, placed in series with a lamp of resistance 100 Ω across a 115-V. line, will reduce the current to 0.50 amp.?

4''. A dynamo supplies 5.00 amp. at 110 V. The two wires leading to a lamp are each 2.00 miles long, and the resistance of each wire is 0.50 ohm per mile. (a) Find the fall of potential in each wire. (b) Find the reading of a voltmeter connected across the lamp terminals. (c) Make a sketch of the connections.

5'. An automobile headlight lamp requires 5.0 amp. Its resistance is 1.25 Ω when so operated. How much resistance should be placed in series with the lamp if the applied voltage is 115 V.?

6''. A trolley car 2.00 miles from the power plant uses 100 amp. If the resistance of the trolley wire is 0.50 Ω/mi., find the drop in voltage along the wire. (b) If the potential of the wire is plus 500 V. at the power plant, find the potential at the trolley car. (c) If two trolley cars at the end of the trolley wire are each using 100 amp. find the voltage as in (b).

7. The filament of the bulb of an automobile headlight carries a current of 6.0 amp. when the potential difference across the terminals is 6.0 V. What is the resistance of the filament?

8'. A motion-picture projector lamp requires a current of 5.00 amp. Its resistance, when operating, is 20 Ω. What additional resistance is required (a) if the potential difference is 115 V., (b) if it is 110 V.?

9'. A generator or dynamo in a farm house causes a potential difference of 32.0 V. Each of two copper wires 0.10 in. in diameter leading to the barn is 250 ft. long, and the resistance is 1.00 Ω per 1,000 ft. (a) What is the total fall of potential in the wires if the current is 5.0 amp.? (b) What is the voltage at the barn?

10. An old radio B battery has an e.m.f. of 20.0 V., and the internal resistance is 40 Ω. What is the voltage across its terminals when it causes a current of 0.100 amp.?

11'. The e.m.f. of a dry cell is 1.50 V. When it is "short-circuited" by connecting a heavy copper wire, of negligibly small resistance, across its terminals, the current is 15 amp. What is the internal resistance of the cell?

12'. An automobile battery has an e.m.f. of 6.0 V. and an internal resistance of 0.010 Ω. Find the potential difference between its terminals when it delivers the following currents: (*a*) 0 amp.; (*b*) 10 amp.; (*c*) 100 amp.; (*d*) 200 amp. Also make a graph plotting currents along the X axis and terminal voltages along the Y axis.

13″. A 12-V. battery of internal resistance 1.00 Ω is connected in series with two coils of resistance 2.00 Ω and 3.00 Ω. What are (*a*) the current, (*b*) the internal voltage drop, (*c*) the external voltage, and (*d*) the voltage across the 2.00-Ω resistance?

14′. What is the current delivered by 16 B-battery dry cells connected in series if the e.m.f. of each is 1.40 V., the internal resistance of each is 2.0 Ω, and the external resistance is 50 Ω?

CHAPTER XL

ELECTRIC CIRCUITS

Ohm's law is very important because it enables one to determine in advance the steady current that will be produced in a conductor of known resistance when the potential difference or "voltage" is given. This law can be used not only for single conductors, but also for com-

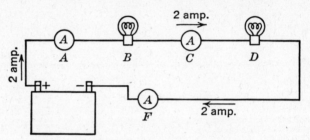

Fig. 1.—The lamps and the ammeters are in series with the battery.

plex combinations or "networks." In this chapter methods for applying Ohm's law to combinations of resistances will be described.

391. Resistances in Series. When the same electric charges must flow through several conductors, they are said to be connected in series. For example, the ammeters and the two automobile lamps

SYMBOLS

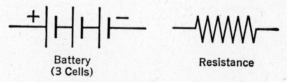

Battery
(3 Cells)

Resistance

Fig. 2.—Symbols for battery and resistance.

represented in Fig. 1 are connected in this manner. It should be emphasized that **in a series combination the current is the same in every part of the circuit.** The electrons distributed through several conductors connected in series are not destroyed, but like air molecules in a series of pipes are merely caused to move forward. This fact puzzles many people who think that the current is used up or consumed.

When several conductors are connected in series, **the resistance of the combination equals the sum of the different resistances.**

In Fig. 3, the two conductors B and C are shown as having resist-

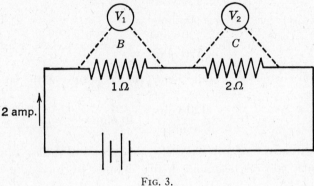

FIG. 3.

ances of 1 ohm and 2 ohms. The current in each part of the circuit is 2 amp.

By Ohm's law, the voltage drops are as follows:

Across B: 1 ohm $\times$ 2 amp. = 2 volts
Across C: 2 ohms $\times$ 2 amp. = 4 volts
Total potential difference across B and C = 6 volts

The single resistance through which the current will be 2 amp. when the potential difference is 6 volts is given by 6 volts $\div$ 2 amp. = 3 ohms. This is the sum of the two resistances.

392. Resistances in Parallel. Electrical energy is usually supplied to a residence through two wires which are kept at a fairly constant potential difference of, say, 120 volts. Suppose that you interconnect the two by a copper wire having a resistance of $R_1 = 60$ ohms. Then the current will be 2 amp. Now interconnect the two by a second, equal, copper wire. Two paths are available for the current and it will be twice as great, that is, 4 amp. Imagine the two wires laid side by side and pushed together to form a single conductor. It has the same length as each of the two, and twice the cross section of each, hence its resistance is one-half as great, that is, 30 ohms. Evidently, then, two equal resistances connected in parallel have a combined resistance one-half that of either. Now replace one of the copper wires by another which is one-half as large in cross section and has twice as great resistance, that is, 120 ohms. How can we find the single resistance which will carry the same total current as the two and hence be equivalent to them?

The currents through the two wires are given by

$$I_1 = \frac{120 \text{ volts}}{60 \text{ ohms}} = 2 \text{ amp.}$$

$$I_2 = \frac{120 \text{ volts}}{120 \text{ ohms}} = 1 \text{ amp.}$$

The total current is 3 amp., hence the resistance of the single conductor is

$$R = \frac{120 \text{ volts}}{3 \text{ amp.}} = 40 \text{ ohms}$$

The resistance R of any parallel combination of resistances R_1, R_2, R_3, etc., may always be found in this manner by imagining that all

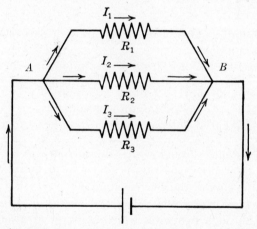

Fig. 4.—The total current through several resistances in parallel equals the sum of the currents through the individual resistances. $1/R = 1/R_1 + 1/R_2 + 1/R_3$

the elements are connected to a 120-volt source or one having any assumed value. However, it is simpler to use the formula

$$\frac{1}{R} = \frac{1}{R_1} + \frac{1}{R_2} + \frac{1}{R_3}, \text{ etc.}$$

Example. An electric lamp of resistance 220 Ω, a toaster of resistance 55 Ω and a percolator of resistance 55 Ω are connected in parallel to a 115-V. source. What is the resistance of an electric iron connected to the same supply wires that takes as much current as all three, and what is the current through it?

$$\frac{1}{R} = \frac{1}{220\ \Omega} + \frac{1}{55\ \Omega} + \frac{1}{55\ \Omega} = \frac{9}{220\ \Omega}$$

$$R = 24.4\ \Omega$$

$$I = V/R = \frac{115\ \text{V.}}{24.4\ \Omega} = 4.71\ \text{amp.}$$

393. Proof of the Formula. Let the potential difference from A to B across any one of the three resistances (Fig. 4) be V, the total current I, and let the resistance of the conductor that would replace the three be R.

The current I must equal the sum of those through the three conductors.

$$I = I_1 + I_2 + I_3 = V/R$$

The potential difference V across the three conductors equals that across the single, equivalent, conductor

$$I = \frac{V}{R_1} + \frac{V}{R_2} + \frac{V}{R_3} = \frac{V}{R}$$

Hence

$$\frac{1}{R_1} + \frac{1}{R_2} + \frac{1}{R_3} = \frac{1}{R}$$

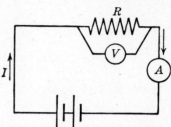

FIG. 5.—Measuring the resistance of a conductor by the ammeter-voltmeter method.

394. Determining Resistances. One of the simplest ways to determine the resistance of a conductor is to connect it in series with a battery and an ammeter A which measures the current I (Fig. 5). A voltmeter V connected in parallel with the conductor indicates the voltage or potential difference across it. The resistance R of the coil is then computed from V and I by Ohm's law. (The resistance of the voltmeter should be very great compared with R so that it carries a negligible fraction of the current. Otherwise the current through the voltmeter will have to be taken into account.)

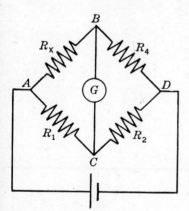

FIG. 6.—The Wheatstone-bridge circuit.

395. The Wheatstone Bridge. The Wheatstone bridge method is more accurate for determining resistances than the ammeter-voltmeter method just described. In Fig. 6, R_1, R_2, R_x, R_4, are four resistances. A current-indicating device called a galvanometer is connected between B and C. In practice the values of the resistances R_1 and R_2 are adjusted until the current through G is zero. Then the value of the unknown resistance R_x is found from

$$\frac{R_x}{R_4} = \frac{R_1}{R_2}$$

396. Derivation of the Wheatstone Bridge Equation. When the galvanometer current is zero, the current I is the same in both resistances of the upper part of the circuit. Similarly the current I' is the same in both parts of the lower branch.

Notice, also, that the potential at B equals that at C, hence the voltage drop from A to B equals that from A to C.

By Ohm's law,

$$IR_x = I'R_1$$

By similar reasoning,

$$IR_4 = I'R_2$$

Dividing one equation by the other,

$$\frac{R_x}{R_4} = \frac{R_1}{R_2}$$

397. A Network Problem. The network represented in Fig. 7 affords exercises which will aid the student to understand how Ohm's law is applied to complicated circuits.

(a) What is the main current if the potential difference is 120 V.? The first step is to find what single resistance is equivalent to the parallel combination BCD.

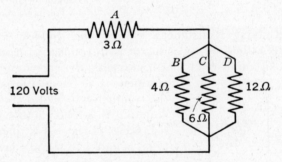

FIG. 7.—A network of resistances.

$$\frac{1}{R} = \frac{1}{4 \ \Omega} + \frac{1}{6.0 \ \Omega} + \frac{1}{12 \ \Omega} = \frac{1}{2.0 \ \Omega}, \ R = 2.0 \ \Omega$$

The total resistance of the circuit is $2.0 \ \Omega + 3.0 \ \Omega = 5.0 \ \Omega$, hence the main current is

$$I = \frac{120 \ \text{V.}}{5.0 \ \Omega} = 24 \ \text{amp.}$$

(b) What is the voltage across the parallel combination? The resistance of the parallel combination is $2.0 \ \Omega$ and the current is 24 amp., hence the voltage is given by

$$V_2 = 24 \ \text{amp.} \times 2.0 \ \Omega = 48 \ \text{V.}$$

(c) What is the current through the 12-Ω coil?

$$I = \frac{V_2}{R} = \frac{48 \ \text{V.}}{12 \ \Omega} = 4.0 \ \text{amp.}$$

SUMMARY

When several conductors of resistances R_1, R_2, and R_3 are connected in series so that the current through each of them is the same, the total resistance R is given by

$$R = R_1 + R_2 + R_3 + \ldots$$

If the conductors are connected in parallel their combined resistance is given by

$$1/R = 1/R_1 + 1/R_2 + 1/R_3 + \ldots$$

The resistance of a conductor can be found by measuring the current through it with an ammeter, and the potential difference between its ends by means of a voltmeter.

The Wheatstone bridge formula is as follows (see Fig. 6):

$$R_x/R_4 = R_1/R_2$$

REVIEW QUESTIONS

1. Define "resistances in series" and "resistances in parallel," and state the two formulas.

2. Prove the formulas for resistance in series and in parallel.

3. Show how to determine the resistance of a coil (*a*) using an ammeter and a voltmeter and (*b*) using a Wheatstone bridge.

4. Make a diagram of a Wheatstone bridge, and show in which two branches the potential differences are equal, and in which two the currents.

5. How much error would there be if the resistance of the voltmeter used in the voltmeter-ammeter method were equal to that of the coil, the resistance of which is being measured?

What is the advantage of using a very sensitive galvanometer in a Wheatstone bridge?

PROBLEMS

1. One of the heating plates of an electric stove carries a current of 12 amp. when connected to a 120-V. lighting system. What is its resistance?

2. A man accidentally touches the two wires of a 115-V. lighting system, one with each hand. The current through his arms and body is 0.00050 amp. What is the resistance opposing the current through his body?

3. An automobile headlight lamp is intended for use with a 6-V. battery and has a resistance of 1.00 Ω. How large a resistance should be put in series with it if it is operated by a 12-V. battery?

4'. A 2-Ω coil is connected in a circuit in parallel with a 4-Ω coil, and the latter carries a current of 10 amp. (*a*) What is the potential difference across the combination? (*b*) What is the current through the 2-Ω coil?

5'. The filament of a radio tube carries a current of 1.00 amp. when connected to a 30-V. source. (*a*) What is its resistance? (*b*) What resistance must be placed in series with it so that it may carry the same current when connected to a 110-V. source?

6′. How many incandescent lamps, each having a resistance of 200 Ω, can be connected in parallel with each other across the two wires of a 100-V. lighting system if the maximum allowable current is 10 amp.?

7′. Resistances of 6.0, 2.0, and 4.0 Ω are connected in series with a 6.0-V. storage battery. Find (a) the current through each resistance, and (b) the voltage across each resistance.

8′. A 6-V. battery of negligibly small internal resistance is connected in series with a 2.0-Ω coil and a 4.0-Ω coil. What is the current in the circuit and the voltage across the 2-Ω coil?

9. What is (a) the greatest and (b) the smallest resistance that can be secured by combinations of four coils of resistance 4, 8, 12, and 24 Ω?

10′. An electric toaster of resistance 40 Ω and a 60-watt lamp of resistance 240 Ω are connected in parallel to a 120-V. house lighting system. Find (a) the total current and (b) the resistance of an electric iron that would have the same current as the two together.

11″. A 9-tube radio set has 8 tubes, each carrying a filament current of 0.25 amp. when the potential difference across it is 5.0 V., and one tube carrying 0.50 amp. at this voltage. What are (a) the resistance of all 9 lamps in parallel, (b) the current, and (c) the necessary resistance of the rheostat, connected in the supply line so that a 6-V. battery may be used?

12″. If the 0.50-amp. tube in problem 11 should "burn out," what would be the current through each of the 8 lamps if all the resistances remained constant?

13. Two wires of total resistance 0.20 Ω lead from a 32-V. battery to a distant barn. Find (a) the total current, (b) the voltage drop in the wires, and (c) the voltage across the lamps, if 10 lamps each of resistance 40 Ω connected in parallel are used at the barn.

14″. Resistances of 2.0, 4.0, 6.0, and 12 Ω are connected in parallel with each other, and the four are connected through a 2-Ω resistance to a 12-V. battery. Find (a) the current through the battery, and (b) that through the 4-Ω resistance.

15″. The potential difference between a trolley wire and the track is 500 V. The 20 incandescent lamps of a streetcar are connected in series so that electricity flows through them from the wire to the track. If the current is 1.00 amp., what is the resistance of each lamp?

CHAPTER XLI

ELECTROLYSIS AND VOLTAIC CELLS

An electric current in a metal is pictured as a swarm of electrons migrating slowly from the negative pole of a battery toward the positive pole—that is, in a direction opposite to the conventional, assumed current. There are many non-metallic conductors, however, in which the currents are not swarms of drifting electrons, but rather of charged atoms and groups of atoms called **ions**. Those substances in which the electricity is carried by ions are called **electrolytes**.

To demonstrate some effects produced by an electric current in an electrolyte, connect a battery in series with a slide-wire rheostat and three cells A, B, C, containing solutions of sulfuric acid (H_2SO_4), copper sulfate ($CuSO_4$), and lead acetate ($Pb[C_2H_3O_2]_23H_2O$) (Fig. 1).

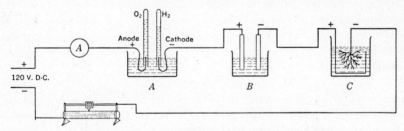

FIG. 1.—Effects produced by an electric current.

The positive electrode of each cell is called its **anode**, the negative electrode the **cathode**. Close the switch and adjust the rheostat so that the current is about an ampere, and notice the effects that are produced. Bubbles appear at both electrodes in A, hydrogen being set free at the cathode and oxygen at the anode. Their source is water, which is decomposed by the current. Copper is deposited on the cathode in B, while the copper anode slowly dissolves. In the third cell lead is deposited on the cathode forming a beautiful tree-like structure.

398. Electrolytic Dissociation. When sodium chloride dissolves in water, the sodium chloride molecules are disrupted forming sodium and chlorine ions. Each chlorine ion is negatively charged, having one excess electron, and each sodium ion is positively charged, having lost one electron. When electrodes connected to the terminals of a battery are dipped into a cell containing a sodium chloride solution, the chlorine ions travel toward the positive electrode, the sodium ions oppositely (Fig. 2). The current consists of these ions drifting in opposite directions.

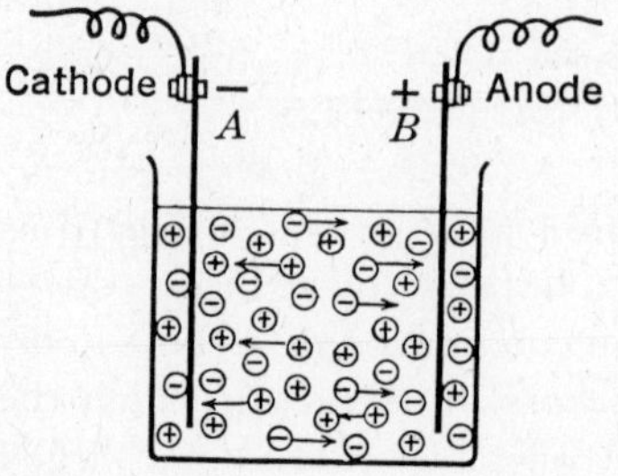

FIG. 2.—In an electrolytic cell, the negatively charged ions drift toward the anode, the positively charged ions toward the cathode.

Acids, alkalies, and salts are ionized when dissolved in water. In all cases, the metallic or the hydrogen ion is positive, the other ion is negative.

399. Electroplating. Electrolysis is widely used in coating metals with gold, silver, nickel, chromium, or copper. Spoons to be electroplated are suspended in a water solution of silver salt and connected to the negative terminal of a battery. Bars of pure silver, dipping into the electrolyte, are connected to the positive electrode. Silver ions are attracted to the spoons; arriving there, each ion receives one electron from the metal and is deposited as ordinary silver. Meanwhile, silver dissolves from the bars and each ion entering the solution leaves an electron on the metal. One atom dissolves from the anode for every atom going out of the liquid at the cathode, so the strength of the solution remains unchanged.

400. Electrotyping. Ordinary type metal is so soft that the type made solely from it becomes deformed after a few thousand impressions. For this reason most books are printed from "electrotype" plates made of copper. In making such a plate, a sheet of wax, plaster, or moist paper pulp is pressed against the type form so that every letter leaves an imprint conforming to the exact shape of that letter. The surface thus indented is then coated with graphite to make it conducting and the mold is suspended as the cathode in a copper sulfate electroplating cell. The flow of electricity causes a film of copper to be deposited over the surface, coating every indentation and reproducing the shapes of all the letters. The mold is then removed from the bath and the thin film of copper is stripped away from the type. Melted lead is poured into the back of the film to give it rigidity, and the electrotype, thus strengthened, is used instead of the original type. In making electrotypes for printing newspapers, the indented molds are laid against cylindrical forms so that the electrotypes are curved and fit onto cylinders which rotate in printing the page of the newspaper. Phonograph records are made by a similar method. The original "master" record is formed on a wax disk from which an electrotype is prepared. This is used to stamp out the records which are sold to the public.

401. Electrolytic Purification. In the electrolytic refining of copper, a huge block of the crude metal is suspended as the anode of a cell, the electrolyte being copper sulfate. As the electricity flows, the copper and the impurities in the block dissolve, but only the pure copper is deposited at the cathode. The impurities such as zinc have greater tendency to dissolve than does copper, that is, they are more difficult to remove from the water solution, hence they remain behind. Among these "impurities" is silver, which is recovered from the "sludge" that accumulates in the cells. A considerable part of the world output of silver is a by-product of the electrolytic purification of copper.

One of the most important industrial applications of electrolysis is the separation of aluminum from its ore. Though this metal is one of the chief constituents of ordinary clay, it was formerly more expensive than platinum. About fifty years ago, a professor at Oberlin College remarked that the man who discovered how to prepare pure aluminum cheaply would bless humanity. One of his students, Charles Martin Hall, attacked the problem, performing experiments in a shed at his home. He succeeded so well that within two years a new industry was born. The price of aluminum soon fell from several dollars per ounce to 22 cents per pound where it has remained for many years. Hall's great discovery was that aluminum ore can be dissolved in a molten mineral, cryolite, forming a liquid electrolyte from which the metal is liberated by an electric current.

402. Electrolysis in Medicine. There is a great deal of quackery in the use of electricity in treating disease, yet, when employed by experts, it becomes a willing and worthy servant. One of the important applications of electrolysis is the introduction of drugs into muscles and other tissues. For example, the skin of an infected finger is painted with iodine, and a damp cotton pad tied around the finger is connected to a platinum or carbon electrode connected to the negative terminal of a battery. Another electrode, fastened to the arm, is connected to the positive terminal. Negative iodine ions pass from the cathode into the finger so that the stain disappears from the skin.

403. Faraday's Laws of Electrolysis. We are familiar with the fact that the amount of silver deposited from a silver nitrate solution is proportional to the time and to the current, that is, to the number of coulombs or ampere-seconds of charge transferred. This fact is expressed by a law stated by Michael Faraday more than a century ago.

Faraday's first law. **The mass m of substance deposited is proportional to the product of the time t and the current I.**

$$m = eIt$$

The constant e, the **electrochemical equivalent** of the substance, is commonly expressed in grams per coulomb.

In order to study the amounts of different substances liberated, connect several electrolytic cells in series as shown in Fig. 3 and let

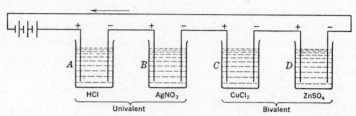

FIG. 3.—One atom of univalent element is liberated for each electron that reaches the cathode.

the current continue until one gram-atom of silver (107.88 grams numerically equal to the atomic weight) is deposited in B. Then 1.008 grams, one gram-atom, of hydrogen is set free in A. The same number of atoms of each element are set free from the solution. This is to be expected, for each ion has the same charge. The amounts of copper deposited in C and of zinc in D are one-half of their atomic weights. This is because each copper ion and zinc ion carries a charge twice that of a silver ion.

These facts are expressed by Faraday's second law.

The mass of an element deposited by a given quantity of electricity is proportional to the atomic weight and inversely proportional to the number of excess protons or electrons on the ions (that is, to the valence of the element).

TABLE I

ELECTROCHEMICAL EQUIVALENTS

	Atomic Weight $\left(\dfrac{\text{Grams}}{\text{Gram-atom}}\right)$	Valence	Electrochemical Equivalent (grams per coulomb)	
Hydrogen.........	1.008	1	0.00001045 =	1.008/96,500
Silver............	107.88	1	0.001118	= 107.88/96,500
Copper..........	63.57	1	0.0006588	= 63.57/96,500
Copper..........	63.57	2	0.0003294	= 63.57/(96,500 × 2)
Lead............	207.20	2	0.0001073	= 207.40/(96,500 × 2)
Oxygen..........	16.00	2	0.0000829	= 16.00/(96,500 × 2)
Nickel...........	58.69	2	0.0003041	= 58.69/(96,500 × 2)
Zinc.............	65.38	2	0.0003387	= 65.38/(96,500 × 2)

404. Computing the Electrochemical Equivalent of an Element. The amount of an electric charge transferred in depositing 107.88 grams of silver (1 gram-atom) is found as follows;

$$m = e\,I\,t = e\,Q$$
$$107.88 \text{ grams} = 0.001118 \text{ gram per coulomb} \times Q$$
$$Q = 96,500 \text{ coulombs}$$

This quantity of charge called the Faraday will liberate 1 gram-atom of any element which, like silver, is univalent. It will liberate one-half of a gram-atom of a bivalent substance, each ion of which is doubly charged. In general, the mass liberated is given by

$$m = \frac{\text{Atomic weight} \times I\,t}{96,500 \text{ coulombs} \times \text{Valence}}$$

405. Weighing Atoms. The mass of a silver atom is so small that it cannot be determined by ordinary weighing, but the task is not difficult when the facts of electrolysis are used. Later it will be pointed out that there are 6.25 billion billion electrons or protons in 1 coulomb or ampere-second of electricity. This amount of charge passing through an electrolytic cell deposits 0.001118 gram of silver. Hence

$$\text{Mass of a silver atom} = \frac{0.001118 \text{ gram}}{6.25 \times 10^{18}} = 1.79 \times 10^{-22} \text{ gram}$$

The number of atoms in a gram of silver is so great that, if they were spread uniformly over the earth's surface, there would be several thousand atoms for each square centimeter.

VOLTAIC CELLS

In the days when Franklin flew the kite and brought down charges from the clouds, electrical machines were scientific toys, incapable of doing the work of the world. In 1790, the year that the American Constitution went into effect, an Italian professor of anatomy, Galvani by name, made a discovery leading to the invention of the voltaic cell. He noticed that sparks from an electrostatic machine caused the legs of a newly killed frog to contract. Greatly interested in this phenomenon, he began to experiment further. One day by chance he hung a pair of frog legs from a copper hook fastened to an iron plate, and noticed that they kept up a merry dance, contracting vigorously whenever they touched the iron. Galvani thought that electric currents were produced by the contact of living tissue with metals. Other workers opposed this view, and the bitter controversy was finally ended by another Italian, Volta, for whom the unit of potential difference is named. He found that currents could be produced by means of a piece of copper and one of zinc, separated by a piece of cloth, moistened with a salt solution. Then he made the first **voltaic cell** by dipping a strip of zinc and one of copper into a vessel of salt water. He found that the voltage could be increased by connecting several cells in series, positive to negative, forming a voltaic battery.

The production of currents by voltaic cells is explained as follows:

Suppose that a rod made of pure zinc is dipped into a solution of acid in water (Fig. 4). Some of the zinc dissolves, and the atoms enter

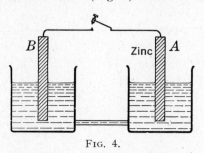

FIG. 4.

the solution as positive ions. Each atom leaves two of its electrons on the zinc rod. These electrons accumulate on the metal, and soon the electrical attractions between these electrons and the ions become so great that no more ions can escape. Hence the action is stopped by electrical forces.

Now let another zinc rod *B* be dipped into another vessel, the two being interconnected by a narrow tube. Ions will dissolve from this rod, and it will be charged negatively like the first one. Connect the two by a wire, and there will be no current because the two are at the same potential. Replace the second rod by one made of copper, which has less tendency to dissolve than zinc, and it therefore becomes less negative in potential with respect to the liquid. When the two are connected by a wire, electrons flow from *A* to *B*, a current is established, and zinc ions continue to dissolve. Hydrogen ions migrate through the narrow tube into the other vessel so that hydrogen gas is liberated at the copper rod. More energy is set free by the zinc in dissolving than is absorbed in liberating the hydrogen. The excess energy evolved is utilized in forcing electrons around the circuit.

A voltaic cell may be formed by placing any two different conductors in an electrolyte. The only essential is that the two substances have different tendencies to dissolve. Place a copper cent and a silver dime in your mouth, separating them by your tongue. Permit the two to touch, and you will experience the nasty taste of the ions. Dentists are careful not to permit a gold filling to touch one made of a silver amalgam, for the two in contact with each other and with the saliva would form a closed circuit, causing the silver to dissolve. A solution of ordinary salt in water would make an excellent antifreeze for automobile engines were it not for the fact that electrolytic action would occur and the soldered seams would be eaten away.

406. Local Action. Ordinary commercial zinc placed in an acid solution dissolves much more rapidly than pure zinc. The bits of iron and the like embedded in the metal are in contact with the zinc, hence tiny voltaic cells are formed when the metal is placed in the acid. "Tin" cans are really made of iron coated with a thin layer of tin. If a little of the surface is scraped off, rusting occurs. The iron, the zinc, and a film of moisture containing a little acid form a voltaic cell. Very pure iron resists rust better than ordinary iron because there is less electrolytic action.

407. Polarization. If an acid electrolyte is used in a voltaic cell, as we have seen, the positive ions are hydrogen. When the cell operates, these ions are forced over to the positive electrode where they pick up electrons, are liberated, and form a gaseous film. The accumulation of the gas around the electrode is called **polarization**. Its bad effects are two. First, the film has high electrical resistance and it opposes the flow of electricity. Second, the hydrogen film effectively changes the nature of the electrode. For example, when the zinc-copper cell just described becomes polarized, no longer is there a zinc-copper cell, but rather a zinc-hydrogen cell, which produces a smaller voltage. Polarization is avoided or diminished in several ways in different types of voltaic cells, as will now be shown.

408. The Dry Cell. The best-known type of voltaic cell is the dry cell used to operate flashlights, doorbells, auto radios, and the like. It consists of a zinc can containing a thick, moist paste of manganese dioxide, graphite, and ammonium chloride solution (Fig. 5). A massive carbon rod at the center serves as the positive electrode. When the cell operates, hydrogen is forced out of solution onto the carbon, forming a polarizing film. Afterward, when the circuit is broken, the hydrogen is slowly oxidized by the manganese dioxide, producing water. The electromotive force of this cell is about 1.5 volts.

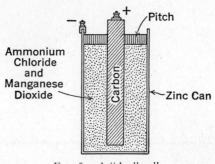

FIG. 5.—A "dry" cell.

409. Storage Batteries. A voltaic cell which can be restored to its original condition by forcing a current through it in a reversed direction is called a storage cell. A familiar example is the lead battery used in automobiles. The positive electrode of each cell is a lead grid containing lead dioxide (PbO_2). The negative electrode is made of pure lead. The electrolyte is a solution of sulfuric acid. When the cell discharges, negatively charged sulfate (SO_4) ions unite with the lead at the negative electrode, forming lead sulfate. Other sulfate ions replace oxygen from the positive electrode. The oxygen which goes into solution unites with hydrogen to form water. The removal of the sulfate ions decreases the density of the solution so that hydrometers may be used to test the condition of charge of the cells. The storage battery is recharged by sending through it a current in a reversed direction. This causes the sulfate ions to reenter the solution from each electrode while oxygen recombines with the lead at the positive plates. It should be

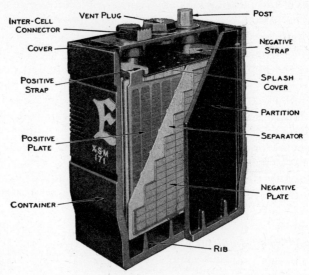

FIG. 6.—Lead storage battery. (Courtesy Electric Storage Battery Co.)

emphasized that, after a cell has been charged, it contains no more electricity than before. It is chemical energy that is stored.

The storage battery of a car must deliver large currents; therefore it is desirable that its internal resistance be low. To this end, the plates or electrodes are placed close together, being separated by thin wooden or rubber strips. Instead of a single pair of plates, a large number are used, alternate plates being positive and negative (Fig. 6). All the positives are connected to one terminal, the negatives to the other. The maximum voltage of a newly charged cell is about 2.2 volts. Three cells connected in series comprise the usual "6-volt" storage battery.

410. The Edison Storage Battery. The lead storage battery deteriorates when kept in an uncharged condition. Its plates buckle or bend when it delivers excessive currents. The Edison-type cell is free from these defects and it is more rugged than the lead cell. On the other hand, it is more expensive and of lower voltage. In this battery the negative plates are of iron oxide, the positive plates of nickel hydroxide. The electrolyte is a solution of potassium hydroxide.

SUMMARY

Water solutions of acids, salts, and alkalies conduct electricity and are called electrolytes. When an electrolyte is dissolved in water the metallic and hydrogen ions are positive. The other ions are negative.

"Univalent" atoms gain or lose one electron each in ionization, and "bivalent" atoms gain or lose two electrons. Faraday's laws of electrolysis are as follows:

1. The mass of substance deposited by an electric current is proportional to the amount of electrical charge transferred.

2. For the same quantity of electricity transferred, the masses of different elements deposited are proportional to their atomic weights divided by their valences.

A voltaic cell consists of two electrodes, made of dissimilar substances, in contact with an electrolyte. The substance forming the negative electrode has a greater tendency to dissolve than that forming the positive electrode.

Polarization is the accumulation of hydrogen around the positive electrode.

A storage cell is a voltaic cell that can be restored to its initial condition by forcing a reversed current through it.

REVIEW QUESTIONS

1. Explain how an electrolytic solution conducts an electric current.
2. Define "dissociation," and discuss it.
3. Discuss "valence."
4. Discuss the electrolytic purification of copper, and show why zinc is not deposited at the cathode.
5. How is aluminum produced from its oxide?
6. Describe the manufacture of an electrotype plate.
7. What are the "secondary reactions" not causing substances to be liberated in the electrolysis of sodium chloride and of sulfuric acid?
8. State Faraday's laws of electrolysis.
9. Define "electrochemical equivalent" and "gram-atom."
10. What is a voltaic cell?
11. If a nickel and a cent are placed in the mouth and are allowed to touch each other, a bitter taste is experienced. Why?
12. Describe the discovery of the voltaic cell.
13. Explain the chemical actions occurring when current is caused by a strip of zinc and one of copper immersed in a hydrochloric acid solution.

14. In such a cell, why does the dissolving of the zinc cease when the circuit is broken?

15. What is polarization?

16. Discuss the construction, operation, and advantages of (a) the dry cell, and (b) the lead storage cell.

17. What is stored in a storage battery?

18. Lead sulfate is a poor conductor of electricity. Why, then, should a lead storage battery not be completely discharged?

19. A copper wire immersed in acid does not oxidize, yet if connected to a terminal of a lead storage battery it soon corrodes. Why?

20. Why is it advisable not to use a salt solution for antifreeze in the radiator of a car?

21. If a clean iron nail is dipped into a copper sulfate solution, it becomes coated with copper. Explain in terms of tendencies to dissolve.

PROBLEMS

1. A current of 2.00 amp. through a water solution of sulfuric acid will cause what gases to escape and at what rates?

2. What time is required to deposit 100 kg. of copper from a $CuSO_4$ solution in an electrolytic purification process if the current is 100 amp.?

3. Two electrolytic cells, A and B, are connected in series. If 107.8 grams of silver are deposited in A, how much bivalent copper will be deposited in B?

4. The storage battery of a car is charged by a current of 15 amp. during a period of 5.0 hr. How much lead at the positive plate unites with sulfate (SO_4) ions to form $PbSO_4$?

5. A current of 2.0 amp. electroplates silver onto a cheap spoon, the current existing for 5.0 min. (a) How much silver is deposited, and what is its cost at a price of 2.0 cents per gram? (b) How many atoms of silver are deposited?

6. The atomic weight of nickel is 58.69 grams/(gram-atom) and it is bivalent. Compute the electrochemical equivalent.

7. The "life" of a certain dry cell is 40 amp-hr. How much zinc dissolves from the negative electrode?

8. A cell delivers 0.10 amp. for 5.0 min. How much copper is deposited, and how much zinc dissolves?

CHAPTER XLII

ELECTRICAL ENERGY AND POWER

Whenever electricity flows in a circuit, work is done, and energy is transformed. This energy may be utilized in many ways, such as in raising a passenger elevator, in starting the motor of an automobile, and in causing chemical changes. By no means the least important is the work done by the electrons in heating the conductor through which they are drifting. In this chapter we consider the factors which determine the amount of work done by the flow of electricity.

411. A Hydraulic Analogy. The amount of work that can be done by water in passing over Niagara depends upon two factors, the **height** of the falls and the **quantity** of water that flows over them. The height is about 160 ft., hence each pound of water that goes over acquires 160 ft-lb. of kinetic energy. Most of this energy is converted into heat, but some is used to turn water wheels. The total energy transformed is given by

$$\text{Energy transformed} = \text{Height of falls} \times \text{Weight of water} \quad (1)$$

412. The Work Done by an Electric Current. The work done by electricity in passing through part of a circuit also depends upon two factors, the voltage, or potential difference V corresponding to the height of the falls, and the quantity of electricity Q that is transferred, corresponding to the weight of the water passing over the falls. The equation is as follows:

$$\textbf{Work} = \textbf{Voltage} \times \textbf{Charge transferred}$$
$$\textbf{Joules} = \textbf{Volts} \times \textbf{Coulombs}$$
$$\textbf{W} = \textbf{QV} \quad (2)$$

Also, since
$$\textbf{Q} = \textbf{It}$$
$$\textbf{W} = \textbf{VIt} \quad (3)$$

Example. In starting the engine of an automobile, a current of 100 amp. existed for 4.0 sec. The voltage across the terminals of the motor was 6.0 V. How much electrical energy was delivered?

$$\textbf{W} = \textbf{IVt}$$
$$= 100 \text{ amp.} \times 6.0 \text{ V.} \times 4.0 \text{ sec.} = 2,400 \text{ joules}$$

413. Another Description of Electromotive Force. In an earlier chapter electromotive force was described as the sum of the (IR) potential differences in all parts of a circuit. Now that the energy relationships have been studied, electromotive force can be defined in another way.

The energy transformed in forcing a charge Q around a circuit is given by

$$W = QV_1 + QV_2 + \ldots = Q(V_1 + V_2 + \ldots)$$

in which V_1, V_2, etc., are the IR potential differences around the circuit. Hence

Energy transformed = Quantity of charge $\times$ E.m.f.

$$\text{E.m.f.} = \frac{\text{Energy transformed}}{\text{Quantity of charge}}$$

Thus an e.m.f. of 1 volt exists in a circuit when 1 joule of work is done in forcing 1 coulomb or ampere-second past any point in the circuit. One volt equals 1 joule per coulomb.

414. Electric Power. Power is defined as the time rate of doing work, and it may be expressed in foot-pounds per second, in horsepower, in watts (joules per second), or in kilowatts. The power of a water fall depends upon the height of the fall and upon the number of pounds of water flowing per unit time. Similarly, in electric circuits the power depends upon the voltage drop and the strength of the electric current.

From (3)

$$\text{W}/t = \text{VI}$$
$$= \text{Voltage} \times \text{Current}$$
$$\text{Joules}/\text{Sec.} = \text{Watts} = \text{Volts} \times \text{Amperes}$$

Example 1. An incandescent lamp connected to a 110-V. battery carries a current of 0.50 amp. What is the power?

$$P = VI$$
$$= 110 \text{ V.} \times 0.50 \text{ amp.} = 55 \text{ watts}$$

Example 2. The starting motor of a car operates at 6.0 V. and the input electric power is 600 watts. What is the current?

$$I = P/V = 600 \text{ watts}/6.0 \text{ V.} = 100 \text{ amp.}$$

The watt is inconveniently small for many purposes, and often **the** kilowatt is used.

One watt = 1 joule/sec. = 10,200 gwt-cm./sec. = ¾ ft-lb./sec.

(approximately)

1 kw. = 1,000 watts = 4/3 horsepower

415. The Kilowatt-Hour is a Unit of Energy or of Work. The householder buys electrical energy at a fixed price per kilowatt-hour. The cost depends upon the amount of current, the time, and the voltage. Suppose that several lamps when operated at the same time carry 10 amp. at 100 volts so that the power is 1 kilowatt, that is, 1,000 watts or 1,000 joules/sec. Then in 1 hour (3,600 sec.) the total input energy is 3,600,000 joules.

One kilowatt-hour = 3.6 million joules = 2.7 million foot-pounds

Example 1. A 5-tube radio set uses 100 watts and operates 5 hr./day for 30 days. What is the expense for energy at 3.0 cents/kw-hr.?

$$100 \text{ watts} \times 5 \text{ hr./day} \times 30 \text{ days} = 15,000 \text{ watt-hr.}$$
$$15 \text{ kw-hr.} \times 3 \text{ cents/(kw-hr.)} = 45 \text{ cents}$$

Example 2. An electric refrigerator requires 200 watts and operates 8 hr./day. What is the energy cost of operation for 30 days at 3 cents/kw-hr.?

$$200 \text{ watts} \times 8.0 \text{ hr./day} \times 30 \text{ days} = 48,000 \text{ watt-hr.}$$
$$48 \text{ kw-hr.} \times 3 \text{ cents/kw-hr.} = \$1.44$$

416. The Convenience of the Electrical Equations. The ampere, ohm, and volt, were defined during the nineteenth century, after the advantages of the decimal system were well understood. It seems peculiar, therefore, that the ampere was defined as the current which deposits 0.001118 gram of silver per second. Why not 0.00100 gram instead? And why is the ohm equal to the resistance of a column of mercury 106.300 cm. long and 1 sq. mm. in cross section instead of 100.00 cm.? The answer is that the makers of the system wished to obtain certain often-used equations based on the centimeter, gram, and second, which would be convenient, involving only small integers or decimals. An examination of the following table shows how well they succeeded.

TABLE I

REVIEW OF IMPORTANT ELECTRICAL EQUATIONS

(1)	Q	$= It$	; Coulombs	$=$ Amperes $\times$ Seconds
(2)	I	$= V/R$	; Amperes	$=$ Volts/Ohms
(3)	W	$= VIt$	; Joules	$=$ Volts $\times$ Amperes $\times$ Seconds
(4)	E.m.f.	$= W/Q$	; Volts	$=$ Joules/Coulombs
(5)	Power	$= VI$	; Watts	$=$ Volts $\times$ Amperes

SUMMARY

The work W done in overcoming resistance to force a charge Q through a conductor is given by

$$W = QV$$

V being the potential difference between the ends of the conductor.

$$\text{Joules} = \text{Coulombs} \times \text{Volts}$$

The electric power is given by

$$\text{Watts} = \text{Volts} \times \text{Amperes}$$
$$1{,}000 \text{ watts} = 1 \text{ kw.}$$
$$1 \text{ kw-hr.} = 3.6 \text{ million joules} = 2.7 \text{ million foot-pounds}$$

The electromotive force in a complete circuit equals the energy expended in forcing a unit quantity of electricity once around the circuit. One volt = 1 joule per coulomb.

REVIEW QUESTIONS

1. Discuss the resemblance between the flow of water over a fall and the flow of electricity through a coil as regards (*a*) energy and (*b*) power. How can you describe the height of a building in terms of energy?

2. Define "potential difference" (*a*) by Ohm's law, (*b*) in terms of energy.

3. What factors determine the power delivered by a current?

4. What is a kilowatt-hour?

5. A small flashlight bulb requires a current of 1 amp., as does also a certain incandescent lamp operated at 110 volts. Why does the lamp require more electrical power than the flashlight?

PROBLEMS

1. An automobile battery having an e.m.f. of 6.0 V. causes a current of 10.0 amp. when the headlights are operated. If the starter motor also is operated the current is 80 amp. Find the electrical power in each case.

2. An incandescent lamp is marked "115 V., 60 watts." What is the current through it under normal conditions?

3. How much does it cost per hour to operate the lamp just described if the price of electrical energy is 3.0 cents/kw-hr.?

4'. A dry cell used to operate an electric doorbell costs 40 cents. Its average e.m.f. is 1.40 V. and it delivers a current of 2.00 amp. for a total time of 80.0 hr. What are (*a*) the power, (*b*) the total energy, and (*c*) the cost of the energy per kilowatt-hour?

5. An automobile storage battery liberated 18,000 joules in the headlight lamps. The current of 10 amp. existed for 5.0 min. What was the potential difference across the terminals of the lamps?

6'. Eight Christmas lamps are connected in series to a 110-V. source and the current is 0.50 amp. What are (*a*) the potential difference across each lamp and (*b*) the wattage or power of each?

7. A small electric clock is connected to a 110-V. source and the current is 0.050 amp. Find (*a*) the power; (*b*) the energy used in 700 hr., or, approximately, 1 month; (*c*) the cost of this energy at 3.0 cents/kw-hr.

8. An elevator motor uses 30 kw. and requires 1.00 min. to raise an elevator to the top of a skyscraper. What does the electrical energy for the trip cost at 2 cents/kw-hr.?

9'. At 3.0 cents/kw-hr., what does it cost per hour to operate an electric range requiring 30 amp. at 115 V.?

10. What is the power used by a 1-Ω resistance coil if the potential difference across it is (*a*) 1.00 V., and (*b*) 2.00 V.?

11'. Two 1-Ω coils are first connected in parallel to a 1-V. battery and later in series with each other. What is the total power developed in each case? (The internal resistance of the cell is negligible.)

CHAPTER XLIII

ELECTRICAL HEATING AND THERMOELECTRICITY

An electric current in a metallic conductor is pictured as a swarm of electrons drifting slowly along in a certain direction. The electrons collide with particles in the wire, give up part of their energy, and produce heat. The amount of energy W transformed in this manner by a current I in a time t is given by the formula developed in the preceding chapter,

$$W = IVt \qquad (1)$$

in which V is the fall of potential or the voltage between the ends of the conductor.

Moreover, by Ohm's law,

$$V = IR$$

hence

$$W = I^2Rt \qquad (2)$$
$$\text{Joules} = (\text{Amperes})^2 \times \text{Ohms} \times \text{Seconds}$$

The amount of energy can be changed from joules to calories by the relation

$$4.18 \text{ joules} = 1 \text{ cal.}$$

Example 1. A coffee percolator is rated at 200 watts. (*a*) How many calories of heat does it produce in 100 sec.?

$$\text{Power} = 200 \text{ watts} = 200 \text{ joules/sec.} = 47.8 \text{ cal./sec.}$$
$$\text{Heat energy} = 47.8 \text{ cal./sec.} \times 100 \text{ sec.} = 4,780 \text{ cal.}$$

(*b*) How much time would be required for this percolator to heat 1 liter (1,000 grams) of water from 20°C. to 100°C., neglecting the heat absorbed by the percolator itself?

$$H = 1.00 \text{ cal./(gram C.°)} \times 1,000 \text{ grams} \times 80 \text{ C.°} = 80,000 \text{ cal.}$$

Therefore

$$H = 47.8 \text{ cal./sec.} \times X = 80,000 \text{ cal.}$$
$$X = 1,673 \text{ sec.} = 27.9 \text{ min.}$$

Since the heat produced by a current in a conductor is proportional to the resistance, the relative heating in the different parts of a circuit can be controlled by using conductors of different resistances. The

387

electric wires of a house lighting system are of large diameter, and their resistances are relatively small, so that little energy is wasted in heating them. The filaments of the incandescent lamps are of smaller diameters and their resistances are higher so that the heat evolved in them is sufficient to raise them to incandescence, causing emission of light.

417. The Incandescent Lamp. A very important application of the heating effect of currents is the incandescent lamp, in which a small filament is heated so as to emit light. Before the development of this light source, householders were limited to the flickering flame of the fireside used by Abraham Lincoln as a boy, to candles, gas flames, and to kerosene lamps. The first incandescent lamps, devised more than a century ago, consisted of platinum wires heated by currents from voltaic cells. The lamps were of little practical utility, both because of their small luminous efficiencies and because the batteries were very expensive and inconvenient. The reason for the small efficiencies of the lamps was that the platinum melted at a red heat and the filaments could not be raised to sufficiently high temperatures for effective light emission. The development of the dynamo, about the middle of the century, provided an economical source of electrical energy and led to a search for more suitable filament materials. Sir Joseph Swan of England devised a lamp the filament of which was a narrow strip of paper carbonized or charred by heating in an oven. The strip of carbon was mounted in an evacuated bulb, but in those days the available air pumps were so ineffective that high vacua could not be produced. The residual oxygen in the bulb soon combined with the hot carbon and ruined the filament. In 1879, twenty years after Swan devised his first crude lamp, Thomas Edison made filaments by carbonizing cotton threads. By that time adequate air pumps had been invented, and there was little trouble because of oxidation. However, the filaments were extremely fragile, and the first lamps operated for only a few hours. Then one was constructed which had a remarkably long life compared with the others. Edison and his assistants anxiously watched it day and night until it "burned out" after the long period of 40 hours! This was such a great improvement that Edison commenced a vigorous search for better materials. Hundreds of substances were tried, and searchers were sent to foreign countries at an expense greater than $100,000. Finally in far-off Japan a kind of bamboo was found that could be split into narrow

Fig. 1.—Structure of a carbon-filament incandescent lamp.

strips which when charred by heating provided rugged carbon filaments (Fig. 1).

The first large-scale use of the new lamps was at the World's Fair at Chicago in 1893. The story is that the manufacturer who secured the contract for supplying the lamps was dismayed to find that the Edison patents prevented him from sealing the lead wires of his lamps into the glass bulbs. He cleverly got around this difficulty by mounting the wires on stoppers which were plugged into the bulbs. A third of a million of these lamps supplied the illumination at the exposition, where they were among the great marvels of science.

418. Improving the Incandescent Lamp. The filament of the Edison lamp could be heated to much higher temperatures than platinum filaments. Therefore it was a better emitter of light. It was, however, less than one-third as efficient as the ordinary tungsten lamp of today. Tungsten is preferable to carbon because the filaments can operate at higher temperatures. The early investigators found it impossible to draw tungsten into fine wires because the metal like cast iron was very brittle. This brittleness was due to traces of other substances, which are now removed by careful purification. By various heat treatments and by hammering at high temperatures the crystal structure is so modified that the wires can be drawn to a hairlike thinness. The filaments thus produced are mounted in evacuated bulbs, giving the vacuum-type tungsten lamp.

The attempts to increase the efficiencies of the incandescent lamps were unceasing, and, a few years after the introduction of the tungsten lamp (1908), Langmuir of the General Electric laboratories made a notable contribution by showing how to retard the evaporation and disintegration of the metal filament. He proved experimentally that, if the bulb contained a gas such as nitrogen or argon, the evaporation of the tungsten was diminished. The explanation was that the blanket of gas impeded the escape of the atoms of metal in the same manner that the atmosphere decreases the rate of evaporation of water from a lake. In the gas-filled lamp the temperature of the filament may be made much higher than in the vacuum type. The lamp is more efficient because a larger fraction of the radiant energy is in the visible part of the spectrum.

419. The Electric Arc. The incandescent filament lamp is admirably adapted to many uses such as household illumination. It is very compact and has no mechanically moving parts. For other purposes the electric arc is preferred because of its great power, its great luminous efficiency, and because the source is very concentrated. An electric arc may be produced in the following manner: two carbon rods, connected through a suitable resistance to a 115-volt source, are first touched together and then separated a few millimeters. An electric discharge forms across the gap, and light is emitted. Part of the light comes from the discharge, part from the hot terminals of the carbon rods. Arcs may also be produced using metal rods, but considerable heat is conducted along the rods. Carbon is preferred because of its low thermal conductivity and because it evaporates very slowly. In the arc lamps for street lighting, mechanisms are used to keep the two electrodes separated at a proper distance from each other as the carbon slowly wastes away.

The improvement in lighting during the last half century has been so gradual that people are scarcely conscious of it; yet there are many older folk who remember the days when the candle was replaced by the kerosene lamp. Today, using a gas-filled incandescent lamp, one can buy light for two cents which would cost two dollars if provided by a paraffin candle.

420. Short Circuits and Fuses. When the electrical supply wires of a residence are accidentally "short-circuited" by being brought into contact with each other, the current becomes very large and except for the fuse it would heat the wires to dangerously high temperatures. To avoid this danger, fuses are connected in the supply lines. Each fuse consists of a wire or strip of lead, aluminum, or other metal melting at a low temperature. The wire or strip is heated to the melting point when the current attains a prescribed value, for instance, 5 amp. Then the metal melts, the circuit is broken, and the fuse must be replaced after the short circuit has been repaired. The fusible wire is mounted in a porcelain receptacle, which prevents the melted metal from doing damage to the surroundings (Fig. 2).

FIG. 2.—A "plug" fuse. (Courtesy of Central Scientific Company.)

THERMOELECTRICITY

Electrical energy is readily changed into heat, but the inverse process, the production of electrical energy by heat, is more difficult. One way to do this is by means of a **thermocouple.** Connect two copper wires to a millivoltmeter or galvanometer and to a piece of iron wire as shown in Fig. 3. Heat one of the iron-copper junctions with a bunsen burner, and the needle of the instrument will be deflected. The essential condition for the production of the voltage is that the two junctions of the two metals be at different temperatures.

The cause of the thermoelectric effect is not well understood, but it is not unlike the evaporation of molecules from a liquid, where they are more numerous, into the space above, where they are less so. The heating of the liquid at A (Fig. 4) causes molecules to vaporize and to travel over to B where they are condensed. The circulation continues as long as the temperature difference is maintained. Similarly in the electric circuit (Fig. 3) electrons evaporate at the hot junction from copper in which they are more numerous and "condense" at the cold junction so that a current is set up. (This analogy is faulty in that it does not explain the fact that the thermoelectric current decreases to zero and then reverses when the temperature of A is raised far enough.)

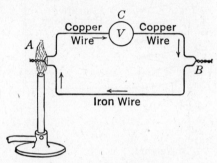

FIG. 3.—A Thermocouple.

Thermocouples may be constructed with any two conducting substances. The potential differences which they produce are only a few hundredths of a volt, hence they do not compete with batteries or dynamos. However, they are very useful for measuring temperatures of furnaces and the like. One junction of the two metals is often kept at constant temperature by means of an ice bath. The other junction, placed in a porcelain tube for protection, is inserted into the furnace. The voltmeter reading is noted, and the temperature is read off from a chart supplied by the manufacturer of the thermocouple.

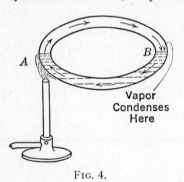

FIG. 4.

421. The Thermopile. Several thermocouples connected in series form a thermopile, which is more sensitive to temperature changes than a single element (Fig. 5). Temperature differences as small as a millionth of a centigrade degree can be measured by these devices. Thermopiles have been used successfully in biological research in studying the heat evolved by living tissue. For instance, a piece of muscle of a newly killed frog is suspended near one set of junctions of a thermopile mounted in a vessel kept at a constant temperature. The heat evolved by the muscle warms the near-by junctions and causes a deflection of the galvanometer to which the thermopile is attached. When the muscle is stretched by suspending a heavier mass from it, the galvanometer deflection increases, showing that more heat is emitted. The generation of heat by the muscle when working and when resting has been studied under various conditions so that better insight has been gained as to the physics of living organisms.

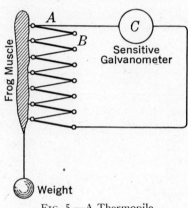

Fig. 5.—A Thermopile.

SUMMARY

The heat produced in a conductor can be computed by $E = IVt = I^2Rt$, and 4.18 joules = 1 cal.

Tungsten lamp filaments are preferable to carbon filaments in that they can be operated at higher temperatures and therefore are more efficient.

In gas-filled incandescent lamps, the gas acts as a blanket impeding evaporation. The lamps, operated at higher temperatures, are generally more efficient than those which are evacuated.

Electric fuses are metal wires or strips which are placed in series in electric supply wires. They afford protection by melting and opening the circuits when the currents rise above prescribed values.

A thermoelectric e.m.f. can be generated by causing a temperature difference between the two junctions of two wires, made of different materials, joined to form a circuit.

REVIEW QUESTIONS

1. Show how to compute the number of calories of heat generated in a coil by an electric current.

2. Discuss the development of the incandescent lamps, showing how each new type of lamp is better than the one preceding it.

3. The glass bulb of a gas-filled 100-watt incandescent lamp is hotter than the bulb of a vacuum lamp of equal wattage. Why?

4. If our coal and oil deposits were exhausted, where could we get energy to run our machines?

5. Describe an electric fuse, and show how it is used.

6. Discuss the thermoelectric effect, and suggest applications not mentioned ˙ the text. (Consult an encyclopedia.)

PROBLEMS

(1 kw-hr. = 3,600,000 joules.)

1. A 6-V., 5-amp. automobile headlight bulb has the same power as a 100-V. lamp. What is the current through the lamp?

2. How many calories of heat are generated per second by a 500-watt electric iron?

3. A flashlight battery delivers a current of 2.0 amp. for a total "life" of 5.0 hr. The e.m.f. is 2.8 V. (*a*) How many joules of energy are liberated? (*b*) How many calories of heat are produced? (*c*) How many grams of water would be heated from 20°C. to 100°C. by this energy?

4′. Two 12-Ω coils are connected first in series, then in parallel across a 6.0-V. battery. What are (*a*) the total current and (*b*) the total wattage, in each case?

5′. An electric heater to be attached to a water faucet uses 5.0 amp. at 120 V. It is advertised as "delivering scalding hot water in 1 minute." What time would be required for it to heat 2,000 grams of water (about 2 quarts) from 20°C. to 80°C. if no heat escaped?

6′. An electric iron uses 720 watts when heating at the maximum rate and 360 watts when the heating is a minimum. The voltage is 120 V. What are the current and the resistance in each case?

7′. An electric iron in a 110-V. circuit uses 5.0 amp. Find (*a*) the resistance and (*b*) the cost of operation for 30 min. at 6.0 cents/kw-hr.

8′. The storage battery of a car when fully charged can deliver a current of 12 amp. for 6.0 hr. Its average e.m.f. is 6.0 V. (*a*) How much energy is liberated? (*b*) How many kilograms of water would this energy heat from 20°C. to 80°C.?

9′. An electric mangle requires a current of 12.0 amp. at 120 V. (*a*) What is its power? (*b*) How much does it cost per hour of operation if the price of electrical energy is 3 cents/kw-hr.?

10′. An electric toaster is used for 6.0 min./day, the current being 2.0 amp. and the potential difference 110 V. What is the cost of the energy per month of 30 days at 3.0 cents/kw-hr.?

11′. If no heat escapes, how much electric energy is required to heat a bathtub of water of mass 40 kg. from 20°C. to 70°C., and how much will the energy cost at 3 cents/kw-hr.?

12′. A coffee percolator requires 5.0 amp. at 110 V. How long will it require to heat 1,000 grams of water from 20°C. to 100°C. if no heat escapes?

13′. How many 110-V., 55-watt lamps can be operated in parallel in a circuit without melting a 20-amp. fuse connected in the circuit?

14′. In problem 3, how many kilowatt-hours of energy are liberated, and how much does the energy cost per kilowatt-hour if the two cells of the battery cost 15 cents?

CHAPTER XLIV

MAGNETISM

We stand today on a bright oasis of knowledge in an illimitable desert of the unknown.
—LORD SALISBURY.

Introduction. The history of magnetism resembles that of electricity in that a few simple facts were known to the ancients. The first records of magnetic phenomena are found in Greek literature. According to one tradition, a shepherd named Magnes observed that the iron head of his staff was strongly attracted by certain black stones made of an iron ore called "magnetite." Perhaps the word "magnet" arose from the name of the shepherd, but more probably it is derived from Magnesia, a province in Asia Minor where magnetic iron ore was found. In Greek literature there are several "tall stories" about magnetism. For instance, it is told that Archimedes used a very strong magnetic stone or "lodestone" to draw nails from the hulls of enemy vessels, causing them to sink. Some of the things recorded have excellent justification. Plato quotes Socrates as saying that an iron ring rubbed against a lodestone acquires the ability to attract other iron objects. These magnetized rings were probably used by the sorcerers to awe the public and, judging by modern quackery, the physicians found them advantageous in treating rheumatism and other ailments.

During the Middle Ages there was little progress in the knowledge of magnetism, but the "figments and falsehoods" about it grew in number, and the lodestones were highly valued. Sometimes, ground to a fine powder, they were used internally as a medicine. Again they were applied externally to cause melancholia or to reconcile estranged husbands to their wives. Men claimed that the lodestone lost its magical powers if rubbed with garlic and regained them when smeared with goat's blood. During this long period, there was one outstanding accomplishment. About two centuries before the discovery of America, someone found that a magnetized steel needle placed on a bit of wood floating on a water surface would turn to a nearly north-south direction. This invention of the magnetic compass enabled the mariner to venture far out to sea, being guided by the magic needle when the skies were obscured by fog.

The reign of Queen Elizabeth was a period of great progress, not only in literature and in geographical exploration, but also in scientific discovery. Gilbert, the queen's physician, made careful investigations of magnetic phenomena similar to those in electricity and discovered many of the laws which will be discussed in this chapter.

422. Magnets and Magnetic Poles. A magnet is a body which attracts pieces of iron, nickel, and a few other materials. Dip a magnetized iron bar into a box of iron filings. Then remove it; the filings will cling to it at regions near the ends. These regions where the filings adhere are called the poles of the magnet. Suspend a magnet by a cord, or place it on a block of wood, floating in a basin of water. It will swing around to a nearly north-south position. The end that points toward the arctic is called the **north-seeking pole** or more briefly the **north pole**. The other one is the **south-seeking pole** or the **south pole**.

Fig. 1.—"Mohammed's Coffin." The upper magnet is supported by magnetic repulsion of the like poles of the lower magnet. (Courtesy of Central Scientific Company.)

423. The Forces Exerted by Magnetic Poles. If the north pole of a magnet is brought near to the north pole of another magnet suspended by a cord, the two repel each other, but if a south pole

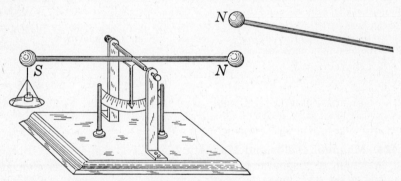

Fig. 2.—Apparatus to measure the forces exerted by magnetic poles.

is brought near, attraction occurs. In general, **like poles repel but unlike poles attract each other**. This law is similar to that for electric charges, but it should be emphasized that the phenomena are different. Poles exert forces on poles, charges on charges, but magnetic poles do not attract or repel electric charges.

The forces exerted upon each other by two magnetic poles can be measured by the apparatus represented in Fig. 2. A magnet with ball ends is pivoted like the beam of a balance or trip scale. Another magnet is supported as shown, and its north pole repels the lower one downward. Then a suitable mass is attached to the other end of the balance to force the pole up to its initial position. The weight of the added mass equals the force of repulsion of one pole on the other. The distance between them may be taken as that between the centers of the balls. (If the balls were not used, the poles would not be concentrated at points but would be distributed over considerable distances along the magnet.)

If the force between two equal poles is 1 dyne when the distance between them is 1 cm., each is said to be a unit pole.

Two like poles of strengths m_1 and m_2 at a distance d apart repel each other with a force F given by

$$F = \frac{m_1 m_2}{d^2} \tag{1}$$

Example. A north pole A of strength 6.0 unit poles (u.p.) is placed in air at a distance of 3.0 cm. from a south pole B of strength 10 u.p. What is the force of attraction on B?

$$F = \frac{m_1 m_2}{d^2}$$

$$F = \frac{6.0 \text{ u.p.} \times 10.0 \text{ u.p.}}{9.0 \text{ cm.}^2} = 6.67 \text{ dynes}$$

Equation (1) calls to mind Newton's equation for the gravitational attraction between two particles. However, the force depends upon the medium surrounding the two magnets. Equation (1) applies rigorously only in a vacuum. When the poles are surrounded by a magnetic material, it should be written

$$F = \frac{m_1 m_2}{\mu d^2} \tag{2}$$

The constant μ, called the permeability of the medium, as will be seen later, measures the ease of magnetization. For air and most other substances the value is nearly unity, the same as that for a vacuum.

424. Magnetic Fields and Magnetic Lines. The region about a magnet in which a magnetic pole would experience a force is called a magnetic field. The existence of the field near a magnet may be demonstrated as follows. Lay a magnetized bar of iron on a table and cover it with a sheet of cardboard. Sprinkle iron filings onto the cardboard and tap it lightly. Then the filings will arrange themselves from pole to pole along curved "magnetic lines" (Fig. 3). Each line shows the direction of the force that would act on a north pole of a magnet if placed at any point on that line. Fig. 4 represents some of the magnetic lines of the field produced by a U-shaped magnet. All of the lines lead from the north pole to the south pole, for each shows the path along which a north pole would be urged to move. Place several small compasses along one of the lines, and each will swing around to a position tangent to the line.

The force exerted on a magnet pole by a field depends upon two

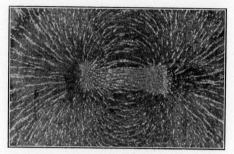

Fig. 3.—The field of a bar magnet.

factors, the pole strength m and the magnetic field strength H at the point where the pole is located. By definition,

$$\text{Force} = \text{Field strength} \times \text{Pole strength}$$
$$F = H \times m$$
$$H = F/m \tag{1}$$

A unit magnetic field (called a gauss or sometimes an oersted) is one in which a unit magnet pole experiences a force of 1 dyne. One gauss or oersted equals 1 dyne per unit pole.

Example 1. A magnetic pole of strength 10 units was placed midway between the poles of a U-magnet. The force acting on it was 20,000 dynes. What was the field strength at that point?

$$H = F/m = \frac{20,000 \text{ dynes}}{10 \text{ u.p.}} = 2,000 \text{ dynes/(u.p.)}$$

Fig. 4.—The field of a U-magnet.

Example 2. What is the field strength at a point which is 5.0 cm. from a magnet pole the strength of which is 100 u.p.?

Imagine that a unit pole is placed at the point. The force acting on it is given by

$$F = \frac{m_1 m_2}{d^2} = \frac{100 \text{ u.p.} \times 1 \text{ u.p.}}{(5 \text{ cm.})^2} = 4.0 \text{ dynes}$$
$$H = F/m_2 = 4.0 \text{ dynes/(u.p.)} \text{ or gauss}$$

Notice that in Fig. 3 the lines are most closely packed together in the regions close to the magnetic poles where the field is strongest. It

is customary to represent the strength of a magnetic field at each point
by the number of lines that are drawn through a square centimeter of
surface at right angles to the field. Thus a field strength of 12 dynes
per unit pole (12 gauss) is represented by drawing 12 lines per square
centimeter (perpendicular to the field).

425. The Process of Magnetization. When a piece of iron is magnetized, no particles are added to it or taken away from it. Instead, the

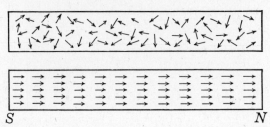

Fig. 5.—In an unmagnetized bar, the little magnets are disorganized. When the bar
is fully magnetized, all the magnets are lined up parallel to the field.

process causes a rearrangement of little magnets already existing in
the metal. These magnets in an unmagnetized piece of iron are believed
to be disorganized, in a helter skelter, random manner. When the iron
is magnetized they are regimented into an orderly array, so that the
north poles point in the same general direction. If all the tiny mag-

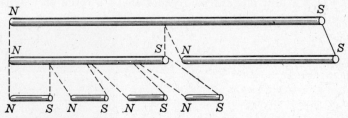

Fig. 6.—Making little magnets out of a large one.

nets are lined up in this manner, the magnet is said to be "saturated" (Fig. 5).

The following experiments help to explain the process of magnetization. Fill a long, narrow, glass tube with iron filings and stroke it from
end to end with the north pole of a bar magnet. This operation causes
many of the magnetic particles to swing around so that they point in
the same direction. Afterward one end of the tube will attract the
north pole of compass, but the other end will repel it. Shake the tube
so as to rearrange the filings and it will be demagnetized so that neither
end will repel the north pole of the compass. Break a magnetized

knitting needle or hacksaw blade into two equal pieces and each will be a magnet (Fig. 6). Then break one of these pieces in two, and again the parts are found to be magnetized. If one could repeat this process time after time, he would eventually arrive at the ultimate magnetic particles. Their nature will be discussed in the next chapter.

426. The Earth is a Great Magnet. Before the experiments of Gilbert, the reason why the compass needle turned to a north-south position was not understood, and it was believed that some object in the skies, such as the north star, was the agent of attraction. Gilbert suggested that the earth is a gigantic magnet with poles acting on the compass needle. In order to show how the earth acts, he fashioned

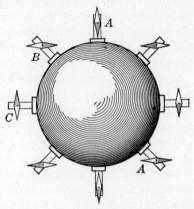

FIG. 7.—A magnetized sphere has a field like that of the earth.

a piece of lodestone into a sphere (Fig. 7) and mounted a magnetized needle on a horizontal axis so that its pole could tilt up and down instead of sidewise. He found that when the tilting needle was located

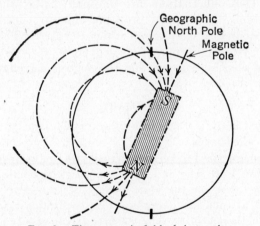

FIG. 8.—The magnetic field of the earth.

near the "equator" of the small, magnetized sphere it became parallel to the axis of the sphere, that is to a line through the two poles. As it was moved toward A, the north pole of the compass titled downward more and more until at A the needle pointed toward the center of the sphere. The effect of the earth on a tilting compass is similar to this. As the compass is carried northward from the equator, the tilt of the "dipping" needle increases until, at a certain location, the needle is vertical. This point is one of the earth's two magnetic poles. The earth's field might be produced by a huge bar magnet about 4,000 miles long placed as shown in Fig. 8. The axis of the magnet is not parallel to the axis of rotation of the earth, and the magnetic poles are several hundred miles distant from the respective geographic poles.

427. The Declination of the Compass. During Columbus' first voyage to America the sailors were greatly alarmed because the compass shifted more and more as the journey continued. Today all sailors know that the declination or deviation from the north-south direction is different for different places. The principal reason for this declination is that the magnetic poles do not coincide with the geographic poles.

428. Variations in Declination. Surveyors and mariners rely upon the magnetic compass in determining directions, and they need to know the declinations for their localities. In America the information is supplied by the U. S. Coast and Geodetic Survey. The declination at a given place is not constant but changes slowly as the years go by; the variation in some places has been several degrees in a century. In addition to this slow change, the earth's magnetic field varies irregularly, hour by hour, during the day, the changes being a few hundredths of a degree. These fluctuations are unusually large when there are "magnetic storms." They are probably due to variations in the strength of the streams of electrons which the earth receives from the sun. Magnetic storms are most prevalent at times when many spots are present on the sun's surface, and the electron currents from sun to earth are most intense.

SUMMARY

A magnetized body attracts iron filings which cling to it at centers of attraction called poles.

A pivoted, magnetized rod comes to rest with its two poles in a nearly north-south direction. The end that is nearer the north is called the north pole, the other one the south pole.

Unlike poles attract and like poles repel each other.

A unit magnetic pole is one which exerts a force of 1 dyne on an equal pole, 1 cm. distant, in a vacuum (or, very closely, in air).

The force exerted by a pole of strength m_1 on another pole of strength m_2 at a distance d is given by

$$F = \frac{m_1 m_2}{\mu d^2}$$

The constant μ depends upon the medium; its value is unity in a vacuum and also, very closely, in most substances.

A magnetic field is a region in which magnetic forces are appreciable. Its strength H, defined by $H = F/m$, is expressed in gauss or dynes per unit pole.

A "magnetic line" is the path along which an isolated, free, north pole would move. The magnetic lines of a magnet are directed from its north pole to its south pole.

In an unmagnetized piece of iron, it is supposed that there are tiny magnets which are arranged at random. Magnetization causes them to "line up" in a certain direction. When all the particles are thus organized, the magnet is said to be "saturated."

The earth is a great magnet, its two poles being located several hundred miles from the geographic poles. At the magnetic equator a "tilting compass" needle is horizontal, and at the magnetic poles it is vertical.

The deviation of the compass from a north-south direction is called the declination. The declination at any location varies slowly from year to year. Smaller changes occur from hour to hour.

REVIEW QUESTIONS

1. What is a magnet? A magnetic pole?

2. Why was the progress in knowledge of magnetism very rapid after the work of Gilbert?

3. Why is magnetism so profitable to quack physicians?

4. Define "unit magnetic pole," and discuss the factors on which the forces between two poles depend. Will a magnetic pole attract an electric charge?

5. Define "magnetic field strength," and state a unit in which it is expressed.

6. What is a magnetic line?

7. Make a rough diagram of the magnetic field produced by two north poles and one south pole located at the corners of an equilateral triangle.

8. In what important respect does magnetization differ from charging a body electrically?

9. Can you produce a magnet with two poles, one of which is stronger than the other? Why?

10. Why does jarring help to magnetize or demagnetize a piece of iron?

11. Why is iron more easily magnetized than steel?

12. Discuss the magnetism of the earth.

13. A vertical iron fence post is magnetized by the earth's field. Would you expect the upper end to be a north pole or a south pole? Why? Would pounding it with a hammer probably increase or decrease the magnetism? (Suggestion—use a small pocket compass to test the magnetism of such a post.)

14. Discuss the variation of the tilt of a dipping needle as it is carried from the arctic to the antarctic regions.

15. What is magnetic declination? Is there any point on the earth where the magnetic compass points southwest? Where?

16. How could you use a dipping needle to locate a large body of iron ore?

17. Why is a compass on an iron ship less reliable than one on a wooden ship?

18. If you were on a desert island and had a compass, how could you determine the declination?

PROBLEMS

1. A force of 2.2 lb. (1,000 gwt. or 980,000 dynes) is required to hold a magnet pole at a distance of 2.0 cm. from an equal pole. Find the strength of either pole.

2. Compute the force of attraction of a north pole of strength 20 u.p. on a south pole of strength 50 u.p. at a distance of 2.00 cm.

3. A north-seeking magnetic pole of strength 20 u.p. is at a distance of 4.0 cm. from a south pole of strength 40 u.p. Find the force of attraction.

4′. A strongly magnetized knitting needle of mass 20 grams is supported in a vertical glass tube with its lower end above the south pole of a bar magnet. The entire weight of the needle is supported by magnetic repulsion. If the distance between the two poles is 1.00 cm., and the pole of the bar magnet is of strength 200 u.p., find the strength of the pole of the knitting needle. (Neglect the influence of the other poles of the two magnets.)

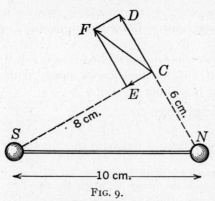

FIG. 9.

5′. A magnet pole of strength 160 u.p. exerts a force of 2.04 gwt. (2,000 dynes) on another pole which is 4.0 cm. away. What is the strength of the other pole?

6. A magnet pole of strength 20 u.p. experiences a force of 40.8 gwt. (40,000 dynes) when supported midway between the poles of a U magnet. What is the field strength at that point?

7. Suppose that a finger ring of area 2.0 cm.² is placed at the point (problem 6). How many magnetic lines pass through the ring if it is perpendicular to the lines?

8. What is the force exerted on a pole of strength 50 u.p. when placed at a point where the field strength is 800 dynes/u.p.?

9. Find the field strength at a point 2.0 cm. from a north pole of strength 100 u.p.

10. Find the field strength at a point midway between the two poles of a U-shaped magnet. The poles are 10 cm. apart, and the strength of each is 200 u.p.

11′. The distance between the two poles of a bar magnet is 10 cm. The strength of each pole is 200 u.p. What is the field strength at a point (on the axis of the magnet) 10 cm. from one pole and 20 cm. from the other?

12″. What is the field strength at the point *C*, Fig. 9? The strength of each magnet pole is 100 u.p.

13′. At a certain point in Arizona the dipping needle is at an angle of 60° with the horizontal. The strength of the earth's magnetic field (parallel to the needle) is 0.53 dyne/u.p. What is the strength of the horizontal component of the earth's field?

14″. The two poles of a tilting compass needle are each of the strength 50 u.p. The strength of the earth's field is 0.50 dynes/u.p. Find the force exerted on each pole by the field, also the sum of the two forces.

CHAPTER XLV

ELECTROMAGNETISM

When Sir William Gilbert made his experiments on static electricity and on magnetism, he noted the resemblances between the forces exerted by magnet poles on each other and those exerted by electric charges. Gilbert suspected that electricity and magnetism were closely related, but he could not prove the relationship by experiments. About two centuries elapsed before electrical theory and magnetic theory formed a partnership and, thus united, began to serve mankind.

429. Electric Currents Produce Magnetic Fields. At the dawn of the nineteenth century, as the reader will recall, the Italian physicists Galvani and Volta had a controversy over whether the electric currents which caused the twitching of frog legs were necessarily produced by living animal tissue. This controversy was finally settled when Volta showed that currents could be produced by a voltaic cell consisting of two dissimilar metal plates in an electrolyte. This important invention provided, for the first time, a source of continuous electric currents and helped greatly in the investigations of

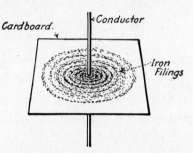

Fig. 1.—(Courtesy of John Wiley & Sons, Wright & Smith, "Automotive Construction and Operation.")

electrical phenomena. Twenty years later, Oersted, a Danish professor of physics, noticed that an electric current in a wire deflected a near-by compass needle, which proved that the current produced a magnetic field. This discovery of a relationship between electricity and magnetism aroused great interest. Soon it was demonstrated that a current in a long straight wire produces magnetic lines which are circular, in a plane at right angles to the wire. To show that this is true, pass a wire vertically through a hole in a horizontal piece of cardboard on which there are iron filings. Establish a current of 30 or 40 amp. in the wire, and the filings will line up in concentric circles (Fig. 1).

430. The Right-Hand Rule. In Fig. 2 several small compasses are placed at equal distances from a vertical wire. When the current is

403

directed upward, the compass needles turn to the position represented, hence the magnetic field is counterclockwise as viewed from above. When

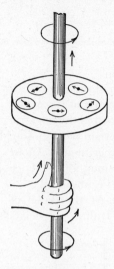

the current is reversed, the needles turn about and point oppositely. The direction of the magnetic field produced by any current can be found by the following rule, which is very useful in studying dynamos, motors, and the like. It should be mastered now.

Grasp the wire with your right hand, the thumb pointing in the direction of the current. Then the fingers will point in the direction of the magnetic field.

431. Magnetic Field Strength and Current. The strength of the magnetic field produced by a current I in a long, straight wire is directly proportional to the strength of the current and inversely proportional to the perpendicular distance R from the wire. When the current is expressed in amperes and the distance in centimeters, the field strength at any point is given by

Fig. 2.—Illustrating the right-hand rule.

$$H = 2\frac{I}{10}\frac{1}{R} \tag{1}$$

If N turns of wire are wound into a circular coil of radius R, the magnetic field strength produced at the center of the coil by a current I is given by

$$H = 2\pi N\frac{I}{10}\frac{1}{R} \tag{2}$$

Suppose that many turns of wire are tightly wound onto a long cylinder, forming a uniform spiral coil called a helix. A current in the wire produces a magnetic field. The magnetic lines thread through the coil as shown in Fig. 3. The field of such a current in a helix closely resembles that produced by a bar magnet. The magnetic field strength inside the coil is given by

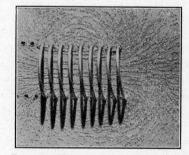

$$H = 4\pi\frac{I}{10}\frac{N}{L} \tag{3}$$

Fig. 3.—The magnetic field produced by a current in a helix.

Example 1. A long trolley wire carries a current of 200 amp. in a south-to-north direction. (a) What is the magnetic field strength produced by the current at a point 100 cm. below the wire? (*b*) What is the direction of the field at this point?

(*a*) From equation (1),

$$H = 2 \times 200 \text{ amp.}/10 \times 1/100 \text{ cm.} = 0.40 \text{ dyne/u.p. or gauss}$$

(*b*) Using the right-hand rule, the magnetic field is found to be directed westward.

Example 2. A helix is 100 cm. long and has 1,000 turns. If the current is 20 amp., what is the magnetic field strength at the center of the coil?

$$\frac{N}{L} = \frac{1,000 \text{ turns}}{100 \text{ cm.}} = 10 \text{ turns/cm.}$$

$$H = 4\pi \frac{10 \text{ turns}}{\text{cm.}} \times \frac{20 \text{ amp.}}{10} = 80\pi \frac{\text{dynes}}{\text{u.p.}} = 80\pi \text{ gauss}$$

432. Magnetic Induction. In the preceding chapter it was pointed out that, when one pole of a magnet is placed near the end of an iron rod, the rod is magnetized, that is, many of the tiny magnets in it line up parallel to one another. It is more convenient to magnetize the iron by means of an electric current. Wrap several hundred turns of insulated wire onto a long iron rod, and establish a current through the coil by means of a battery. The field inside the coil will cause the tiny magnets in the iron to line up, producing a strong electromagnet. Electromagnets are much more useful than permanent magnets because their strengths can be readily controlled by changing the current through the windings. Most of the electrical devices which do the work of the world have electromagnets as important components. The strength of an electromagnet depends not only upon the number of turns of wire around the iron "core" and upon the current in the wire, but also upon the "permeability" of the iron.

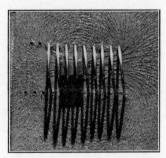

433. What is Magnetic Permeability? When an iron bar is placed inside a coil carrying a current, the strength of the magnetic field at the ends of the bar is increased many fold because of the magnetization of the iron (Fig. 4). It follows that more magnetic lines emerge from each

FIG. 4.—A small iron bar, placed inside a helix carrying a current, causes the magnetic field to become stronger near its ends.

square centimeter at the ends of the bar. We think of these lines as extending through the iron; hence we say that the number of magnetic lines in the iron is greater than the number if the bar were removed from the coil. The ratio of the "flux" or number of lines per square centimeter inside the metal, to the number per square centimeter of the magnetic field (if the core were removed), is the "permeability" μ of the substance. The value for iron may be many thousand, so that an electromagnet may be much stronger than if its core were made of wood, copper, or the like.

$$\text{Permeability } (\mu) = \frac{B}{H} = \frac{\text{No. of lines/cm.}^2 \text{ in substance}}{\text{No. of lines/cm.}^2 \text{ in magnetizing field}}$$

For example, a long helix has 100 turns of wire per centimeter. If the current is 10 amp., the field inside the coil is

$$H = 4\pi \times 100 \text{ turns/cm.} \times 10 \text{ amp.}/10 = 400\pi \text{ dynes/u.p. or gauss}$$

If an iron rod is placed inside the coil and the permeability is 1,000, the number of lines per square centimeter inside the coil is given by

$$B = \mu H = 1,000 \times 400\pi \text{ lines/cm.}^2 = 400,000\pi \text{ lines/cm.}^2$$

434. Permeabilities of Different Substances. The great importance of electromagnets in motors, dynamos, and other machinery has led

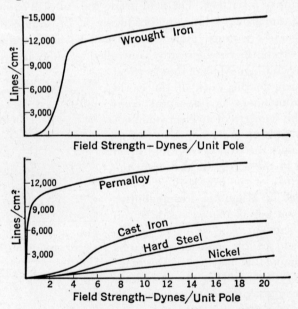

FIG. 5.—Magnetization curves for different materials.

to careful studies of the magnetic properties of different kinds of iron and steel as well as of other materials. Permanent magnets are made of hard steels which require high fields for magnetization. The permeabilities of these steels are low but they retain most of the magnetization after the field is reduced to zero. Most electromagnets have cores made of wrought iron. A nickel-steel alloy called "permalloy" can be strongly magnetized by very weak fields. For this reason it has many applications in the electrical industry, particularly in telephony.

The magnetization curves for several materials are given in Fig. 5. Notice that the number of lines per square centimeter increases rapidly at first and more slowly afterward. When all the magnetic particles are lined up parallel to the field, the magnet is said to be saturated and the number of lines per square centimeter is nearly constant.

435. Magnetism Caused by Spinning Electrons. The fact that moving electric charges produce magnetic fields leads us to suspect that the magnetism of iron is caused by electric currents. The important question arises: What is the nature of the magnetic particles? In recent years much evidence has been accumulated which indicates that these particles are electrons each of which rotates on its axis like a tiny earth. According to this view each spinning electron is a magnet. When iron is placed in a field these particles tend to line up with the field. The next question is: Why are most substances not strongly magnetized like iron? Is it because there are no spinning electrons in these materials? On the contrary, the opinion holds that in these materials the spinning electrons are present, but that all of them are "paired off," as it were, so that when one spinning electron lines up with the field its partner turns in the opposite direction. Since the effect of each electron is neutralized by that of its mate, the resultant magnetization is zero.

436. All Substances are Slightly Magnetic. Iron, cobalt, and nickel can be strongly magnetized, but the permeabilities of most materials are nearly unity. Their magnetizations probably arise not from the spinning of electrons but from their motions in orbits around their atomic nuclei. In some "paramagnetic" substances the electrons move in such a way as to increase the number of magnetic lines. In other, "diamagnetic" substances the revolving electrons tend to weaken the field.

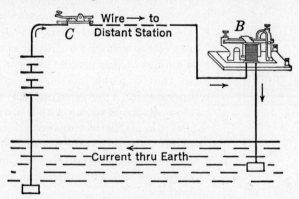

FIG. 6.—A simple telegraph system.

437. The Electric Telegraph Sounder. One of the simplest applications of electromagnetism is the telegraph sounder. As shown in Fig. 6

it consists of an electromagnet above which is an iron plate, called an "armature," attached to a pivoted bar. When the operator at a distant

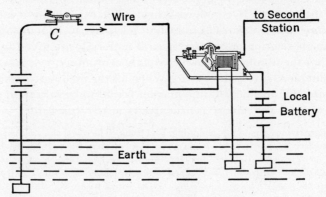

FIG. 7.—A telegraph relay system.

station pushes the telegraph key C, an electric circuit is closed, and a current energizes the electromagnet, which pulls the armature down.

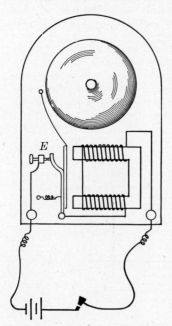

FIG. 8.—An electric bell.

When the key is opened, the armature is pulled upward by a spring. A short closing of the key produces a "dot," a longer one a "dash," so that messages can be transmitted.

438. The Relay. In long-distance telegraphy, the resistance of the wires is too great to use a single battery and hence a system of relays is employed (Fig. 7). The key C is closed, energizing the electromagnet of the relay at a distant station. The windings of this magnet have many turns so that a feeble current is sufficient to operate it. The armature of the relay closes a second circuit with its own battery, and the signal is transmitted to a more distant station. At the terminal station, the relay closes the circuit through an ordinary telegraph sounder operated by a local battery.

439. The Electric Bell. In the electric bell (Fig. 8), current from a battery energizes an electromagnet which attracts an armature as in the telegraph sounder. When the armature moves toward the magnet, the circuit is broken at E and the armature is then drawn back to its initial position by a spring, thus reclosing the circuit. In consequence the armature vibrates and the gong rings. Notice that an electric bell will operate just as well if the terminals of the battery are reversed. It would therefore operate if the current changed direction many times per second. Hence it can be energized by "alternating" current.

440. The Moving-Coil Galvanometer. The ordinary galvanometer consists of a flat coil of wire mounted on pivots between the poles of a

FIG. 9.—A moving-coil galvanometer. The coil is at right angles to the needle.

U-shaped magnet (Fig. 9). To make clear its operation, we review a few facts as to the magnetic field produced by a current. Fig. 10A rep-

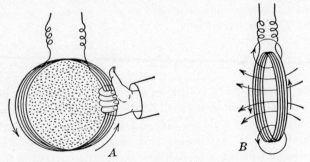

FIG. 10.—The magnetic field due to a current in a coil.

resents a coil of wire lying on a table top. The direction of the current in the coil is indicated by the arrows. Grasp the coil with your right hand, the thumb pointing in the direction of the current. Then the fingers point in the direction of the magnetic lines. These lines emerge from the upper face of the coil, which therefore acts like the north pole of a magnet. Tilt the coil to a vertical plane as shown in Fig. 10B and its left face is the north pole. The current in the coil of the galvanometer represented in Fig. 9 is directed upward and to the right along the near side. Hence the left face of the coil acts like a north pole of a bar magnet. This face is repelled by the nearby (north) pole of the U magnet. The coil therefore turns on its pivots and the pointer is deflected. The motion is opposed by one or more spiral springs. The angle of twist increases as the current becomes greater. Hence the pointer and scale, which indicate the angle deflection, show the intensity of the current.

441. The Ammeter. A galvanometer may be modified so as to measure larger currents, forming an ammeter. This is done by attaching across the terminals of the movable coil a metal strip or wire called a shunt. Most of the electricity flows through the shunt and only a little through the coil. The resistance of the shunt is so adjusted that the total current through the shunt and coil in parallel is indicated by the pointer and scale (Fig. 11).

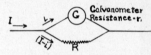

FIG. 11.—A shunted galvanometer.

Example. The scale reading of a galvanometer is 10.00 when the current in the coil is 10 milliamperes (0.010 amp.). The resistance of the coil is 20 Ω. What is the resistance of the shunt so that the total current shall be 10.00 amp. when the scale reading is 10.0 divisions?

The voltage across the terminals of the moving coil is given by Ohm's law.

$V = 0.010$ amp. $\times 20$ Ω $= 0.20$ V.

Since the total ammeter current is 10.00 amp. that through the shunt must be 9.99 amp. Its resistance is, therefore,

$$R = \frac{0.20 \text{ V.}}{9.99 \text{ amp.}} = 0.020 \text{ Ω}$$

442. The Voltmeter. A voltmeter is merely a galvanometer having a very high resistance in series with it. The value of this series resistance is so adjusted that the scale reading equals the applied voltage between the terminals of the instrument. For example, suppose that a galvanometer has a resistance of 20 ohms and that a current of 0.010 amp. causes a deflection of 10 scale divisions. What resistance must be connected in series with it to convert it into a 10-volt voltmeter? The required current to cause this scale reading is 0.010 amp., hence

$$R = V/I = 10 \text{ volts}/0.01 \text{ amp.} = 1,000 \, \Omega$$

The coil resistance being 20 Ω, that of the series coil must be 980 Ω.

FIG. 12.—A combined voltmeter-ammeter. (Courtesy of Central Scientific Company.)

SUMMARY

The magnetic lines caused by an electric current in a long, straight wire are a set of circles around the wire, each being in a plane at right angles to it. The right-hand rule is as follows: Grasp the wire with the right hand, the thumb pointing in the direction of the current; then the fingers will point in the direction of the field.

The magnetic field strength H at a distance R caused by a current I in a long, straight wire is given by $H = 2I/10 \; 1/R$.

The field strength inside a long helix is given by $H = 4\pi \dfrac{I}{10} \times \dfrac{N}{L}$, N/L being the number of coils per unit length of the helix.

The magnetic permeability μ of a substance is defined as the ratio of the number of magnetic lines per square centimeter inside a long rod of the substance to the number of lines per square centimeter of the magnetic field. $\mu = B/H$.

The magnetic particles producing the strong magnetization of iron, nickel, etc., are believed to be spinning electrons. In other materials the weak magnetization is ascribed to the motions of electrons in their orbits.

A coil carrying a current tends to set itself at right angles to a magnetic field.

An ammeter is a galvanometer fitted with a shunt of suitable resistance. A voltmeter is a galvanometer with a resistance coil in series with the pivoted coil.

REVIEW QUESTIONS

1. State the right-hand rule, and use it to determine the direction of the magnetic field below a trolley wire in which a current flows from west to east.

2. Make a drawing showing the magnetic field due to a current in a helix. How can you find which of its ends is a north pole?

3. From Fig. 4, do you think that permeability of iron is dependent upon its degree of magnetization?

4. From Fig. 4, estimate the approximate permeabilities of the iron for fields of 6, 10, and 20 dynes per unit pole.

5. Discuss the causes of the magnetization of (a) iron and (b) weakly magnetic materials.

6. Describe the structure and operation of the telegraphic sounder and relay; also of the electric bell.

7. Describe a pivoted-coil galvanometer, and show how it can be converted (a) into an ammeter and (b) into a voltmeter.

PROBLEMS

1. A trolley wire carries a current of 300 amp. What is the field strength at a point 150 cm. from the wire?

2'. What is the magnetic field strength at a point midway between two long, parallel, straight wires, 20 cm. apart, carrying currents in opposite directions, each current being 10.0 amp.?

3. What is the magnetic field strength inside a coil 100 cm. long having 10,000 turns, if the current is 2.00 amp.?

4'. (a) What is magnetic permeability? (b) When a long iron rod is placed in the helix described in problem 3, the number of lines per square centimeter is 251,000. What is the permeability of the iron?

5''. The coil resistance of a galvanometer is 50 Ω and the scale reading is 10 divisions when the current through the coil is 1.00 milliampere. What is the resistance of the shunt which will convert it into an ammeter reading 10.0 amperes when the scale reading is 10?

6''. What resistance must be connected in series with the galvanometer described above in order to convert it into a voltmeter reading 10 V. when the scale reading is 10?

7'. A voltmeter has a resistance of 200 Ω and its maximum reading is 1.50 V. What resistance must be connected in series with it to make its maximum reading 150 V.?

CHAPTER XLVI

INDUCED CURRENTS

I could trust a fact and always cross-question an assertion.—FARADAY.

Introduction. After Oersted's momentous discovery that an electric current produces a magnetic field, physicists soon began to ask the question, "If electric currents produce magnetic fields, should not magnetic fields produce currents?" Among those who considered this matter was Michael Faraday. It took him several years to find the answer. His discovery of electromagnetic induction in 1831 is one of the great triumphs of science. It is interesting to note that the honor

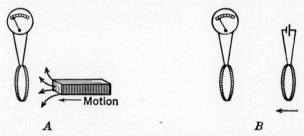

FIG. 1.—Inducing a current in a coil by changing the number of lines that thread through it.

is shared by Joseph Henry, then an obscure school teacher in West Albany, New York, but later a renowned scientist. The official credit is given to Faraday because he was the first to publish his results.

Electromagnetic induction can be illustrated by a few simple demonstrations. Place a bar magnet near one face of the coil connected to a galvanometer (Fig. 1A). Move the magnet toward the coil and the galvanometer needle is deflected, revealing the existence of a current. When the motion ceases, the current does also. Move the magnet away from the coil, and the galvanometer needle moves in the opposite direction, showing that the current is reversed. Now replace the magnet by a second coil connected to a battery (Fig. 1B). When this coil is moved toward the first one, or away from it, the galvanometer deflects as it did when the magnet was shifted. As a third experiment, keep the coil at a fixed position, and open the circuit so as to interrupt the current. Then the galvanometer needle is deflected as though the coil were removed. When the circuit is closed again, the deflection is in the opposite direction.

To gain further insight into the matter, consider the field of the magnet used in the first experiment. When the coil is at a considerable distance from the north pole, few of the magnetic lines pass through the coil. When it is moved closer, the number increases; when it is moved farther away, the number of lines through it diminishes. In both cases currents are induced. **A current is induced in a closed circuit whenever the number of magnetic lines threading through that circuit is changed.**

443. The Induced Current Opposes the Change—Lenz's Law. When a magnet pole is moved toward one face of a coil or ring, the current

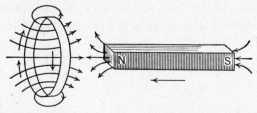

FIG. 2.—The induced current causes a magnetic field opposing the change.

induced in the coil produces a magnetic field so that one face of the coil becomes a north pole and the other a south pole. Moreover, these induced magnetic poles always oppose the change that is occurring. For example: Move the north pole of a magnet closer to one face of a finger ring, and this face becomes a north magnetic pole, opposing the motion (Fig. 2). Remove the bar magnet, and the current in the ring will reverse, so that the nearer face becomes a south magnetic pole, again opposing the motion. This rule is expressed by Lenz's law, as follows:

Whenever a current is induced, its magnetic field opposes the change that is occurring.

Lenz's law and the right-hand rule can be used to predict the direction of induced currents. When the north pole of a magnet is moved closer to a vertical ring (Fig. 2), the induced current opposes the motion, producing a north pole on the nearer face of the ring. To cause this north pole, magnetic lines must emerge from this face of the ring as shown in the figure. Now grasp the ring with your right hand, so that the fingers point in the direction of the induced field, and the thumb will point in the direction of the current, that is, downward in the nearer side of the ring.

444. Lenz's Law from Conservation of Energy. Though Lenz's law was first discovered experimentally, it might have been predicted from the principle of the conservation of energy. When a magnet pole is pushed toward a coil and a current is set up, the wire is heated, energy must be supplied, and work must be done. If the induced current aided the motion, no work would be required to bring up the magnet and energy would be created out of nothing. Since this is impossible, it follows that Lenz's law must be true.

445. Induced Electromotive Force. When the number of magnetic lines threading through a coil changes, a current is induced if the circuit is closed. If it is open, there will be no current, but in either case there always is an induced **electromotive force** tending to cause a current. The amount of induced electromotive force (e.m.f.) is proportional to the rate of change of the magnetic lines through the coil and to N the number of turns of wire.

In a single loop of wire, an e.m.f. of 1 volt is induced when the rate of change is 100 million magnetic lines per second.

In a coil of N turns the induced e.m.f. is N times as great.

$$\text{E.m.f.(volts)} = \frac{N \times \text{Change of number of magnetic lines per second}}{100,000,000}$$

Example. When a bar magnet is near a coil of 1,000 turns, the number of magnetic lines through the coil is 2,000. If in 2.0 sec. the magnet is removed so that no lines pass through the coil, find the average induced e.m.f.

$$\text{E.m.f.} = \frac{(1,000 \text{ turns} \times 2,000 \text{ lines})/2.0 \text{ sec.}}{100,000,000}$$
$$= 1/100 \text{ V.}$$

446. Direct and Alternating Current. Hitherto we have dealt principally with direct currents, in which electricity is transferred in a constant direction. Most of the electrical energy which we use is transferred by alternating current: The electrons in a wire do not progress but are continually pushed to and fro, each oscillating about a certain position. The unit of alternating current is defined as follows.

An alternating-current ampere is that alternating current which heats a conductor at the same rate as an international ampere.

In like manner **an alternating-current volt is that alternating voltage which produces in 1 ohm a current of 1 alternating-current ampere.**

The great advantage of alternating current over direct current is the ease with which the voltage may be raised or lowered. The device used for these purposes is the transformer.

447. The Transformer. The transformer is an astonishingly simple device having no mechanically moving parts. It consists of a ring or rectangle of iron on which there are two separate sets of coils (Fig. 3).

Suppose that the coil *A* is connected to a battery. When the circuit is closed, the iron will be magnetized and the magnetic lines will follow the iron path and will thread through the other set of coils *B* and *C*. The changing of the magnetic lines will induce an e.m.f. in each coil which will persist only as long as the field is changing. Open the circuit and the magnetic field will die down so that an opposite e.m.f. is induced. Now connect the coil *A* (through a suitable resistance) to the house-lighting system which provides an alternating voltage of, say, 110 volts. The current through the coil will reverse 120 times per second (60 cycles) and magnetic lines will be thrust through

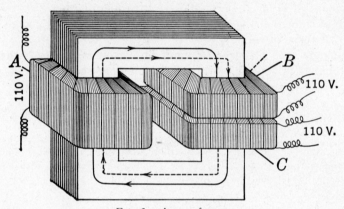

FIG. 3.—A transformer.

the other coils, first in one direction, then in the other, repeatedly. Suppose that the three coils have the same number of windings. Then the voltage induced in *B* and that in *C* will each be about equal to that supplied to *A*. The two coils *B* and *C* can be connected in series so that the output voltage across them is twice that across the input coil *A*. A transformer in which the output coils have more turns than the input coils is called a "step-up" transformer. In the step-down transformer the output coils have fewer windings than the input coils and the voltage is lowered. A doorbell transformer having one-tenth as many windings in the output as in the input coils "steps the voltage down" from 110 volts to 11 volts. In general, **the ratio of the number of windings on the two coils approximately equals the ratio of the voltages.**

A transformer does not produce energy, hence the output power cannot be greater than the input power. Therefore, if the voltage is stepped up by a transformer, the current must be reduced.

Example. The input current to a transformer is 1 amp. at 2,000 V. What is the output current at 100 V. if the efficiency is 100 per cent?

Input power   Output power

2,000 V. × 1.0 amp. = 2,000 watts = 100 V. × x, x = 20 amp.

448. Electrical Energy is Usually Transmitted at High Voltage. The power supplied by a dynamo is equal to the product of the voltage by the current. Thus 2,000 watts is transmitted either by 1 amp. at 2,000 volts or by 20 amp. at 100 volts. The heating of the wires is proportional to the square of the current, so that it is 400 times greater at the lower voltage than it is at the higher. In a typical electrical system, the electrical energy is generated at 2,300 volts (Fig. 4). Then it is stepped up to 115,000 volts by huge transformers at the power station. After

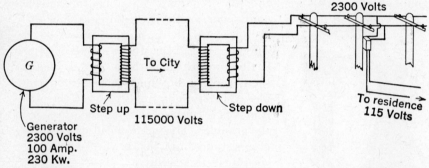

Fig. 4.—Transformers raise the voltage at the power house, lower it at the city and still more at the residences.

the energy is transmitted to central points in the city, transformers reduce the voltage to 2,300 volts. Smaller step-down transformers mounted in iron boxes on poles near the residences lower the voltage to 115 volts, and from these the energy is delivered to the householders. Other smaller transformers may be used to operate electric bells, radios, and the like. A huge silent transformer transmitting power equal to that of fifty thousand horses, is one of the most important devices in the electrical industry.

449. The Telephone. The first successful telephone, constructed by Alexander Graham Bell in 1875, was a very crude affair (Fig. 5). The transmitter A and the receiver B were electromagnets, each having a thin steel plate or diaphragm near one of its poles. When the diaphragm of A was pushed closer to the electromagnet, the magnetization of the iron was increased, and an e.m.f. was induced in its coil, causing a current in the wire. This changed the magnetization of the receiver magnet B, forcing its plate to move. Therefore, when someone spoke

near the transmitter, the sounds caused the diaphragm to vibrate and
the induced currents produced corresponding motions in the receiver.

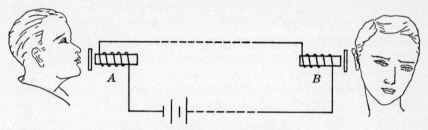

FIG. 5.—Bell's simple telephone.

Numerous improvements have made modern telephone systems very
complicated. There are hundreds of patents revealing the achievements. One of the most important of these
is the carbon transmitter, invented by
Thomas A. Edison. In its modern form a
flexible metal diaphragm pushes against
the cover of a box filled with carbon granules. When sounds are incident on the plate,
it moves to and fro, varying the pressure of
the granules. This motion causes variations
of resistance and hence variations of the
current in the circuit.

FIG. 6.—A telephone receiver.
(Courtesy of Central Scientific
Company.)

The modern telephone receiver (Fig. 6)
is essentially the same as the one invented
by Bell, differing from it only in that, instead of a bar magnet and single coil, a U-
magnet is used with two coils, one mounted
near each pole.

The essential parts of a transmitter and receiver system are diagrammed in Fig. 7. The battery in the circuit A causes a current through

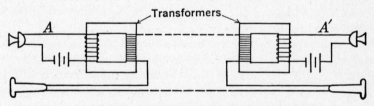

FIG. 7.—A simple telephone system.

the in-put coil of the transformer. Sound waves impinging on the diaphragm of the transmitter force it to vibrate, changing the pressure of

the carbon granules, causing variations in the electric current, and varying the magnetization of the iron core of the transformer. The output coil has many turns, so that the output e.m.f. is high, hence relatively large currents are induced in the external circuit, and the telephone receiver at the distant station responds. The receiver at the transmitting station also emits sound, but this is usually unnoticed by the person speaking.

450. The Spark Coil or Induction Coil. A spark coil or induction coil is used to produce high voltages by means of a battery or other

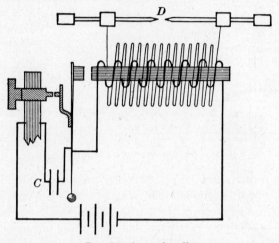

FIG. 8.—A spark coil.

direct-current source (Fig. 8). It somewhat resembles a step-up transformer, the input coil having a few turns of heavy wire while the output coil has many thousand turns of fine wire. When the switch in the battery circuit is closed, the iron core is magnetized. Opening the circuit causes a sudden demagnetization and induces a very great e.m.f. in the output coil. The circuit is opened and closed automatically by a vibrator, like that of an electric bell, and a series of sparks are produced at D.

The condenser C acts like a reservoir into which electricity moves when the vibrator contact is opened. It tends to prevent sparks from occurring at the contact points, which would tend to melt the metal there. The theory of the condenser will be treated in a later chapter.

451. The Ignition System of a Car. In automobile engines the explosive mixtures of air and gasoline are ignited by means of electric sparks. The ignition coil used to produce them differs from an induction coil in that the contacts are closed and opened by a rotating device driven by the engine. As shown in Fig. 9, the input windings of the ignition coil are connected in series with the battery and the circuit breaker. The circuit is opened several times for each revolution of the wheel W which is geared to the engine. Whenever the circuit is broken, a high e.m.f. is induced in the output windings of the ignition coil. Let us now see how sparks from the single coil are produced in a six-cylinder motor. In the "distributor" there is a revolving arm which touches

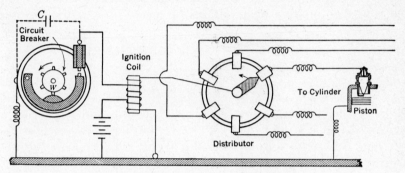

Fig. 9.—Ignition system of an automobile.

six contacts in turn, each being connected to a spark plug in a separate cylinder. This arm is driven at the same speed as the circuit breaker so that sparks are produced in the various cylinders in a sequence.

452. Self-Induction. We have learned that induced e.m.f.'s are caused by varying the number of magnetic lines threading through a circuit and that the induced current always opposes the change that is occurring. This is true no matter what causes the change of magnetic lines. It may be due to the bringing up of a magnet pole toward a coil, or to the change of current in a near-by electrical circuit. Lastly, the change of magnetic lines may be due to variations of the current in the coil itself. When the current in a coil is increasing, the building up of the magnetic lines always causes an e.m.f. opposing the increase. On the contrary, when the current is decreasing, the dying down of the magnetic lines tends to maintain the flow of electricity. **The tendency of a circuit to oppose changes of the current in that circuit is called self-induction.** (This is similar to the tendency of a body to oppose changes in its velocity and therefore it is sometimes called "electrical inertia.")

Self-induction may be demonstrated as follows. Connect an incandescent lamp and an electromagnet in parallel with each other through a resistance to a direct-current source (Fig. 10). When the switch is first closed, the current through the electromagnet is impeded by self-induction. That through the lamp is great because it has little self-induction, hence it glows brightly. After a small fraction of a second, the current through the electro-magnet builds up to its full value (determined by Ohm's law) and the magnetic field becomes constant. Most of the flow is through the coil, so that the lamp becomes dim. When the switch is opened, the lamp flashes up brightly for an instant. The disappearance of the magnetic lines

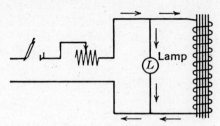

FIG. 10.—An inductance coil.

in the coil induces an e.m.f. which causes the current through the lamp. Repeat the experiment using 60-cycle alternating current, and the lamp will continue to glow brightly. The reason is that the current reverses periodically before the iron core has been fully magnetized. The time between reversals is insufficient for the current in the coils to grow to its full value.

When the trolley of a streetcar slips from the trolley wire, sometimes a long electric arc is produced. It is caused chiefly by the self-induction of the coils in the electric motors.

453. Self-Inductance—The Henry. The amount of self-induction produced in a coil depends upon the rate of change of the current and upon the *self-inductance* of the coil. **A coil has a self-inductance of 1 henry if an e.m.f. of 1 volt is induced when the current changes 1 amp./sec.**

Example. The current in an electro-magnet decreased from 8 amp. to 3 amp. in 1/100 sec. The average induced e.m.f. was 500 volts. What was the self-inductance of the coil?

A change of 5 amp. in 1/100 sec. is 500 amp./sec. This rate of change induces an e.m.f. of 500 volts. It follows that a change of 1 amp./sec would cause 1 volt. The self-inductance is therefore 1 henry.

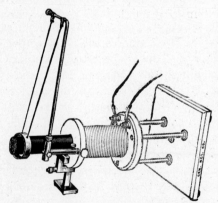

FIG. 11.—Currents induced in the suspended ring cause it to be momentarily repelled. (Courtesy of the Central Scientific Company.)

454. Eddy Currents. Support an aluminum ring like a pendulum around one pole of an electromagnet connected to a battery (Fig. 11). Close the switch, and magnetic lines will be thrust through the aluminum ring. The current in the ring will oppose this change, hence the ring is pushed outward. Soon the induced current dies down and the ring moves back to its initial position. Open the switch so that the coil is demagnetized. This is equivalent to withdrawing a magnet pole. The induced current opposes the change and the ring is pulled toward the electromagnet. Repeat these experiments after replacing the ring by a solid aluminum disk suspended in front of the iron core. The disk will behave as the ring did. Consequently we know that **currents are induced in a solid conductor by a varying magnetic field.** The whirlpools of electrons set up in this manner are called "eddy" currents.

If an aluminum frying pan is placed close to one pole of a powerful electromagnet connected to an alternating-current source, the metal can be heated sufficiently by the eddy currents to boil water or to fry eggs. Thus eddy currents may be useful in producing heat. However, in alternating-current machinery it is usually desirable to prevent them, and to this end the cores of transformers and of field magnets and the armatures of dynamos and motors are built up of varnished sheets of iron so that the insulation between layers may prevent eddy currents.

SUMMARY

Whenever the number of magnetic lines threading through a coil or circuit is changed, an electromotive force is induced tending to cause a current. The induced current is in such a direction as to cause a magnetic field opposing the change. The induced e.m.f. is proportional to the rate of change of magnetic lines. One volt is induced in a single loop of wire when the rate of change is 100 million lines per second.

A transformer consists of an "input" coil and an "output" coil wound on an iron ring. The ratio of the output to the input voltages approximately equals that of the numbers of windings on the respective coils. The output power cannot be greater than the input power.

Self-induction is the production of an e.m.f. in a circuit by the variations of the current in that circuit. The induced currents always oppose the variations.

If a circuit has a self-inductance of 1 henry, the induced e.m.f. is 1 volt when the current changes at a rate of 1 amp./sec.

Eddy currents are whirlpools of electrons produced in conductors by varying magnetic fields.

REVIEW QUESTIONS

1. What is electromagnetic induction? Describe some experiments by which it can be demonstrated.

2. State Lenz's law, and show how it may be proved (*a*) by experiment and (*b*) by the law of the conservation of energy.

3. A finger ring lies against a wall of a room. When the north pole of a magnet is moved toward it, is the induced current counterclockwise or clockwise?

4. Are (a) a current and (b) an e.m.f. always induced when the number of magnetic lines passing through a coil is changed?

5. How can you compute the e.m.f. produced by a changing magnetic field?

6. Describe a "step-up" transformer.

7. Describe a simple telephone system, showing the purpose of each part.

8. Describe a spark coil or induction coil and also an ignition system for an automobile.

9. (a) What is self-induction? How can it be demonstrated? (b) Show how to increase the self-inductance of a coil.

10. What is a "henry"?

11. A metal disk vibrates like a pendulum near one pole of an electromagnet. Describe what happens (a) when the coil is magnetized and (b) when it is not magnetized.

12. Describe the heating effect and the "damping" effect of eddy currents.

PROBLEMS

1. The number of magnetic lines threading through a single loop of wire changes from 200,000 to 50,000 in 1/6 sec. What is the average induced e.m.f.?

2. An induction coil has 100,000 turns. The number of lines through it changes from 400,000 to 0 in 1/100 sec. What is the average induced e.m.f.?

3'. Ten thousand magnetic lines emerge from the north pole of a bar magnet. If a finger ring is moved from a considerable distance and is slipped onto the bar magnet in 1/10 sec., what is the average induced e.m.f.?

4'. The input coil of a transformer has 10,000 turns; the output coil has 100 turns. The output current is 2.0 effective amperes at 120 effective volts. (a) What is the input current and voltage if the efficiency is 100 per cent? (b) What is the input power?

5'. The voltage of a power transmission line is 200,000 effective volts, and the current is 20 effective amperes. What are (a) the power and (b) the power loss (I^2R) in heating each kilometer of wire, the resistance being 0.40 Ω/km.?

6''. An electromagnet has a self-inductance of 3.0 henries. What is the induced e.m.f. when the current is reduced from 10.0 amp. to 0 amp. in (a) 1 sec., (b) 1/100 sec.?

7'. The strength of the vertical component of the earth's magnetic field at a certain place is 0.60 dyne/u.p. A boy's hoop, having a cross-sectional area of 10,000 cm.², is tilted from a horizontal position to a vertical, north-south, plane in 0.25 sec. What is the average e.m.f. induced in the hoop?

CHAPTER XLVII

GENERATORS AND MOTORS

When Faraday discovered that electric currents can be produced by varying the number of magnetic lines threading through a coil, people were greatly interested. One day at a public lecture the prime minister of Great Britain asked a question which is often heard today. "Mr. Faraday," he said, "this discovery is very interesting, but of what use is it?" Faraday replied rather dryly, "Perhaps it will give rise to a great industry on which you can levy taxes." Faraday's prediction came true half a century later when practical *generators* or *dynamos* were invented and began to supply electrical energy to homes and factories.

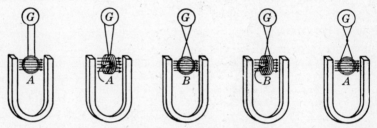

Fig. 1.—Rotating the coil changes the number of magnetic lines through it and induces an electromotive force.

A generator consists of one or more coils, rotating in a magnetic field, producing an electromotive force. A simple experiment will make clear the theory of its operation. Connect a coil of wire to a galvanometer and suspend the coil between the poles of a U-magnet (Fig. 1). Rotate the coil 90° so that the side A faces the north pole of the magnet. This operation causes magnetic lines to enter the coil and the galvanometer needle deflects, say, to the right. Turn the coil through another 90°, removing all the magnetic lines from the coil, and the galvanometer deflects to the left. A third rotation of 90° brings the face A next to the south pole of the magnet and causes a deflection to the left. Finally, bring the coil back to its initial position and the needle moves to the right. During the complete rotation, the magnetic lines were thrust through the coil twice and were twice removed from it. If

424

the turning of the coil were continued, an alternating current would be generated.

455. The Slip Rings. The coil just described could not be rotated continuously because of the twisting of the wires. This difficulty is avoided in practical generators by the use of "slip rings" mounted on the axle on which the coil revolves (Fig. 2). Brushes pushing against the revolving rings conduct the energy away from the generator.

When the circuit is open and no electricity flows, little effort is required to turn the coil. If the circuit is closed, the current produces a magnetic field which opposes the motion (Lenz's law). More work must be done, and mechanical energy is transformed into electrical energy.

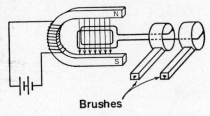

Fig. 2.—A simple alternating-current generator.

456. The Sine Curve. When the coil of a simple generator turns at constant speed, the electromotive force varies as shown in Fig. 3. It is zero when the coil is at right angles to the field, and rises to a maximum when it has turned 90°. Then the electromotive force decreases to zero at 180°, reaches a negative maximum at 270°, and goes back to zero at

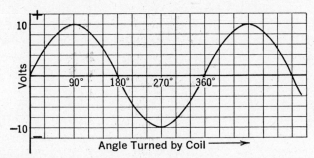

Fig. 3.—The induced electromotive force varies with the angular position of the coil.

360°. This curve is repeated for each complete revolution of the coil. It is called a "sine curve" because its equation is $Y = A \sin \theta$. A is the maximum value of the e.m.f., and θ the angle through which the coil has turned.

457. Direct-Current Generators. Alternating current can be used for electric lights and for operating some types of electric motors. It cannot be used for charging storage batteries or for some other purposes. Fig. 4 represents a simple direct-current generator. Particular attention should be given to the "commutator" C which reverses the connections to the outer part of the circuit whenever the e.m.f. of the coil reverses. Therefore, though the current in the coil is alternating, that in the external part of the circuit is constant in direction. If slip rings were used, the output voltage would be represented by the dotted line in Fig. 5. In fact, the commutator reverses the connections at A,

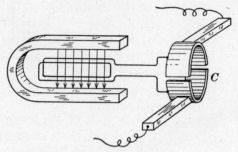

FIG. 4.—A simple direct-current generator.

B, C, and D, so that the output voltage is as represented by the heavy line.

The current produced by the device just described is constant in direction but not in magnitude. In practical direct-current generators, the "drum" type of armature is employed. Numerous coils are wound in slots in a cylindrical iron core (Fig. 6). The commutator has many segments. In this arrangement the brushes make contact with the various coils in turn. Moreover, the contact with each coil is made at

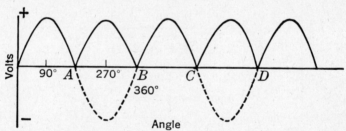

FIG. 5.—The current in the coils is alternating; that in the external circuit is pulsating and direct.

the time when the induced e.m.f. in that coil is a maximum. For this reason the voltage across the brushes is nearly constant.

458. The Magnetic "Cut-Out." The output voltage of a generator depends upon the speed of rotation of the armature. When an automobile is traveling at a speed lower than 6 or 8 mi./hr. the armature or rotating system of the generator turns so slowly that the e.m.f. is less

than that of the storage battery. Therefore the generator must be dis-
connected from the battery to prevent it from being uselessly dis-

Fig. 6.—A generator, showing a drum armature and commutator. (Courtesy Chicago
Apparatus Company.)

charged. This is accomplished automatically by means of a magnetic
"cut-out" (Fig. 7). When the generator is driven at high speed, its
current energizes the cut-out magnet which closes the contact C. Then
the generator supplies the energy to charge the storage battery and also
to operate the ignition coil and lights. When the engine slows down

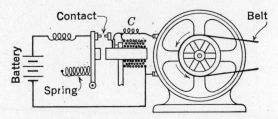

Fig. 7.—The magnetic cut-out of an automobile.

sufficiently, the cut-out magnet weakens so that a spring opens the
contact. The battery then supplies the energy for the ignition coil and
the lights.

MOTORS

A generator produces electrical energy by the expenditure of work,
but a motor performs the opposite service. That is, it uses electrical
energy to do work. The device sketched in Fig. 8 may be used either

as a generator or as a motor. If it were driven by a steam engine, the repeated thrusting of magnetic lines through the coils would generate a pulsing e.m.f. Suppose, instead, that it is connected to a battery. The poles will be magnetized as shown and the armature will turn to

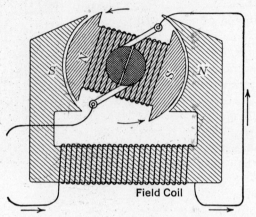

Field Coil

Fig. 8.—A simple two-pole motor.

a horizontal position. Then the commutator will reverse the current through the coils. Each pole will be repelled by the near-by pole of the U-magnet, and the rotation will continue. Attraction always occurs

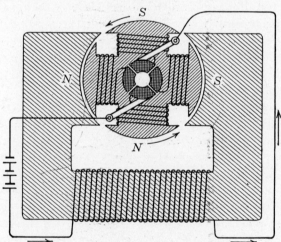

FIG. 9.—A simple four-pole motor.

when the poles are approaching each other, repulsion as they move away, so that the forces tend to maintain the motion.

The motor represented in Fig. 9 is more desirable than the one just described because it produces a more uniform torque. Its armature has two electromagnets mounted at right angles to each other. The commutator is divided into four parts or segments. In the position shown, the vertical magnet is energized so that the armature rotates counterclockwise. After it turns 45°, the brushes will pass from one pair of segments to the other so that the other electromagnet is energized. Thus the upper pole is always south, the lower one north, and the forces maintain the motion. The drum type of armature is used in the starting motors of automobiles and in most other motors. It is magnetized by the current as shown by the iron filings in Fig. 10. The forces between the poles and those of the field magnet maintain the rotation just as in the simple motor.

FIG. 10.—Magnetic field of an armature.

459. "Universal" Motors. If the input current to the motor shown in Fig. 9 were reversed, the upper end of the armature would become a north pole and the lower one a south pole. Meanwhile the polarity of the U-magnet would also reverse, and the armature would rotate in the same direction as before. The rotation is unaffected by the reversal of the current, hence these motors can be driven either by direct or by alternating current. They are often used in washing machines and vacuum sweepers and are called "universal" motors.

In order to reverse the direction of rotation, the direction of the current in the armature coils is reversed, without changing the current in the field coils.

460. The Counter Electromotive Force of a Motor. Connect an incandescent lamp to the lighting system, in series with a small motor. If the armature is prevented from rotating, the lamp glows brightly but it becomes dim as the speed increases. The reason is that the flux of magnetic lines in the coils varies just as in the generator. Moreover, the electromotive force always opposes the current, hence it is called a counter electromotive force. When the motor is turning at high speed, the counter e.m.f. is large and the current through the coils is small. As the load on the motor increases and it slows down, the back e.m.f. diminishes and the current increases. Thus the input current increases with the load.

Let the resistance of the coils be R, the applied voltage V, and the counter e.m.f. e. Then, by Ohm's law, the current I is given by

$$I = (V - e)/R$$

Example. The starting motor of an automobile has an armature resistance of 0.050 Ω. The applied potential difference is 6.0 V. and the counter e.m.f. is 3.00 V.

(a) What is the current? (b) If the armature did not turn, what would the current be?

(a)
$$I = \frac{(V - e)}{R} = \frac{6.0 \text{ V.} - 3.00 \text{ V.}}{0.050 \, \Omega} = 60 \text{ amp.}$$

(b)
$$I = \frac{V}{R} = \frac{6.0 \text{ V.}}{0.050 \, \Omega} = 120 \text{ amp.}$$

461. The Controller of a Streetcar. In a large motor the excessive starting current is likely to do damage, and it must be reduced by means of resistances which are cut out as the motor speeds up and the back e.m.f. increases. In most streetcars the connections are changed by means of "controllers." To start a car, the motorman moves the

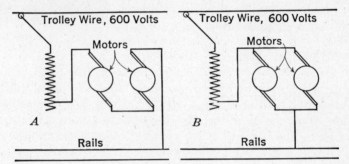

FIG. 11.—When a street car is starting, the motors are connected first in series (A), later in parallel (B).

controller handle to the first notch so that the two motors and the rheostat are in series (Fig. 11A). As the speed of the motor increases, the handle is moved forward step by step, gradually reducing the rheostat resistance to zero. In this position of the handle, the full potential difference, say 600 volts, is applied across the two motors in series, and that across each is 300 volts. The next shift of the handle connects the two motors in parallel with each other and in series with the rheostat (Fig. 11B). Then the rheostat is gradually cut out, and finally each motor operates at 600 volts and maximum power.

462. Series, Shunt, and Compound Motors. In some motors the armature coils and the field magnet coils are connected in series (Fig. 12A). When the motor is turning slowly, the back e.m.f. is small and the current is large. This current energizes both the field and the coils so that the torque is very great. These motors are used for streetcars, rock crushers, and other machines in which the load varies greatly. A streetcar can travel fast on a level street, but when climbing a steep hill it must slow down in order that the motors may exert a great torque. **The torque of a series motor at low speed is much greater than at high speed.**

In "shunt" motors (Fig. 12*B*) the field magnet coils and the armature coils are connected in parallel so that the full voltage is if you wish applied across the field magnets and their strength is constant. Hence the torque varies less with speed than that of the series motor.

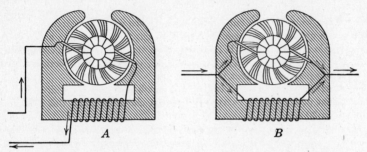

FIG. 12. (A) A series-wound motor, (B) A shunt-wound motor.

In the "compound" motor the armature has two sets of windings, one in series with the field coils, the other in parallel. The torque is nearly independent of the speed.

SUMMARY

A generator consists of one or more coils rotating in the field of an electromagnet so as to produce an electromotive force.

When the armature of a motor rotates, a counter e.m.f. is induced, tending to decrease the current.

In series motors the torque is much greater at low speed than at high speed. In shunt motors the two sets of windings are in parallel and the torque varies less with speed than that of a series motor.

REVIEW QUESTIONS

1. Describe a simple generator, and show how the e.m.f. varies when the coil is turned at constant speed. Also show how to change an alternating-current generator so that it will produce direct current.

2. Why does the input current of a motor decrease as the speed increases?

3. Describe the difference in structure between series and shunt motors and also in their operation. Which would be preferable for operating a rock crusher?

4. Describe the operation of a "cut-out."

PROBLEMS

(1 horsepower = 0.746 kw.)

1'. A wire is fastened around the edges of a screen door, forming a 1.0 m. by 3.0 m. rectangle. The door is rotated 90° in 2.0 sec., turning from an east-west to a north-south plane. The strength of the horizontal component of the earth's field is 0.20 dyne/u.p. (a) How many magnetic lines pass through the rectangle in the first position? (b) What average e.m.f. was induced by the rotation of the door?

2″. The armature coil of a simple generator has 1,000 turns; 10,000 magnetic lines thread through the coil when it is at right angles to the field. What is the average effective induced e.m.f. when the coil makes 10 rev./sec.?

3′. A shunt motor in which the field is constant is connected to a battery having an e.m.f. of 6.0 V. The total resistance in the armature circuit is 0.30 Ω. When the motor runs at full speed (zero load) the counter e.m.f. is 5.0 V. (a) What is the armature current? (b) What is the current when the motor runs at half speed (full load)? (c) What would be the current if the armature were prevented from turning?

4. When the generator of a car delivers zero current, 100 watts are required to overcome friction. What power is required when the generator causes a current of 10 amp., the e.m.f. being 6.4 V.? (Assume that, excepting the frictional loss, the generator is 100 per cent efficient.)

5′. The starting motor of a car is 70 per cent efficient and it requires 50 amp. at 6.0 V. (a) What power does it exert? (b) To what elevation could this power raise a 3,000-lb. car in 20 sec.?

6″. The motor of a fan used to circulate the air through the "cold air return" of the furnace of a residence has an output power of 0.30 hp. The motor is 70 per cent efficient, and it operates 1/3 of the time. Find: (a) the input power; (b) the cost of operation per month of 30 days, the price of electrical energy being 3 cents/kw-hr.

7′. An up-force of 1,000 kgwt. is required to raise a fully loaded passenger elevator. (a) What input power is required to raise the elevator 3.0 m./sec. if the motor is 80 per cent efficient? (b) What is the cost of the energy required to lift the elevator 200 m. to the top of a building, the price being 1 cent/kw-hr.?

CHAPTER XLVIII

RADIO

Civilization and the Speed of Communication. In primitive societies there was little need of communication between distant tribes: messengers on foot or horseback sufficed for ordinary purposes. In times of war the flaming beacon carried warnings with the speed of light but over comparatively small distances. These means of transmitting messages were highly developed in the days of the Roman Empire. There was little increase in the speed of communication from the days of the Caesars until the nineteenth century which gave us the steamship, the railroad, the electric telegraph, and the telephone. With the railroad, speeds of 60 mi./hr. were possible, and the electric telegraph, first used in 1843, raised the value to that of light: namely, 186,000 mi./sec. Since then there has been no increase in speed, nor is any expected, for there is evidence that nothing can travel faster than light. Telegraphy without wires was not successful until the present century. As is usually true, the necessary achievements to make it possible were made during a long period. A hundred years ago, Faraday found that variations of the electric current in one circuit cause corresponding variations in another one near by. The explanation suggested by Faraday was that, when the current increased, magnetic lines traveled outward and caused induced currents in the second circuit. The question then arose, with what speed did the disturbance travel? In 1873, Clerk Maxwell, a British mathematical physicist, published an important paper giving evidence that the electromagnetic disturbances produced by alternating currents travel with the same speed as light and are of the same nature as light, though of different wave lengths. Soon investigators set about discovering means of producing and detecting these electromagnetic waves, and fifteen years later a German professor, Heinrich Hertz, devised the first radio transmitter and detected its signals at distances of a few yards. He proved that the radio waves are reflected, like light, by large metal mirrors, that they are refracted by prisms, and that they are plane polarized. Further he was able to measure their wave lengths, which were a few meters. As a result of these pioneer experiments, it was shown that radio waves are like light though of much greater wave lengths and of lower frequencies.

433

Before discussing methods of radio transmission and reception, it will be helpful to review briefly some of the facts previously presented regarding wave motion.

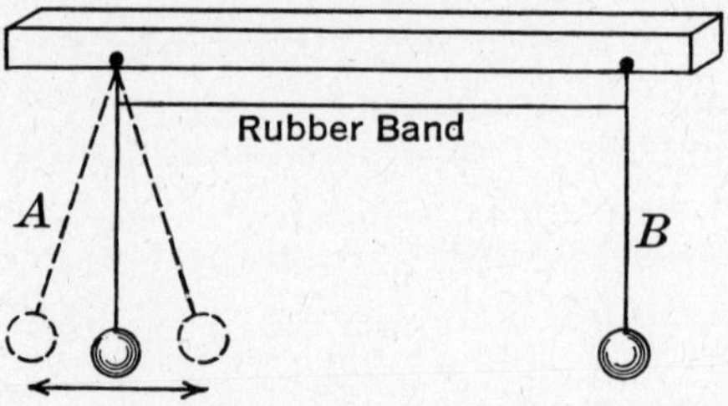

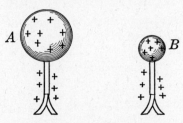

463. Resonance. Interconnect two pendulums by a rubber band (Fig. 1) and set one of them into vibration. The pulls of the rubber band will cause the other to vibrate also. Energy traveling along the rubber band is transmitted from one vibrator to the other. Moreover, the second pendulum is most readily caused to vibrate if the two have the same natural period and are "in resonance" with each other.

FIG. 1.—One pendulum readily sets the other into vibration if their periods are the same.

Place two tuning forks A and B close to one another and cause A to vibrate (Fig. 2). The sound waves travel outward and tend to set B also into vibration. In this experiment, as in the previous one, the response of B is greatest if the two have the same frequency.

These are familiar examples of the principle of resonance, namely, that when two vibrators have the

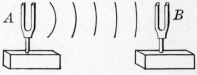

FIG. 2.—Tuning forks in resonance.

same natural frequency, one of them is easily set into vibration by the other.

464. Electromagnetic Induction. Let us also review a few facts about electromagnetic induction. Place two coils adjacent to each other, and establish a current in one of them. Then a magnetic field is produced and some of the magnetic lines thread through the other coil. When the current in the first coil varies, the number of lines through the other changes and an induced current flows in its wires. If one coil were connected to an alternating current source, the varying magnetic field would induce an alternating current in the other. This is the foundation fact of radio communication.

FIG. 3.—At a given potential, A has a larger charge than B, hence its "capacitance" is greater.

465. Electrical Capacitance. Before showing how radio waves are generated, it is necessary to describe a certain property of electrical systems called **capacitance.** Consider two metal spheres A and B, of different diameters, connected to gold leaves which serve as electroscopes (Fig. 3). Suppose that equal electric charges are imparted to both spheres. The charges on A less closely crowded together than those on B, repel one another with smaller forces and have smaller tendencies to escape. The electrical potential of A is smaller than that of B, and its gold leaves diverge less. The larger sphere requires a greater charge to produce a given potential, hence we say that it has a greater electrical capacitance or capacity. The capacitance of a body or system is defined as the charge it contains per unit of potential. If 1 coulomb changes the potential of a body 1 volt, its capacitance is 1 farad.

$$\text{Capacitance (farads)} = \frac{\text{Quantity (coulombs)}}{\text{Voltage (volts)}} \qquad (1)$$

466. Electrical Condensers. Every radio set includes several **condensers**, which are devices so constructed as to have considerable electrical capacitance. The simple condenser pictured in Fig. 4 consists of

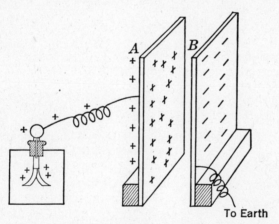

Fig. 4.—A simple condenser.

two parallel metal plates, one insulated and connected to a gold-leaf electroscope, the other grounded. When the insulated plate is charged positively, electrons are attracted from the earth to the grounded plate which is therefore charged negatively by induction. The induced negative charges on B attract the positive charges on A, decreasing their tendencies to escape, so that the potential of A is diminished and the gold leaves converge. More charges would now be required to restore the potential to its initial value, so that the capacitance is increased by the presence of the grounded plate.

The capacitance of a condenser may be made greater by using larger plates or by moving them closer together. A third way is to change the medium between them. If a large plate of glass or of ebonite is inserted between A and B, the leaves of the electroscope converge, and more charges must be added to bring them back to their previous positions. The condenser now contains a larger charge at a given voltage, hence the capacitance is increased.

The capacitance of a condenser with two parallel plates each of area A (cm.²) at a distance d(cm.) apart is given in farads, by

$$C(\text{farads}) = \frac{1}{9 \times 10^{11}} \frac{KA}{4\pi d}$$

K is the *dielectric constant* of the medium between the plates. Its value is unity for a vacuum and, approximately, for air.

TABLE I

DIELECTRIC CONSTANTS

Ebonite	2.7
Glass	5.4—9.9
Mica	5.66—5.97
Paraffin	2.10
Air at 0°C. (**normal pressure**)	1.0006
Hydrogen at 0°C. (**normal pressure**)	1.0003
Ethyl alcohol at 0°C.	28.4
Petroleum	2.13
Water	81.1
Vacuum (by definition)	1.0000

The condensers used in radio sets are either of constant or of variable capacitance. "Fixed" condensers are often made by placing sheets of paraffin paper between layers of tinfoil, and connecting alternate metal sheets together to form sets of "plates" which may be oppositely charged. The capacitance of such a condenser is relatively great because the total area of the plates is large and because they are close together.

FIG. 5.—A variable condenser for a radio set. (Courtesy of the National Company.)

We shall see presently that variable condensers are used to "tune" radio receivers so that they are in resonance with the transmitting station to which one is listening. One set of plates is rigidly mounted and connected to one terminal (Fig. 5). The other set of alternate plates, connected to the other terminal, is mounted on an axle and may be rotated so as to be completely within the other set. In this position the capacitance of the condenser has its maximum value. The capacitance is varied by turning a knob attached to the axle.

467. An Electrical Oscillator. A device in which electric charges can surge to and fro repeatedly with a certain frequency is called an **oscillator**. A very simple type is diagrammed in Fig. 6. Two metal spheres are electrically connected through a spiral coil or helix. Suppose that a negative charge is suddenly imparted to A. The electrons will repel one another and will flow along the connecting wire, as an electric current. The spiral coil, having self-inductance, will impede the growth of current at first, and afterward it will tend to maintain the flow. The electrons will accumulate on B, charging it negatively. Then a reverse current will carry the charges back to A. This surging to and fro will occur repeatedly, the current

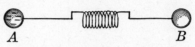

A B

Fig. 6.—Electrical oscillator.

gradually decreasing in amplitude. The period of the oscillation depends upon two factors, the capacitance and the self-inductance of the oscillator. If the two spheres are replaced by larger ones, of greater capacitance, the electrons will repel one another less strongly than before; they will travel more slowly along the wire and a greater time will be required for an oscillation. Replace the coil by another having a greater number of turns and greater self-inductance. This coil will afford greater opposition to the growth of current so that more time will be required for the charges to flow from sphere to sphere. Hence the period of oscillation is made greater by increasing either the capacitance or the self-inductance of the system.

The period T of an oscillator of capacitance C (in farads) and self-inductance L (in henries) is given by

$$T = 2\pi\sqrt{L/(1/C)} \tag{1}$$

Example. The capacitance of an oscillator is 9×10^{-10} farad, and the self-inductance is 0.040 henry. What are the period and the frequency of oscillation?

$$T = 2\pi\sqrt{\frac{0.040 \text{ henry}}{1/(9 \times 10^{-10} \text{ farad})}} = 1.2\pi \times 10^{-5} \text{ sec.}$$

Frequency $= 1/T = 26,500$ per sec. $= 26.5$ kilocycles/sec.

Equation (1) is analogous to that for the period of a simple harmonic vibrator. The self-inductance L corresponds to the mass m of the vibrating body; the quantity $1/C$, to the force constant of the spring.

468. How Radio Waves Cause Oscillations in a Circuit. In Fig. 7, B represents an "antenna," which is a long wire preferably mounted in an exposed position. It is connected to the earth through the input coil of a transformer. The radio waves from a distant transmitting station induce electromotive forces in the antenna and cause electrons to surge through the coil to the earth and back again repeatedly. The

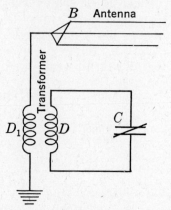

FIG. 7.—Antenna, transformer and oscillator.

transformer causes in the adjoining circuit an alternating electromotive force which forces the electrons to and fro, first one side of condenser C and then the other. When this circuit is in tune with the sending station, the oscillations are of greatest amplitude.

469. A Simple Receiving Set. Connect a telephone receiver or "head phone" across the condenser and in series with a "detector valve" (Fig. 8). This valve consists of a crystal of galena or some other suitable material, against which the point of the needle is pressed. The arrangement, called a rectifier, acts like a leaky check valve in a waterpipe. When

the upper plate of the condenser is negative, electrons flow to the right through the valve, but they cannot flow back when the plate is positive because of this valve action. Thus the alternating current is changed to a pulsating direct current. Suppose that the so-called "carrier" radio

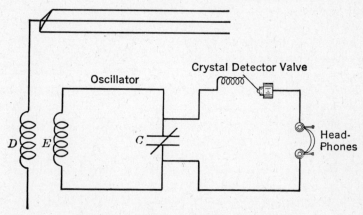

FIG. 8.—A simple crystal-detector receiver.

waves incident on the antenna are of constant amplitude. Then the alternating current in the oscillator circuit is also constant (Fig. 9A). The current through the valve does not vary, hence the head-phone diaphragms do not vibrate and no sound is heard. There are two reasons why the diaphragm does not respond. First, it is too sluggish to vibrate readily with a frequency of many thousand cycles per second. Second, the electromagnets of the head phones have large self-inductances, and the large counter electromotive forces in them "choke out" the pulsations and make the flow uniform (Fig. 9B).

When radio messages are received, the "carrier" waves are "modulated" and the current in the oscillator rises and falls (Fig. 9C). Hence the pulsating current through the valve varies and the diaphragms of the head phone vibrate so that sounds are emitted.

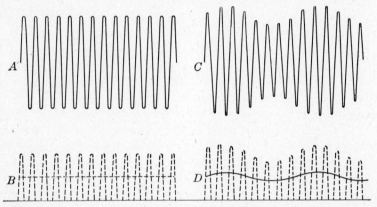

FIG. 9. (A) When no message is being received, the alternating current in the oscillator is of constant magnitude. (B) The direct current through the headphones is also constant. (C) The current in the oscillator varies when a message is being received. (D) The headphone current also varies.

470. The Three-Electrode Radio Tube. Radio tubes play important roles in modern radio sets. The three-electrode tube diagrammed in Fig. 10A has, as important parts, the "filament," the "grid," and the "plate." The filament is a fine wire of tungsten or some suitable alloy, which is heated to incandescence by current from a battery. Because of high temperature, the free electrons in the filament move about with greater speeds than at ordinary temperatures. Some of them plunge through the surface of the wire, evaporating like the molecules of a liquid. These evaporated electrons form an invisible swarm or cloud inside the evacuated tube. If a "B" battery is connected so as to make the plate more positive than the filament, electrons are attracted from the cloud to the plate. They travel from it through the battery and back again to the filament, so that a current exists in the circuit.

Now consider the action of the grid, which is a wire mesh or screen interposed between filament and plate. When the grid is more negative than the filament, it repels the electrons, opposing their flow; but when it is positive it assists the flow. Hence the current to the positively charged plate can be controlled by varying the potential of the grid.

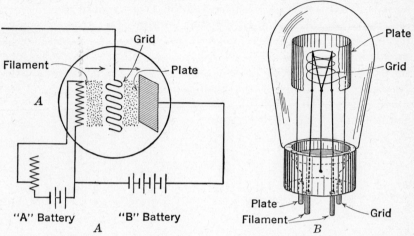

FIG. 10.—(A) Diagram of a three-electrode tube. (B) Sketch showing actual design.

471. A One-Tube Receiver. The simple receiver set shown in Fig. 11 is identical with the one previously described as to antenna and oscil-

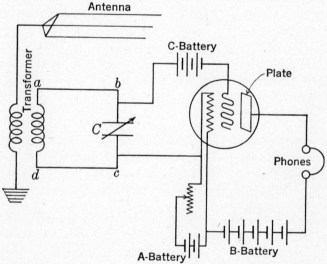

FIG. 11.—A three-electrode tube serving as a detector valve.

lator, but the crystal rectifier or "detector" is replaced by a three-electrode tube. The "C" battery causes in the grid a negative potential barely sufficient to stop the current in the plate circuit when no radio waves are being received. When the circuit is oscillating, however, the grid potential rises and falls and currents exist whenever the grid is positive. Thus a direct current flows through the head phones just as in the crystal set. Moreover, this current will increase and decrease with the "modulations" or variations of the oscillating current caused by the sounds at the transmitting station, hence sounds will be emitted by the head phones. When used in this manner, the tube serves as a "detector."

472. Amplification. In most radio sets there are several amplifier circuits interconnected by transformers, the current in each being

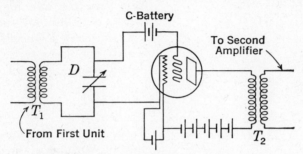

FIG. 12.—An amplifier circuit.

greater than that of the preceding one. In the circuit diagrammed in Fig. 12 the C battery is so adjusted that normally there is a current in the plate circuit. Now let an oscillating current flow in the input coil of the transformer T_1, inducing currents in the oscillator D. In consequence the potential of the grid will vary as will the current in the plate circuit. This varying current induces larger currents in the output coil of the transformer T_2 connected in the next circuit. By linking several such amplifiers in series, the oscillations can be increased many thousand fold.

Two types of amplification are used in radio receivers. Radio-frequency amplifiers are connected between the main oscillator and the detector. They magnify the "carrier" wave, reproducing all its alternations even when the amplitude is constant and no message is being received. Audiofrequency amplifiers are connected between the detector and the loud speaker. Their transformers have iron cores which are so sluggish that they are not magnetized by high-frequency oscillations of the carrier waves. Therefore they are not affected by constant carrier waves but they are affected when the waves are "modulated."

473. The Electrodynamic Loud Speaker. A very important part of a radio receiver is the loud speaker. The most important requirement is that it should emit sounds of all frequencies equally well without introducing any distortion. In the electrodynamic speaker (Fig. 13), a small coil of wire is fastened to a paper cone. This coil is suspended in the field of a strong electromagnet. The varying electric currents from the radio circuit cause the coil and cone to vibrate so that sounds are emitted.

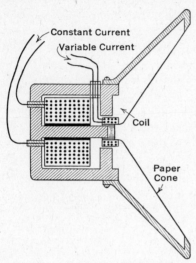

FIG. 13.—A dynamic loud speaker.

474. Alternating-Current Receivers. Most radio receiving sets get their electrical energy from alternating-current circuits instead of from batteries. The filament of an "alternating-current" tube is a hollow tungsten cylinder, which is heated indirectly by a wire supported inside it (Fig. 14). This wire is energized by alternating current from a small step-down transformer. The temperature of the heater wire varies with the alternations of the current, but that of the cylinder itself is nearly constant so that it emits a steady stream of electrons. (When a radio set is turned on, it does not respond at first because the filaments require time to heat up.)

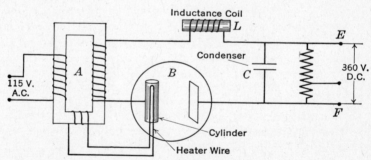

FIG. 14.—Rectifier for alternating-current sets (simplified).

The B batteries in the plate circuit are replaced by a step-up transformer A which increases the potential difference to 350 volts or so. The current from the output coil of the transformer is "rectified," or changed from alternating current to direct current, by means of the radio tube just described. The electrons can flow from filament to plate, but not from plate to filament. The tube acts like a check valve, and a direct, pulsating, current is produced. The pulsations would cause a "60-cycle hum"; hence it is necessary to make the current nearly constant. This is done by means of an inductance coil L and a condenser C. The coil, having large electrical inertia, opposes any increase or decrease of current through it. Therefore it partly smooths out the pulsations. The condenser provides a reservoir for electricity which also tends to prevent the variations in current. The inductance coil and the condenser smooth out the current so that the voltage across the terminals EF is nearly constant. The three-electrode radio tubes of the set also have cylindrical filaments like the one just described.

475. A Radio Transmitter. Having given a good deal of attention to the apparatus which receives radio messages, we now consider

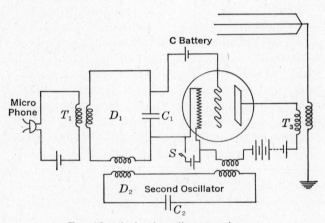

Fig. 15.—A simple radio transmitter.

briefly equipment necessary for sending them. The transmitter represented in Fig. 15 differs from the one-tube receiver in several respects. There is a second oscillator D_2 which is linked by transformers to the plate battery circuit and also to the main oscillator D_1, which has the same frequency. When the switch S is closed, the increasing current sets up oscillations in D_2 in much the same way that a single push causes a pendulum to vibrate. These oscillations cause others in D_1 (resonance) so that the grid in the tube sets up variations in the plate current. Notice that the process is self-exciting. Small oscillations set up in D_2 cause others in D_1; the grid produces larger ones in the plate circuit and hence larger effects in D_2. Thus the radio set oscillates with a certain definite frequency determined by the capacitance and self-induction. The antenna is connected to the transformer T_3, and the transmitter sends out a "carrier" radio wave of fixed frequency and constant amplitude (Fig. 9A). (In practical equipment, several stages of amplification serve to increase the amplitude of the waves.) The microphone of the transmitter, like that of a telephone, is linked to the main oscillator by means of a transformer T_1. When someone speaks into the microphone, his voice causes variations in the microphone current which induce electromotive forces in the main oscillator. These cause the radio waves to wax and wane, producing modulation (Fig. 9C).

476. Long Waves and Short Waves in Radio. The frequency of the carrier wave sent out by a station is determined by the capacitance and inductance of the oscillators. Different frequencies are assigned to different stations by the Government. Commercial broadcasting stations use "long" radio waves of length greater than 100 m. and of frequencies less than 300 kc. Shorter waves of lengths from 10 m. to 100 m. are employed for many purposes such as in sending messages by police cars, in directing airplanes, and in amateur transmitting. The most important difference in behavior between the two is that long waves are readily diffracted. They bend around obstacles easily and hence spread out fairly uniformly from the station. Short waves, on the other hand, do not bend around corners, and they can be concentrated into fairly narrow beams like light. One way to do this is to erect, behind the antenna, a curved screen of wires, which directs the waves forward in a beam.

Directed radio beams are of great service in guiding aviators. Usually two narrow beams side by side are sent out from the airport. One of these sends the signal dot-dash, the other dash-dot. Hence if an air pilot traveling from Newark, New Jersey, to Pittsburgh hears dot-dash signals, he is south of his true course. If he hears dash-dot, he is north. When the two are blended in a hum, he is exactly on the course.

An aviator flying through the fog is directed by means of the radio beam, and he can keep at a chosen elevation by means of the aneroid barometer, but how does he know when he reaches his destination? This information he gets by the "zone of silence." The radio beams sent out from the airport are directed sidewise and upward at an acute angle so that there is a region directly above the station in which no signals are received. The pilot flies through this silent zone, turns around and returns at a lower elevation, so that he can see the lights of the "runway" and can bring down his plane in safety. If the fog extends to the ground, he does not attempt to land but seeks another airport.

477. The Upper Atmosphere Acts Like a Mirror. Short-wave radio sets are amazingly effective at times in sending messages long distances.

Schoolboys have built 10-watt outfits which have been heard in Australia as clearly as the 50,000-watt, long-wave transmitters of KDKA or WLW. This great range of short waves is due to their reflection by highly ionized, conducting layers of air at elevations of 50 to 150 miles above the earth's surface. These layers act like mirrors and bend the rays back toward the earth. The ionization of the air is caused in part by ultra-violet radiations from the sun so that short waves are transmitted better in daylight than in darkness. The great trouble is that short-wave sending is very erratic. A set may be able to send messages 10,000 miles at one time, but only 1,000 miles at another.

478. Producing Heat by High-Frequency Oscillations. A high-frequency oscillator may be used not only in sending out radio waves but also in producing heat. Suppose that the antenna were removed from the transmitter diagrammed in Fig. 15 and that a piece of metal were placed inside the input coil of T_3. Then the rapidly varying magnetic field would induce eddy currents in the metal, which would be heated. High-frequency induction furnaces of this type are widely used in the manufacture of high-grade alloys such as stainless steel. The great advantage is that the metal is not contaminated by gaseous impurities as it would be in an ordinary furnace. Recently the method has been applied to the drying of lacquers on automobile bodies. The newly painted body is placed inside an enormous coil and high-frequency currents cause eddy currents in the metal. The heat thus generated causes the lacquer to harden more quickly and, what is more important, to harden first next to the metal rather than at the outer surface of the film.

479. Friendly Fevers. An ordinary fever is one of nature's ways of combating disease. Some ailments can be cured by "friendly" fevers induced by high-frequency electrical oscillations. In one type of treatment, the patient is placed in a cabinet around which is wound a coil of wire. High-frequency currents in this coil induce currents in the tissues and raise the temperature above 106°F. The artificial fever is not a cure-all, and, like other electrical methods, it is especially liable to quackery. (One way of testing whether or not a "specialist" knows a little physics is to ask him to explain the difference between a volt and an ampere!)

SUMMARY

The quantity of electrical charge Q on a body at a potential V is given by $Q = CV$, C being the electrical capacitance of the body. One farad equals 1 coulomb per volt. An electrical condenser usually consists of a number of parallel plates, alternate plates being so connected that voltage may be applied between them.

An electrical oscillator is a device in which electric charges can surge to and fro with a natural frequency of vibration. Its period is given by $T = 2\pi\sqrt{L/(1/C)}$.

The detector in a radio receiver changes the current from alternating to pulsating.

In a three-electrode tube, the current may be controlled by varying the potential of the grid.

The "carrier" wave of a transmitter is the radio wave of constant amplitude sent out when no message is being transmitted. Modulation causes the amplitude of the emitted waves to vary.

Short radio waves may be directed into fairly narrow beams, but long waves are readily diffracted.

REVIEW QUESTIONS

1. Define (a) electrical capacitance, (b) farad, (c) condenser.

2. Upon what factors does the period of a simple oscillator depend? What is meant by "tuning" a radio set? In what two ways can it be accomplished? Point out the resemblances between electrical oscillations and those of a body suspended by a spring.

3. Do you increase or decrease the capacitance of your radio set in shifting from KDKA (980 kc.) to WCAE (1,250 kc.)?

4. Explain the action of the crystal in a simple receiving set. Show how it may be replaced by a three-electrode tube. What is the purpose of the C battery?

5. Explain the operation of an amplifier circuit. How does the amount of C battery voltage differ from that in a detector circuit?

6. Explain the structure and operation of the device, in an alternating-current set, that replaces the B batteries.

7. Make a drawing of a radio transmitter, and explain its operation.

8. Discuss the advantages and disadvantages of "short" radio waves. Why do short-wave transmitters have such great ranges?

9. Explain how airplanes are guided by a radio beam.

10. What is a "friendly fever"?

PROBLEMS

1. What is the period of an oscillator having a natural frequency of 1.59×10^5 cycles/sec. or 159 kc./sec.?

2. What is the wave length of the radio waves that the oscillator in problem 1 emits?

3′. What is the capacitance of a condenser that may be combined with a self-inductance of 0.090 henry to form an oscillator having a frequency of 1.59×10^5 cycles/sec.?

THE NEW PHYSICS

CHAPTER XLIX

IONS AND ELECTRONS

The achievements made during the nineteenth century were so great that it seemed that the pioneer work of physics was accomplished and that the future would yield merely increased refinements in measurement, together with better engineering applications. Contrary to these expectations, the twentieth century has brought forth a new physics rivaling the old in grandeur. It deals for the most part with the structures of atoms, with the "building blocks" of which they are composed, and the nature of light. The new physics does not supplant the physics of Newton, Galileo, and Faraday, for the old laws hold as well as ever when applied to the motions and energies of visible bodies. However, some of the laws are no longer valid in describing the behavior of atoms and of electrons.

480. The Ionization of Gases. Much of the new knowledge has been obtained by the study of the ionization which is produced in gases by

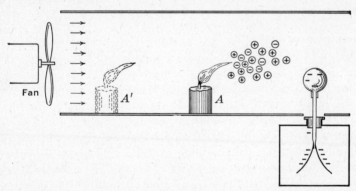

Fig. 1.—The ions produced by the flame gradually recombine.

electric fields, by flames, by X-rays, and by particles shot off by radium. To demonstrate the production of gaseous ions, mount a charged electroscope with its knob in a metal tube and place a lighted candle at A (Fig. 1). The molecules of the air are ionized by the flame, and some of the ions, carried forward by the breeze, are attracted to the knob of the electroscope thus discharging it. Move the candle to a position A' farther from the electroscope. Thereafter the gold leaf will move downward slowly. In explaining this decrease in speed it should be pointed out that the flame produces both positive and negative ions and that the oppositely charged particles gradually recombine as they move forward in the air stream. When the flame is farther away from the electroscope, a greater time elapses before the ions reach the knob and hence more of them are neutralized and fewer are available to discharge it. Place a barrier of cotton across the tube so that the air must pass through it before reaching the electroscope. Afterward the discharge rate is greatly diminished. The positive and negative ions adhere to the fibers of the cotton where both kinds accumulate and neutralize one another.

481. Gaseous Conduction at Low Pressures. Connect a narrow spark gap across the terminals of a glass tube which has two electrodes

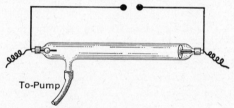

To-Pump

FIG. 2.—At reduced pressure the air conducts electricity more readily than at normal pressure.

mounted near its ends (Fig. 2). Connect the system to an electrostatic machine, and sparks are produced at the gap, but none inside the vessel. This proves that the resistance to the passage of currents is greater inside the tube than it is across the spark gap. Now connect the system to an air pump which reduces the pressure to a few millimeters-of-mercury. In this condition no sparks occur at the gap but a luminous discharge is visible inside. This shows that at the reduced pressure the air conducts electricity more readily than at normal pressure. The current in a gas does not consist of a stream of electrons as in metals, but of two opposite "traffic streams" as in liquids. The positive and negative ions are probably charged clusters of air molecules. They travel more freely at reduced pressures than at ordinary pressures because there are fewer molecules to obstruct their motions.

482. Cathode Rays are Electrons Traveling at High Speeds. When the pressure is reduced to a few hundredths of a millimeter-of-mercury, the appearance of the tube changes markedly. The discharge itself is invisible, but the glass walls glow with a yellowish light. This light is caused by bombardment of the glass by trillions of electrons shot off from the negatively charged cathode. The density of the gas is so small that the particles can make the entire journey through the tube without being stopped. Streams of electrons traveling at high speed are called **cathode rays**.

Fig. 3 represents a highly evacuated enclosure in which a metal cross is mounted in front of the cathode. When the tube is operated by an electrostatic machine, a sharply defined image of the cross is seen on the wall opposite to the cathode. This proves that the electrons travel in straight lines.

FIG. 3.—Cathode rays travel in straight lines. (Courtesy of Central Scientific Company.)

Cathode rays produce heat when they strike the target. This fact can be demonstrated by a tube in which a piece of platinum is mounted in front of the curved cathode (Fig. 4). Operating the tube causes streams of electrons from the cathode to bombard the platinum, heating it to incandescence.

FIG. 4.—Heating effect of cathode rays. (Courtesy of Central Scientific Company.)

483. The Charge of the Electron. The amount of charge carried by an electron was first accurately determined in 1910 by Dr. R. A. Millikan, who was awarded the Nobel prize of $40,000 for this achievement. The essential parts of his apparatus are shown in Fig. 5. Two horizontal metal plates, supported one above the other, are connected to the terminals of a battery, the potential difference being several hundred volts. By means of an atomizer or sprayer, a fine mist or fog of oil is produced in the space above the plates. The droplets drift slowly downward, and a few of them pass through a small hole in the upper plate. A strong beam of light focused on these droplets makes them visible like motes in a sunbeam, and they are viewed through a low-power microscope. A beam of X-rays directed between the plates ionizes the air. This process of ionization of a molecule consists in the ejection from it of a single electron which afterward adheres to some other molecule so that one positive and one negative ion are produced. Let us assume that one of the negative ions strikes against a slowly falling droplet, charging it negatively. Then the droplet will fall more slowly than before since it is attracted by the positively charged upper plate. When sufficient cells are added to the battery, the droplet ceases to fall, because the pull of gravity is balanced by the upward pull of electrical attraction. Suppose that in a particular experiment 1,200 volts are required to balance a singly charged droplet. If one more negative ion were captured, doubling the charge on the droplet, the necessary voltage would be one-half as great, and 600 volts would be

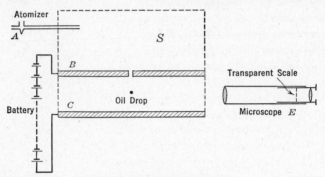

Fig. 5.—Apparatus to determine the charge of the electron. (From the Pittsburgh Atomic Physics.)

required to produce equilibrium. The excess electrons on a certain droplet and the required voltages are as follows:

Number of Excess Electrons	Required Voltage
1	1,200
2	600
3	400
4	300
5	240
6	200

By experiments of this nature, consisting in the capture of ions carrying one excess electron and of others carrying one excess proton, Millikan was able to show that the charges on the different electrons and protons were all numerically equal. Further, these charges were equal to those carried by the ions of silver, chlorine, etc., in electrolytic solutions. The charge of the electron is so small that a current of 1 amp. delivers 6.25 billion billion electrons per second. This number of electrons, spread uniformly over the earth's surface, would give about 50 electrons to the square inch.

484. The Mass of an Electron. As the electron is far too small to be weighed on a chemical balance, its mass must be found by indirect methods. One type of apparatus for this purpose is represented in Fig. 6. A heated filament, mounted in front of the cathode A, emits electrons as in the radio tube. These electrons are driven across to the plate B and some of them passing through a small hole in it travel onward, striking the glass wall of the tube at C where they cause a luminous spot. Suppose, now, that the part of the tube beyond B is placed between the poles of a large U-shaped electromagnet, the magnetic lines being perpendicular to the plane of the paper. This magnetic field deflects the electrons, causing them to move along curved paths. If the electrons were of different masses, the heavier ones, having greater inertias, would be less deflected than the lighter ones and several

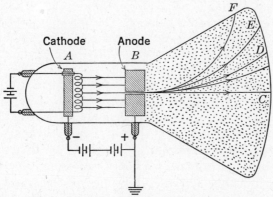

Fig. 6.—Apparatus for determining the mass of the electron.

luminous spots (D, E, and F) would be seen. In fact, only one spot is visible and we infer that all the electrons have the same mass. Moreover, if the potential difference between A and B is known, together with the strength of the magnetic field, the radius of the curved path, and the charge of the electron, the mass can be computed. (The equations are too complicated to be given here.) The mass of the electron has been measured by this and other methods, the accepted value being

$$m = 8.994 \times 10^{-28} \text{ gram}$$

The mass of an electron is about 1/1,840 times that of a hydrogen atom, and no smaller charged particle has as yet been discovered. The reader can show that about 1.1 billion billion billion electrons would be required to make 1 gram of mass. An ordinary 115-volt, 100-watt lamp would have to operate for more than 50 years before 1 gram of electrons would pass through its filament.

485. The Mass of an Electron Varies as the Velocity Increases. In the apparatus just described, greater velocities can be imparted to the electrons by using greater voltages between the cathode and the anode. When this is done, at velocities of 100,000 mi./sec. or more, the masses of the electrons are appreciably greater than at slower speeds. At a velocity nine-tenths that of light the mass is twice that of an electron at rest.

This astonishing result was the first experimental evidence that the principle of the conservation of mass is not always true. It holds for ordinary bodies because their speeds are relatively small, but inside the atom electrons move with speeds approaching that of light and variations of mass must be taken into account when we apply mechanics to problems of atomic behavior.

486. Is Matter a Form of Energy? The mass of an electron can be increased by doing work upon it in causing acceleration, hence it would appear that mass is not a fundamental, non-varying property of a body. The question then arises, what is it that we must add to the electron when we increase its velocity and its mass? To this question the most plausible answer is "energy." In recent years physicists have come to believe that matter is merely another manifestation of energy. Thus to previously known forms such as heat, light, electrical and chemical energy, a new type is added, namely mass energy. In accord with this view, whenever work is done on a body, increasing its energy, its mass and its inertia are also augmented. The mass of an express train traveling 60 mi./hr. is believed to be a trifle greater (a few millionths of a milligram) than if it were at rest.

487. The Masses of Atoms. The apparatus described above can be modified so as to measure the masses of atoms. To do this for lithium, for example, a little lithium chloride is smeared onto the coil of wire mounted at A and the battery terminals are reversed so that A is now positive with respect to B. When the coiled wire is heated, lithium atoms evaporate from it and some of them are singly charged, having lost one electron. These positive ions are driven toward B, and some of them pass through the hole and strike the glass at C producing a luminous spot just as the electrons did. A very strong magnetic field is applied, and the beam of positive ions is deflected downward instead of upward as before. (Why?) In this case, two luminous spots are seen instead of one, which indicates that the lithium ions are of two different kinds, having different masses. The two constituents are the "isotopes" of lithium, and their atomic masses are found to be 6.012 and 7.012. Ordinary lithium is a mixture of these isotopes in such proportions as to give its atomic weight as found by chemical methods. The masses of

heavier atoms and molecules can be determined by this and similar
means (Fig. 7). The fact that the experimental values are nearly
exact integers leads to the belief that all heavier nuclei are built up of
protons and neutrons. The great obstacle to the acceptance of this view
is that hydrogen is a little too heavy. If helium is composed of four
hydrogen atoms its atomic weight should be 4.032 instead of 4.001. To
meet this difficulty it is assumed that, when two protons and two

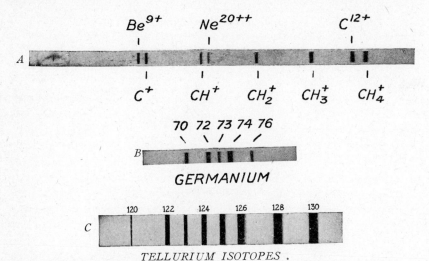

FIG. 7.—Mass spectra. (A after Bainbridge, B and C after Dempster.) ("Pittsburgh
Atomic Physics.")

neutrons are packed close together to form a helium nucleus, some of
the mass is transformed into radiant energy. Strange as this suggestion
may seem, it is now widely accepted by astrophysicists who believe
that part, at least, of the energy emitted by the stars is supplied by the
conversion of hydrogen into helium. Thus the stars give out their substance in radiations, sink into senile decay, and become mere wasted
specters of their former greatness.

SUMMARY

Ionization can be produced in gases by X-rays, by radioactive rays,
by flames, and by strong electric fields. Positive and negative gaseous
ions, produced in equal numbers, may recombine with one another.

Gases at pressures of a few millimeters-of-mercury conduct electricity
better than at ordinary pressures. At very low pressures the current
consists almost entirely of electrons.

The charge of the electron numerically equals that of the proton.

The mass of an electron increases with its velocity, which leads to the belief that matter is a form of energy.

Isotopes of an element are atoms of different masses but the same atomic number and the same chemical properties.

REVIEW QUESTIONS

1. Discuss ionization and recombination of ions.

2. How can cathode rays be produced? Describe some of their effects.

3. Show how to prove that different ions in the atmosphere carry equal charges.

4. In Millikan's oil-drop experiment, a certain oil droplet carrying one excess electron was balanced when the potential difference between the plates was 1,000 V. What voltage would be required to balance it if it carried four excess electrons?

5. How can the mass of the electron be determined?

6. Would you expect the deflection caused by a magnetic field to increase or to decrease if (a) the charge, (b) the velocity, (c) the mass of the moving particle were doubled?

7. Discuss the variation of mass with velocity and explain it in terms of energy.

8. How can the masses of atoms be measured?

9. What are "isotopes"?

10. What is the difficulty in accepting the view that heavier atoms are built up of hydrogen, and how can this difficulty be met?

PROBLEMS

1. In starting an automobile, a current of 50 amp. existed for 10.0 sec. How many electrons passed through the motor?

2″. When mass is converted into other forms of energy, the relationship is

$$\text{Energy in ergs} = \text{Mass in grams} \times (\text{Speed of light})^2$$

(a) How many ergs and joules of energy would be liberated if 1.00 gram of mass were transformed into radiant energy?

(b) How much coal, heat of combustion = 8,000 cal./gram, would liberate this amount of heat in burning? (Speed of light = 3.0×10^{10} cm./sec.)

CHAPTER L

X-RAYS, AND PHOTOELECTRICITY

It is more desirable to be approaching truth perpetually than to attain it.—Lessing.

A few years after Hertz demonstrated the existence of radio waves, another kind of radiation called X-rays was discovered by Roentgen. This discovery was in a sense accidental, for Roentgen was looking for something else. One day while he was experimenting with cathode rays, the thought occurred to him that perhaps the yellowish light from the glass walls of the tube might pass through paper. Accordingly he enclosed the tube in a pasteboard box and found that his "hunch" was wrong for the tube was quite invisible even in a darkened room. However, he was delighted to observe that something did penetrate the pasteboard and caused near-by objects to emit light. Roentgen was uncertain as to the nature of the radiations, and so he called them "X-rays" because X in algebra represented the unknown quantity. The radiations, being in themselves invisible, are detected indirectly by the **light** which they cause when incident on zinc sulfide and other substances, by their **blackening** effect on a photographic plate, and by the **ionization** which they produce in gases. These invisible radiations differ from light in that they penetrate all known substances, even steel and lead.

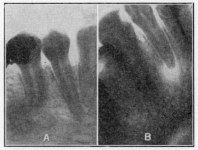

FIG. 1.—X-ray photograph. (A) showing crooked tooth, (B) showing an abscess at the root of a tooth.

Sometimes many years elapse between a discovery by the physicist and its adoption for practical purposes. X-rays are unique in this regard, for they were used by surgeons for examining broken bones only a few weeks after their discovery. An injured hand, for example, was held between the X-ray tube and a "fluoroscope" or glass plate coated with a material sensitive to the radiations. The bones absorbed more of the X-rays than the flesh, hence their shadows were seen on the glowing plate (Fig. 1). This method is still used. Sometimes the behavior of the intestines is determined after the patient swallows a liquid containing a salt of barium. This metal, being dense, absorbs a considerable fraction of the radiations, and the passage of the salt through the digestive tract is observed by the shadows on the fluoroscope.

488. The Coolidge X-ray Tube. X-rays are produced by the sudden stopping or the deceleration of electrons. In Roentgen's experiment, the electrons were stopped by impact on the glass walls of the enclosure, but it is better to use a massive metal target. In the Coolidge type of tube, the electrons are emitted by a glowing filament at the cathode C (Fig. 2). A potential difference of many thousand volts causes these electrons to speed toward the target, and they acquire velocities of thousands of miles per second. When they strike the metal, most of

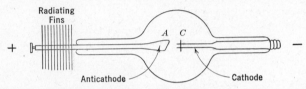

FIG. 2.—A Coolidge X-ray tube. (Pittsburgh Atomic Physics, 1937.)

their kinetic energy is converted into heat, but a small fraction of 1 per cent is emitted as X-rays. (The voltage to operate the tube is provided by a step-up transformer. The current is "rectified" by a vacuum tube like that used in alternating-current radio sets.)

489. X-rays Are of the Same Nature As Light. X-rays are not charged particles but are of the same nature as light. However, their wave lengths are thousands of times smaller than those of light. Ordinary diffraction gratings cannot be conveniently used to measure the wave lengths, for two reasons. First, the rays would penetrate the grating; and secondly, the grating lines are too widely spaced. Fortunately natural crystals are available for this purpose. A rock salt crystal, for example, is built up of parallel layers of atoms at a known distance apart. When a beam of X-rays is incident on the crystal, some of the radiation is reflected at the first layer, and some at other layers below the surface. Consider the rays reflected by the various layers at an angle θ (Fig. 3). If the reflected radiations are in phase they will produce a maximum effect; otherwise they annul one another and the effect will be nearly zero. The waves will be in phase if the difference in path is one wave length λ.

But this distance is $2d \sin \theta$. Hence

$$\lambda = 2d \sin \theta \tag{1}$$

In this equation λ is the wave length, d the distance between the planes of the crystal, and θ the angle of incidence.

In measuring the wave lengths of X-rays the experimenter directs the incident beam against the crystal planes at some angle θ. He sets the detecting device, for example a fluoroscope, so that it will detect the radiations, and then he varies the angle until waves are copiously reflected, measures θ, and applies equation (1). (The radiations are also in phase when θ has larger values such that the difference in path for successive layers is 2λ, 3λ, . . .)

A very important use of X-rays is the determination of the distance d between the planes of crystals. This distance is measured by using radiations of known wave length, determining θ, and calculating d by

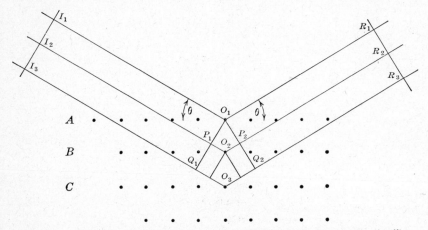

Fig. 3.—Reflection of X-rays by a crystal. ("Pittsburgh Atomic Physics.")

equation (1). Often a finely divided powder is used instead of a large single crystal. The millions of tiny crystals lie at all possible angles, and only those for which θ has the appropriate value cause copious reflection. This method is very simple to apply. One merely directs a beam of X-rays onto the powder, places a photographic film around the target, and exposes the film. Then θ is measured and d is evaluated. If all the crystals are of the same structure, only one spectrum is produced, but if impurities are present, there will be several spectra. This method of spectrum analysis is being rapidly adopted in industry.

490. "Hard" and "Soft" X-rays. The absorption of X-rays increases with the **thickness** of the screen, the **density** of the material, and the **atomic weights** of the elements of which it is composed. Lead is commonly used for shielding the tube because it is very dense, has a high atomic weight, is cheap, and is easily formed into sheets. The penetration also depends upon the wave lengths which, in turn, depend upon the voltage at which the tube operates. "Hard" X-rays that can penetrate a millimeter of lead are produced when the potential difference is 100,000 volts or so, "soft" rays, which are absorbed by a sheet of paper, when the potential difference is 10,000 volts. When a physician uses X-rays to treat a skin disease, he operates the machine at low voltage producing "soft" radiation; but in treating diseased organs inside the body, the voltage should be high. Huge electrostatic machines (Chapter XXXVII) operating at a million volts or more are employed in "deep therapy." Measurements with the crystal grating prove that "soft" X-rays are of greater wave length than "hard" X-rays.

491. Light "Bullets" or "Photons." The Photoelectric Effect. When Roentgen demonstrated that X-rays behave like light, he thought that

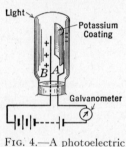

FIG. 4.—A photoelectric cell.

the puzzle as to their nature was solved and that they were nothing else but electromagnetic vibrations in a tenuous medium called the "ether." The twentieth century has brought forth new evidence as to the nature of light and of X-rays, proving that they consist of streams of "bullets" or "photons" like the "corpuscles" pictured by Newton nearly three hundred years ago. The complete evidence is presented in more advanced textbooks. Here we shall discuss only the **photoelectric effect.** This is the ejection of electrons from a body by light, or by other radiations. Fig. 4 represents a photoelectric cell. It is an evacuated tube in which is a curved metal plate A coated with potassium. This plate is connected to the negative terminal of a battery, the other electrode B to the positive terminal. When the tube is in a dark room, there is no current in the circuit. When light is incident on the potassium, electrons are ejected from it, travel across to the positive terminal and thence around the circuit. The light supplies the energy to eject the electrons with considerable velocities. A candle a mile or so away would afford weak illumination, and we should expect that a period of several minutes would elapse before sufficient energy would be received by an atom to eject an electron with the observed velocity and energy. In fact, electrons begin to be shot off from the surface within a millionth of a second after the light reaches the cell. This fact defies explanation if we assume that the energy is carried by ever-spreading waves. It is easy to understand assuming that the energy is carried by "light bullets" or "photons," for each particle can deliver all its energy to an atom, whether the light comes from a near-by candle, a distant candle, or even from a star which is millions of light years away.

492. Light as "Bullets" and Waves. The facts of diffraction, interference, and polarization lead to the belief that light is a wave phenomenon, but the photoelectric effect and many other facts discovered during the last forty years force us to believe that the energy is carried by bullet-like particles. The present view is that light has a dual nature. A candle sends out light-bullets or **photons** and also **waves** to guide the photons on their journey. When light passes through a narrow slit, the waves act like "traffic policemen" directing some of the photons forward, others sidewise into the shadow of the obstacle.

493. The Energies of Photons. The amount of energy imparted to the electrons in the photoelectric cell is greater for blue light than for red light. In general the kinetic energies of the photons are directly proportional to the frequencies of the light. Infra-red photons, of low frequency, do not have sufficient energy to eject electrons from potassium. The photons of visible radiations can eject electrons with considerable velocities. Those of ultra-violet radiations, still more energetic, can cause numerous chemical effects in other substances. An X-ray photon having thousands of times as much energy can ionize hundreds of atoms. If we represent a photon of visible light by a speeding rifle bullet, an X-ray photon would be a 6-in. shell traveling at the same speed.

The amount of energy E in a photon is computed by the equation

$$E = h\nu$$

in which ν (Greek nu) is the frequency of the waves, and h, Planck's constant, is 6.59×10^{-27} erg-sec. The frequency of the yellow light from a sodium burner is about 5×10^{14} per second, hence the energy of a photon is

$$E = 6.59 \times 10^{-27} \text{ erg-sec.} \times \frac{5 \times 10^{14}}{\text{sec.}} = 33 \times 10^{-13} \text{ erg} = 33.0 \times 10^{-20} \text{ joule}$$

It follows that a sodium burner emitting energy at the rate of 1 watt would send out about 3 billion billion photons per second.

494. The "Electric Eye." Not only have studies of the photoelectric effect given better understanding of light but also they have yielded many devices which are useful in the automatic operation of machinery. The photoelectric cell employed for this purpose is popularly called the "electric eye." A familiar example of such use is the operation of traffic signals on highways. When an automobile approaches on the side street, it cuts off a beam of light incident on the cell. The interruption of the electric current operates a relay which reverses the red and green signals so that the car can enter the main street safely. Then after a short period the lamps are again reversed automatically, permitting the main street traffic to proceed.

The most important application of all is in talking pictures. When the pictures are taken, the film is drawn, at constant speed, past a variable aperture illuminated by a beam of light. The width of the opening, and hence the blackening of the film, is controlled by the sounds incident on the microphone. When the pictures are projected, a beam of light passes through the sound track into a photoelectric cell. The variable absorption causes pulsations of current in the photoelectric cell which, after being amplified, actuate the loud speaker and reproduce the sounds.

SUMMARY

X-rays, of the same nature as light, are generated when electrons are suddenly decelerated or accelerated. The rays are invisible and can be detected by the phosphorescence which they produce in certain substances, by their "blackening" effect on photographic films, and by the ionization which they cause in gases.

X-rays have higher frequencies and smaller wave lengths than light. In measuring their wave lengths crystals are used as diffraction gratings. The successive planes in the crystal serve as partially reflecting mirrors, and the angle of maximum reflection is used to determine the wave length.

"Soft" X-rays have longer wave lengths and are more easily absorbed than "hard" X-rays.

In X-rays and in light the energy is carried by particles called photons. The energy of each photon is proportional to the frequency. The photons are accompanied by "guiding" waves which cause diffraction.

The photoelectric effect is the ejection of electrons from a body by light.

REVIEW QUESTIONS

1. Describe the discovery of X-rays.

2. Is it preferable in research work (a) to have no hypothesis to guide one or (b) to have an erroneous hypothesis?

3. In what ways can X-rays be detected and what apparatus is required in each case?

4. Describe the Coolidge X-ray tube. In operating it, how can (a) the "hardness" and (b) the amount of radiation be increased?

5. Why are physicists convinced that X-rays and light are of the same nature?

6. How can rock salt crystal be used to measure the wave lengths of X-rays? How can the distance between the planes of another kind of crystal then be determined?

7. What is the difference between hard and soft X-rays as regards (a) absorption and (b) wave length?

8. What is the photoelectric effect? What determines the amount of energy of a photon?

9. Why can X-ray photons ionize nitrogen though light cannot? Why is red light used in a photographic dark room rather than blue light?

10. Why can light ionize sodium though it cannot ionize nitrogen?

11. How can the "electric eye" be used to sort out dark cigars from lighter ones?

12. Describe the use of the photoelectric cell in talking pictures.

13. What is Planck's constant? How is it used?

PROBLEMS

1. The electron current to the target is 1.00 milliampere and the potential difference is 100,000 V. (a) What is the wattage used? (b) How many electrons strike the target each second?

2″. When X-rays of wave length 10^{-8} cm. are incident on a crystal at an angle $\theta = 30°$, the rays are copiously reflected at an equal angle. Using equation (1), find the distance between the adjacent lattice planes.

3″. (a) What is the frequency of light of wave length 0.000050 cm.? (b) What is the energy of each photon, and how many are emitted per second by a 2-watt source?

CHAPTER LI

RADIOACTIVITY AND COSMIC RAYS

"Atoms or systems into ruins hurled,
And now a bubble burst, and now a world."

—ALEXANDER POPE, *Essay on Man.*

Introduction. The wide interest aroused by the discovery of X-rays in 1895 caused a vigorous search for other new radiations. In the following year the French physicist, Becquerel, made another very important finding, and it is interesting to notice that he was led to do so by a false hypothesis. The discovery arose in the following way. Becquerel knew that certain salts of the metal uranium become phosphorescent and emit light on exposure to the sun's radiation. He thought that perhaps this phosphorescent light would be able to pass through paper, and so he devised the following experiment. First he placed the crystals in sunlight until they glowed brightly, and then he laid them on a photographic plate wrapped in black paper. After a few days, he developed the plate and observed that it was blackened in several spots. Later experiments showed that the effect was produced not only by the phosphorescent uranium salt, but equally well by the pure metal which does not emit visible light. Thus his first "guess" had been wrong, yet he made a very significant discovery. The moral of this is that a skilled investigator who asks questions of nature by experiment is likely to find something worth while even though it may not be that for which he was looking.

Becquerel's announcement aroused great interest, and physicists soon discovered other "radioactive" elements such as thorium, polonium, and radium. The discovery of radium came about in the following manner. Madame Curie and her husband Pierre observed that a certain ore called pitchblende was more active than either pure uranium or thorium, and so they set about the separation of its radioactive constituent. Starting with a ton of the ore, they gradually isolated a few milligrams of nearly pure radium which proved to be more than four million times as active as uranium.

495. What is Radioactivity? Radioactivity is different from chemical change in that it is spontaneous, and its rate cannot be altered by any means ordinarily at our disposal. When a photographic plate is located near a radioactive substance, the rate of blackening is precisely the same when the substance is in a hot furnace or in liquid oxygen boiling at −183°C. Chemical changes, on the contrary, are

very sensitive to temperature variations, and their rates are doubled by a rise of a few centigrade degrees.

Radioactive changes are very difficult to influence because they occur deep down inside the atom, within the nucleus. Radioactivity may be defined as **a spontaneous nuclear transformation causing radiations to be emitted.**

496. How Radioactivity is Measured. The emissions from radioactive sources can be detected by the same methods as X-rays. They "blacken" photographic films, they cause phosphorescence in certain materials, and they produce ionization in gases. Of these the last-named is most frequently used. A convenient apparatus for measur-

FIG. 1.—Electroscope for measuring radioactivity. (Courtesy of Central Scientific Company.)

ing radioactivity is represented in Fig. 1. The gold leaf of the electroscope is mounted on a rod attached to a horizontal metal plate in the ionization chamber below it. The radioactive mineral is placed on the floor of the chamber, and ions which it produces are drawn to the plate above, gradually discharging the electroscope. The rate of motion of the leaf measures the amount of radioactivity of the substance.

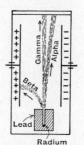

497. Introducing Some New Members of the "Ray" Family. Let a few milligrams of pitchblende be placed at the bottom of a narrow hole in a block of lead and let a photographic plate be supported above the hole, the system being in a highly evacuated chamber (Fig. 2). Then the radiations passing upward "blacken" the plate in a small region directly above the hole. Suppose, now, that two parallel plates are mounted as shown in the figure, and that they are oppositely charged, producing

FIG. 2.—The separation of alpha, beta, and gamma rays by an electric field.

an electric field between them. In this case the beam divides into three parts, showing the existence of three kinds of radiations which are called **alpha, beta,** and **gamma** rays.

Alpha Particles. The rays that are deviated toward the negative plate are streams of "alpha particles," each being a doubly charged helium ion of mass four times that of the hydrogen atom. The initial speeds of alpha particles are from 5,000 to 20,000 mi./sec., and they are totally absorbed by one or two sheets of writing paper.

Beta Particles. The beta rays consist of negatively charged particles which are, in fact, electrons. Their speeds are much greater than those of the alpha particles and are as high as 180,000 mi./sec., within 3 per cent of the speed of light. These rays being smaller than alpha particles and having higher velocities are more penetrating. The most speedy ones pass through a sheet of aluminum 1 mm. thick.

Gamma Rays. The gamma rays, being undeviated by the electric field, are uncharged. They are identical with extremely "hard" X-rays and have been detected after passing through several centimeters of lead.

498. The Disintegration of Atoms. In earlier parts of this volume the structures of atoms were discussed. They are believed to be tiny solar systems each having a positively charged nucleus. The planets are electrons which, negatively charged, are attracted by the nucleus. The number of protons in the nucleus is the **atomic number** of the element. Let us see how radioactive emissions affect the mass of the nucleus and its atomic number. The atomic mass of radium is 226, and its atomic number 88. When a radium atom explodes, hurling out an alpha particle, the atomic mass changes from 226 to 222 and the atomic number decreases to 86. In consequence of this change, the element radium changes to another one called radon which has quite different chemical properties. Radium is a bivalent metal similar to barium, but radon is a gas resembling helium. This "daughter product" is much more unstable than radium and soon disintegrates to another, and so the process continues until a stable atom is produced, namely, lead. Some elements, in exploding, eject alpha particles; others throw out beta particles. When an alpha particle is ejected, the atomic weight decreases 4 and the atomic number decreases 2. When a beta particle is emitted, the atomic weight changes very little and the atomic number increases by 1. The descendants of uranium, the most massive atom of all, are shown in Table I. In the right-hand column the "half life" tells us the time required for half of the atoms initially present to be transformed into the "daughter" substance.

For example, starting with 2 million atoms of uranium, 1 million atoms would remain after 4.6 billion years. The half period of radium is only 1,700 years, so we see that it is much more unstable and much more radioactive than uranium. Radon, the daughter product of radium, is even more unstable. Its half life is less than 4 days, and it is highly active.

TABLE I

DESCENDANTS OF URANIUM

Element	Nature	Atomic Weight	Atomic Number	Rays Emitted	Half Life
Uranium	Metal................	238	92	α	4.6×10^9 yr.
Uranium X₁	Metal................	234	90	β and γ	24.6 days
Uranium X₂	Metal................	234	91	β and γ	1.15 min.
Uranium II	Isotope of Ur.........	234	92	α	
					2×10^6 yr.
Ionium	Metal................	230	90	α	7×10^4 yr.
Radium	Metal................	226	88	α	1700 yrs.
Radon	Gas.................	222	86	α	3.85 days
Radium A	(Polonium isotope)....	218	84	α	3.0 min.
Radium B	(Lead isotope)........	214	82	β	26.3 min.
Radium C	(Bismuth isotope).....	214	83	β and γ	19.5 min.
Radium C'	(Polonium isotope)....	214	84	α	10^{-6} sec.
Radium D	(Lead isotope)........	210	82	β and γ	16 yr.
Radium E	(Bismuth isotope).....	210	83	β	5.0 days
Radium F	Polonium.............	210	84	α	136 days
Lead (end product)	Metal................	206	82	None	

499. Biological Effects of the Rays. When a radioactive source is placed in contact with the skin of a patient the alpha rays are readily absorbed near the surface and produce "burns." The beta rays penetrate to a depth of a millimeter or so, and the gamma rays, very penetrating like hard X-rays, are effective at much greater depths in the tissues. To prevent the surface burns, sometimes the radioactive material is enclosed in a glass capsule to cut off the alpha rays. The three kinds of radiation all tend to damage living cells, but fortunately cancer cells are more readily killed than normal cells; hence, the utility of radium.

Radium costs $20,000 or more per gram, and therefore the supplies of this precious metal are carefully guarded against theft or loss. In hospitals frequently radon is used for treatments. The radon is pumped off from the radium at intervals of a few days, and the gas thus secured is enclosed in small capsules which are inserted into the diseased tissue.

The effects of radioactive rays are very complex, and treatments with radium may be dangerous so that they should be given only by specialists. Sometimes quack doctors persuade their patients to drink water which contains radon. The gas is carried throughout the body by the blood stream. When it decays, other non-gaseous radioactive elements are formed and deposited in the tissues. This treatment has frequently produced disastrous consequences, and even death.

500. The "Age" of the Earth. It is believed that several billion years have elapsed since the earth's solid crust was formed. This belief is justified in part by the evidence of radioactivity. It is assumed that when the earth solidified some pure uranium was imprisoned in the rocks and that through the ages this element was transformed, producing lead as the end product. As time went on, the amount of uranium present diminished and the lead accumulated. The age of the rock is estimated by the relative amounts of the two metals which are found in it. Suppose, as a particular case, that the number of atoms of each metal are found to be equal. Then at least one half of the uranium has decayed, and hence the period since the solidification of the rock occurred would be greater than the half-period of uranium, that is 46 billion years.

501. Cosmic Rays. About thirty years ago the Swiss physicist Gockel made a balloon ascension which resulted in a remarkable discovery. The purpose of his journey was to study the variation with altitude of the intensity of the gamma rays from radioactive matter in the earth. To this end he used a gold-leaf electroscope in a lead-covered box, so that its discharge rate would measure the ionization produced in the confined air by the penetrating gamma rays. He had predicted that the rate would diminish as the balloon rose because the rays would be absorbed in the atmosphere below. To his great astonishment he found that, contrary to expectations, the discharge rate increased with elevation. This result led to the view that the ionization was produced by agencies not coming from the earth but from outer space, and these are called **cosmic rays.**

Since Gockel's pioneer voyage of discovery, numerous other workers have studied the cosmic rays. Millikan constructed ingenious electroscopes weighing but a few ounces. Each instrument was self-recording and included a barometer and clock. These devices, attached to small balloons, were carried to elevations of 10 miles or more. When they descended and were returned by the persons finding them, the records told the story of the discharge rate at each elevation (indicated by the recording barometers) and one could determine the intensity of the rays at various heights above the earth's surface. By such experiments it was proved that the rays can pass through a wall of lead 1 m. thick and hence they are much more penetrating than the hardest gamma rays. These results have been confirmed by more recent balloon voyages into the stratosphere.

502. What are Cosmic Rays? The question as to the nature of cosmic rays is not completely answered. It has been shown fairly conclusively that they are made up, for the most part, of charged particles, but we do not know whether these are electrons, protons, alpha particles, or something else. Possibly they are partly composed of extremely hard and penetrating gamma rays.

503. A Unit of Energy—The Electron Volt. In stating the energies of molecules and electrons, of beta particles, alpha particles, and the particles in cosmic rays it is convenient to use the **electron volt**, which is defined as the energy acquired by an electron in moving from one point to another, the potential difference being 1 volt. Thus if 50,000 volts are applied between the cathode and the target of an X-ray tube, each electron acquires 50,000 electron volts of energy. With this fact in mind, it is startling to learn that some of the particles in cosmic rays have energies as large as 100 billion electron volts!

TABLE II

ENERGIES OF PARTICLES

(630 billion electron volts equal 1 erg)

	Electron Volts
Translational kinetic energy (average) of molecule at 0°C..	35/1000
A photon of red light (longest wave length).............	1.7
A photon of violet light (shortest wave length)..........	3.4
X-ray photons (usual)................................	20,000–100,000
Alpha particles.....................................	6– 10 million
Cosmic-ray particles................................	2–100 billion

504. Fog Trails Revealing the Paths of Atoms. In recent years physicists have had great fun at the new game of "atomic billiards." With alpha particles, and other particles as projectiles, they observe the behavior of atomic nuclei when hit by these missiles. The particles themselves are invisible, but their paths are revealed by the fog trails which they produce in moist air. A simple form of the apparatus to generate the fog trails is shown in Fig. 3. When the rubber bulb is squeezed, water rises in the tube, compressing the air confined above it. When the bulb is released the air expands suddenly and is chilled. This sudden chilling causes the space to be supersaturated with water vapor. In this condition fog particles form on ions that are present. Alpha particles are shot out at random from a speck of radium mounted on a rod in the chamber, and as each particle plows through the air it produces thousands of ions along its path. A water droplet forms on each of these ions, and the path is made visible by the smoke-like trail of fog.

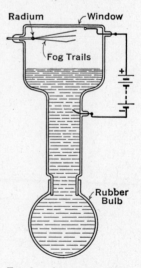

FIG. 3.—Apparatus to produce fog trails.

(The battery causes an electric field between the water surface and a transparent, conducting film on the window. This electric field sweeps out all the ions excepting those produced at the instant of the expansion. Therefore the fog particles form on these only.)

FIG. 4.—A fog trail revealing the transmutation of nitrogen into oxygen. (After Blackett.)

Typical fog trails caused by this apparatus are pictured in Fig. 4. It will be noted that all but one of the trails are fairly straight, showing that the alpha particles encountered no massive obstacles. This proves that the nuclei are much smaller than the atoms of the gas, for each projectile must have passed through thousands of atoms. One trail near the left tells an interesting story. The alpha particle struck a nitrogen nucleus nearly head on, dealt it a smashing impact, was captured by the nucleus, and a proton was ejected. The short path of the recoiling nucleus is plainly seen, as is the longer path of the proton.

FIG. 5.—Collision of two deuterons, producing two isotopes of hydrogen. (Courtesy of Dr. P. I. Dee and of the Royal Society.) ("Pittsburgh Atomic Physics," 1937.)

505. The Disintegration of Atoms. The word atom, derived from a Greek term meaning "uncut," is justified by the fact that atoms are not broken up by ordinary chemical methods. The attempts of the alchemists to convert mercury into gold were futile because they did not have at their disposal projectiles which were sufficiently energetic to penetrate the nucleus of an atom. The discovery of radioactivity provided the necessary artillery, and Rutherford in 1910 first succeeded in attaining the dream of the alchemist—the transmutation of an element. The fog trails in Fig. 4 enable us to "witness" the transmutation of nitrogen into oxygen. When the alpha particle of atomic mass

Fig. 6.—A famous photograph that proved the existence of the positron. The particle traveling upward was slowed down in passing through a lead plate. It was deviated by a magnetic field. (Courtesy of Dr. Carl Anderson.)

4 and atomic number 2 was captured by the nucleus, and the proton was ejected, the atomic weight increased 3, becoming 17. The atomic number increased 1, becoming 8 and an isotope of oxygen was produced.

Experiments on disintegration were formerly hampered because radium, the only convenient source of atomic projectiles, is very expensive. Today it has been replaced by several types of "atom guns" which can speed up hydrogen ions to velocities approaching those of alpha particles. One of these guns resembles the apparatus previously described for measuring the masses of electrons and ions (Chapter 49, Fig. 6). Two electrodes mounted in a long tube are kept at a potential difference of a million volts or so. (The Van de Graaff generator described in Chapter 37 is suitable for this purpose.) Hydrogen ions liberated at the positive electrode are accelerated toward the cathode, pass through a hole in it, and strike the substance which is to be disintegrated. The paths of the ejected particles may be studied by their fog trails. Fig. 5 pictures an encounter in which one heavy hydrogen (H^2) nucleus struck another. The two particles that resulted were a proton and an isotope of hydrogen of atomic mass 3.

506. Subatomic Energy. When a boron nucleus is broken up into three helium nuclei, the total kinetic energy of the three particles is much greater than that of the proton that struck the nucleus. This is extremely interesting, for it proves that some of the energy inside the boron nucleus was set free. There is reason to believe that tremendous quantities of energy reside in the nuclei of atoms. It is probable that a spoonful of water contains energy equal to that set free by the burning of several tons of coal. Why not use the atom gun to liberate this energy? Unfortunately, the nuclei of atoms are so small that many thousands of "shots" must be fired for every disintegration that is produced. As Einstein once said, "It is like a blindfolded man shooting birds in a country where there are not many birds." It is unlikely, though not impossible, that subatomic energy will ever replace that from coal and oil. It is interesting to learn that probably the heat of the sun is maintained by the release of subatomic energy and that the sun is slowly wasting away as it pours out its substance in radiations.

507. Particles Ejected from Nuclei. When atoms disintegrate, several kinds of particles may be ejected. Of these the electron, proton, and the alpha particle have been described. The **positron** is of the same mass as the electron, but it is positively charged (Fig. 6). The **neutron** is about as massive as the proton but it is uncharged. Traveling at high speed, it can pass through atoms without exerting much force on their electrons or their charged nuclei. Hence it does not lose much momentum, and can travel enormous distances. Neutrons can penetrate a slab of lead 1 m. thick, though an alpha particle would be stopped by a single sheet of paper. Lastly there is the **deuteron**, which is about twice as massive as a proton but has the same charge. The deuteron is the nucleus of "heavy hydrogen" which combines with ordinary hydrogen and oxygen forming "heavy water." A few thousandths of a per cent of this substance is present in ordinary water and may be separated from it by repeated distillations. The process is fairly difficult, so that the price of heavy water is about one dollar per gram. This is unfortunate, for its properties are different from those of ordinary water, and a promising field of research has been opened.

TABLE III

PARTICLES EJECTED FROM NUCLEI

Name	Mass (Hydrogen = 1)	Charge, (Proton = + 1)
Electrons............	1/1,840	−1
Positrons...........	1/1,840	+1
Protons.............	1	+1
Neutrons...........	1	0
Deuterons...........	2	+1
Alpha particles......	4	+2

SUMMARY

Radioactivity is a spontaneous nuclear transformation accompanied by the emission of radiations. It may be detected and measured by its effects in producing (a) ionization, (b) blackening of photographic films, and (c) phosphorescence.

Alpha particles are doubly charged helium ions; beta particles are electrons; and gamma rays are like hard X-rays.

In radioactive disintegrations atoms emit alpha particles, beta particles, and gamma rays. When an alpha particle is ejected the atomic weight decreases 4 and the atomic number decreases 2. If a beta particle is emitted the atomic weight is little changed and the atomic number increases by 1.

The "half life" of a radioactive element is the period required for one-half of the atoms to disintegrate.

The "age" of a rock can be estimated from the relative amounts of uranium and of lead found in it.

Cosmic rays are very penetrating radiations probably coming from the depths of space. They are believed to be made up mostly of charged particles.

One electron volt equals the energy of an electron after "falling" through a potential difference of 1 volt; 630 billion electron volts equal 1 erg.

The following particles have been ejected from atoms: electrons, positrons, protons, deuterons, alpha particles, and neutrons.

REVIEW QUESTIONS

1. Define radioactivity and tell the story of its discovery.
2. Describe the three types of radioactive rays.
3. Discuss the effects of radioactive rays.
4. Discuss the changes of atomic weight and of atomic number occurring when an atom ejects (a) an alpha particle and (b) a beta particle.
5. Describe some biological effects of radioactive rays, and show how radon is used
6. How can the "age" of the earth be determined?

7. What are cosmic rays, and how were they discovered?

8. What is an electron volt?

9. Show how the transmutation of an element can be accomplished. Why is it more difficult to disintegrate heavy atoms than lighter ones?

10. Show how fog trails are produced.

11. Describe the different kinds of particles which have been ejected from atomic nuclei.

12. Why is there little prospect of making subatomic energy available by artificially disrupting atoms?

13. In an atomic disintegration experiment a proton entered, and was captured by a lithium nucleus of atomic weight 7 and atomic number 3. The nucleus was then broken into equal parts. What was the element thus produced?

PROBLEMS

1. The atomic weight of radium is 226 and its atomic number is 88. What will the corresponding values be after two alpha particles have been ejected from a nucleus, producing radium A?

2′. When an atom of radium B (atomic weight 214, atomic number 82) disintegrates, first radium C and then radium C′ are produced. In each case one electron is expelled. (a) Find the atomic weight and the atomic number of this element. (b) How do its chemical properties compare with those of radium A?

3′. The "half life" of radon is 3.85 days. If initially 4 billion atoms of this element are present, how many will remain after 3.85 days and after 7.70 days?

4′. An alpha particle had an initial kinetic energy of 2.4 million electron volts, and it produced 80,000 pairs of nitrogen ions. How much work was required to produce each ion pair?

APPENDIX

AIDS IN THE SOLUTION OF PROBLEMS

A. APPROXIMATE NUMERICAL EQUIVALENTS

LENGTH

1 in. = 2.54 cm.

1 ft. = 30.5 cm.

1 mi. = 5,280 ft. = 1.61 km.

1 cm. = 0.394 in.

1 m. = 1.094 yd. = 39.4 in.

1 km. = 1,000 m. = 5/8 mi.

VOLUME

1 (liquid) qt. = 0.946 liter.

1 liter = 1.06 qt.

MASS

1 pound (avoirdupois) = 454 grams.

1 kg. = 1,000 grams = 2.20 pounds.

FORCE

1 pound-weight (lb.) = 454 gwt.

1 gwt. = 980 dynes.

WORK, ENERGY, AND POWER

1 erg = 1 dyne-cm.

1 ft-lb. = 4/3 joule.

1 B.t.u. = 778 ft-lb. = 252 cal.

1 horsepower-hour = 198,000 ft-lb.

1 horsepower = 3/4 kw.

1 joule = 3/4 ft-lb. = 10^7 ergs = 10,200 gwt-cm.

1 cal. = 4.18 joules.

1 kw-hr. = 3,600,000 joules = 2,700,000 ft-lb.

1 kw. = 4/3 horsepower.

B. MISCELLANEOUS

1 ft.^{3} of water at 70°F. weighs 62.4 lb. = 1,000 ounces.

1 cm.^{3} of mercury at 0°C. weighs 13.6 gwt.

76 cm.-of-mercury = 1,034 cm.-of-water = 30 in.-of-mercury = 14.7 lb./in.^{2}

π = 3 1/7 = 3.142.

Area of circle = πr^2.

Surface of sphere = $4\pi r^2$.

Volume of sphere = $4/3\pi r^3$.

$\sqrt{2}$ = 1.41; $\sqrt{3}$ = 1.73.

C. CONCERNING TRIANGLES

Area of triangle = ½ (base × altitude).

Two triangles are similar if their corresponding angles are equal. The corresponding sides of similar triangles are proportional.

In any right-angled triangle, ABC (Fig. 1):

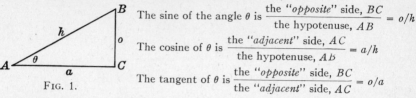

The sine of the angle θ is $\dfrac{\text{the "}\textit{opposite}\text{" side, } BC}{\text{the hypotenuse, } AB} = o/h$

The cosine of θ is $\dfrac{\text{the "}\textit{adjacent}\text{" side, } AC}{\text{the hypotenuse, } Ab} = a/h$

Fig. 1.

The tangent of θ is $\dfrac{\text{the "}\textit{opposite}\text{" side, } BC}{\text{the "}\textit{adjacent}\text{" side, } AC} = o/a$

The angles 30°, 60°, and 45° are used often in this text; hence the following table should be studied.

Angle	30°	60°	45°
Sine	½	$0.866 = \frac{1}{2}\sqrt{3}$	$0.71 = \frac{1}{2}\sqrt{2}$
Cosine	$0.866 = \frac{1}{2}\sqrt{3}$	½	$0.71 = \frac{1}{2}\sqrt{2}$

D. CONCERNING ALGEBRA

(1) $k(a + b + c) = ka + kb + kc.$

(2) $a^m \times a^n = a^{(m+n)}.$

(3) $a^m/a^n = a^{(m-n)}.$

(4) $a + (- b) = a - b.$

(5) $a \times (- b) = - ab, \ - a \times (- b) = ab.$

(6) $(a^m)^n = a^{mn}.$

(7) $\dfrac{a/b}{c/d} = \dfrac{a/b \times d/c}{c/d \times d/c} = a/b \times d/c = ad/bc.$

(8) $ax^2 = by^2 + k; \ \therefore \ ax^2 - by^2 = by^2 - by^2 + k = k.$

(9) $(x \pm y)^2 = x^2 \pm 2xy + y^2.$

(10) $ax^2 \pm bx + c = 0; \ \therefore \ x = \dfrac{- b \pm \sqrt{b^2 - 4ac}}{2a}.$

(11) $1/a + 1/b = \dfrac{b}{ab} + \dfrac{a}{ab} = \dfrac{a + b}{ab}.$

E. SQUARES OF NUMBERS

No.	(With 1/10 per cent approximations)									
	(Plus) 0	1	2	3	4	5	6	7	8	9
10	100	121	144	169	196	225	256	289	324	361
20	400	441	484	529	576	625	676	729	784	840
30	900	960	1024	1090	1156	1225	1296	1370	1444	1520
40	1600	1680	1764	1850	1936	2025	2116	2210	2304	2400
50	2500	2600	2704	2810	2916	3025	3136	3250	3364	3480
60	3600	3720	3844	3970	4100	4225	4360	4490	4620	4760
70	4900	5040	5180	5330	5480	5630	5780	5930	6080	6240
80	6400	6560	6720	6890	7060	7230	7400	7570	7740	7920
90	8100	8280	8460	8650	8840	9030	9220	9400	9600	9801

ANSWERS TO PROBLEMS

CHAPTER II (pp. 17–18)

2. 30 lb. **3.** 12.7 lb. **4.** 500 lb. **5.** 29 lb. **6.** (*a*) 50 lb. (*b*) 100 lb. **7.** 50 lb. **8.** 2,010 lb. **9.** 2,000 lb. **10.** 1,000 lb. **11.** 40 lb. **12.** 100 lb. **13.** (*a*) 16 lb. (*b*) 12 lb. **14.** 1.00 lb. **15.** 160 lb.; 120 lb. **16.** (*a*) 1.73 lb. (*b*) 4.73 lb. **17.** (*a*) 200 lb. (*b*) 141 lb.

CHAPTER III (pp. 23–24)

1. (*a*) 40 lb-ft. (*b*) 20 lb-ft. **2.** 300 lb. **3.** 320 lb. **4.** 1.50 lb-ft. **5.** (*a*) 50 lb-ft. (*b*) 43.3 lb-ft. (*c*) 25 lb-ft. (*d*) 0. **7.** 5.0 ft. **8.** (*a*) 5.0 lb. (*b*) 15 lb. **9.** 45.5 in. **10.** 90 lb.; 60 lb. **11.** (*a*) 3.0 kgwt. (*b*) 5.0 kgwt. **12.** 50 lb. **13.** 9.0 ft. from *B*.

CHAPTER IV (pp. 35–36)

1. (*a*) 80 ft-lb. **2.** (*a*) 2,800 ft-lb. (*b*) 700 ft-lb. **3.** 28.0 kgwt-m. = 2,800,000 gwt-cm. **4.** 0.60 hp. **5.** 312,000 ft-lb. **6.** 1.89 hp. **7.** (*a*) 240,000 kgwt-m. = 2,350,000 joules. (*b*) 23.5 kw. **8.** 11.5 ft-lb. **9.** 100 ft-lb. **10.** (*a*) 0.10 ft. (*b*) 10. (*c*) 50 lb. **11.** (*a*) 6.00. (*b*) 5.0 lb. **12.** (*a*) 200,000 ft-lb. (*b*) 40 lb. **13.** (*a*) 120π. (*b*) 41.7 lb. **14.** (*a*) 12 ft. (*b*) 13.3 ft.

CHAPTER V (p. 46)

1. (*a*) 3.0 lb. (*b*) 180 ft-lb. **2.** 0.0109 hp. **3.** (*a*) 100 lb. (*b*) 0.20 hp. **4.** (*a*) 15.0 lb. (*b*) 8.66 lb. (*c*) 6.00 lb. **5.** (*a*) 5.0 lb. (*b*) 8.66 lb. (*c*) 2.0 lb. **6.** (*a*) 16.0 lb. (*b*) **12.0 lb.** (*c*) 3.6 lb. **7.** (*a*) 400 lb. (*b*) 0.80 hp.; 6.4 hp. **8.** (*a*) 15 lb. (*b*) 25 lb. (*c*) 5.0 lb.

CHAPTER VI (pp. 53–54)

1. 88 ft./sec. **2.** 26.4 ft./sec.² **3.** 4,000 ft./sec.² **4.** (*a*) 0 ft./sec. (*b*) 200 ft./sec. **5.** 10 ft./sec.² **6.** 196 ft./sec. **7.** (*a*) 7.81 sec. (*b*) 76.5 m./sec. **8.** 30 sec. **9.** 4.0 sec. **10.** 16 ft.; 48 ft.; 80 ft.; 112 ft. **11.** (*a*) 6.00 ft./sec.² (*b*) 128 ft. **12.** (*a*) 900 ft./sec.² (*b*) 126 ft. **13.** (*a*) 1,000 ft./sec. (*b*) 0.0020 sec. (*c*) 1,000,000 ft./sec.² **14.** (*a*) 148 ft./sec. (*b*) 444 ft. **15.** (*a*) 22 ft./sec.² (*b*) 44 ft. **16.** (*a*) 3.0 sec. (*b*) 144 ft. **17.** (*a*) 12.5 ft./sec.² (*b*) 100 ft. **18.** (*a*) 4.75 sec. (*b*) 66 ft. (*c*) 242 ft. **19.** 187 ft./sec.

CHAPTER VII (pp. 61–62)

1. 3.2 ft./sec.² **2.** 1.60 ft./sec.² **3.** 441 lb. **4.** 6.4 ft./sec.² **5.** 98 cm./sec.² **6.** 100 lb. **7.** (*a*) 10,000 ft./sec.² (*b*) 97.7 lb. **8.** (*a*) 100 gwt. (*b*) 200 gwt. **9.** (*a*) 400 cm./sec.² (*b*) 2.04 gwt. (*c*) 0.41. **10.** 15 lb. **11.** 8.0 ft./sec.² **12.** (*a*) 16×10^6 cm./sec.² (*b*) 163,000 gwt. **13.** 0.68 ft./sec.² **14.** 1/16 lb. **15.** (*a*) 200 lb. (*b*) 250 lb. **16.** (*a*) 50 lb. (*b*) 50 lb. (*c*) 86.6 lb. (*d*) 0.58.

CHAPTER VIII (pp. 72–73)

1. 16 ft. **2.** 50 ft./sec. **4.** (*a*) 1.56 sec. (*b*) 39 ft. (*c*) 270 ft. **5.** (*a*) 25 sec. (*b*) 2,500 ft. **6.** (*a*) 96 ft./sec., − 96 ft./sec. (*b*) 0 ft./sec., 192 ft./sec. **7.** (*a*) 55.4 ft./sec. (*b*) − 32 ft./sec. (*c*) 8.6 ft./sec. **8.** 1,000 gwt. **9.** 1.60 lb. **10.** (*a*) 50π ft./sec. (*b*) 3,080 lb. **11.** 50 lb.

12. 600 cm./sec. **13.** 1,250 lb. **14.** (a) 25,200 ft./sec. = 4.8 mi./sec. (b) 1.38 hr.
15. (a) 0.56 lb. (b) 2.56 lb. **16.** (a) 720 lb. (b) 6.75 ft. **17.** (a) 80 ft./sec. (b) 40 ft./sec.
18. (a) 9.6 lb. (b) 4.0 ft./sec.

CHAPTER IX (pp. 82–83)

1. 4,000 ft-lb. **2.** (a) 48.7 ft-lb. (b) 156 ft. **3.** (a) 80 ft. (b) 1,410 lb. **4.** (a) 24 ft./sec.
(b) 17 ft./sec. **5.** (a) 405,000 ft-lb. (b) 126.5 ft. **6.** 64 ft./sec. **7.** 86 lb. **8.** 10,200 gwt. =
10^6 dynes. **9.** (a) 9,000 lb-sec. (b) 1,800 lb.; 90.0 lb. **10.** (a) 200 gwt-sec. (b) 20,000 gwt.
(20 kgwt.) **11.** (a) 0.100 lb-sec. (b) 10.0 lb. **12.** 2.0 lb-sec., −250 lb-sec. **13.** (a) 4.0
ft./sec. (b) 8.0 lb. **14.** (a) 3,000 lb-sec. (b) 2.86 ft./sec.

CHAPTER X (pp. 91–92)

1. (a) $2\pi/60$ rad./sec. = 0.105 rad./sec. (b) $2\pi/6$ cm./sec. = 1.05 cm./sec.
2. (a) 1.50 lb-ft-sec.^{2} (b) 2π rad./sec. = 6.28 rad./sec. **3.** (a) 12π rad./sec. = 37.7
rad./sec. (b) 12π cm./sec. **4.** (a) 2.0 lb-ft. (b) 1.33 rad./sec.^{2} (c) 0.67 rad. **5.** 2.00
lb-ft-sec.^{2} **6.** (a) 0.020 lb-ft-sec.^{2} (b) 2π rad./sec. (c) $0.04\pi^2$ ft-lb. = 0.40 ft-lb. **7.** (a) 0.25
lb-ft-sec.^{2} (b) 4,440 ft-lb. (c) 1.62 hp. **8.** (a) 4.32 lb-ft-sec.^{2} (b) 8.64π lb-ft-sec. (c) 85.3
ft.-lb. **9.** (a) 62 lb-ft-sec.^{2} (b) 10/31 rad./sec.^{2}

CHAPTER XI (p. 104)

1. 37.5 lb. **2.** (a) 30 lb. (b) 30 ft. **3.** (a) 40 lb. (b) 10 lb. **4.** (a) 6.66 dynes. (b)
3.33 cm.

CHAPTER XIII (p. 118)

1. 294 dynes = 0.300 gwt. **2.** (a) 1.50 cm. (b) 0.150 cm. (c) 0.00150 cm. **3.** 1,400
dynes = 1.43 gwt. **4.** 294 dynes = 0.300 gwt. **5.** 943 dynes = 0.960 gwt. **6.** 300
dynes/cm.^{2} **7.** (a) 420. (b) 2,100 ergs. (c) 70 cm.^{2} (d) 30 ergs/cm.^{2} **8.** 40 dynes = 0.041
gwt.

CHAPTER XIV (pp. 124–125)

1. (a) 60 lb./in.^{2} (b) 1/24. **2.** (a) 200,000 lb./in.^{2} (b) 4/1,000. (c) 50,000,000 lb./in.^{2}
3. (a) 50,000 gwt./cm.^{2} (b) 1/1,000. (c) 50,000,000 gwt./cm.^{2} **4.** (a) 10 lb. (b) 40 lb.
5. 0.086 ft. **6.** (a) 1,600 lb. (b) 3,000 lb. **7.** (a) 30,000,000 lb./in.^{2} (b) 10,000,000 lb./in.^{2}
8. 5,000 lb./in.^{2} **9.** 1.3 mm. **10.** (a) 290 lb. (b) 250 lb. (c) 650 lb. (d) 750 lb. **11.** (a) 4.0
lb./ft.^{2} (b) 0.10. (c) 40 lb./ft.^{2}

CHAPTER XV (pp. 138–140)

1. 200 lb./in.^{2} **2.** 86.6 lb./in.^{2} **3.** 8,900 lb./in.^{2} **4.** 56.7 lb./in.^{2} **5.** 0.94 gwt./cm.^{2}
6. 350,000 lb. **7.** 62,400 lb. **8.** (a) 80 gwt./cm.^{2} (b) 64 gwt./cm.^{2} **9.** 146 gwt./cm.^{2}
10. 15 gwt./cm.^{2} **11.** 80 lb. **12.** 110 lb./in.^{2} **13.** 0.16 ft.^{3} **14.** 3.2 ft.^{3} **15.** 0.60 gwt./cm.^{3}
16. 660 gwt. **17.** (a) 12.5 gwt./cm.^{3} (b) 2.0 gwt./cm.^{3} **18.** (a) 0.60 cm.^{3} **19.** 2.0 ft.^{3} **20.**
0.90 gwt./cm.^{3} **21.** 7.4 cm.^{3} **22.** 0.933 gwt./cm.^{3} **23.** (a) 200 lb./in.^{2} (b) 400 lb. **24.** 112
cm.^{3} **25.** 2,337 lb. **26.** 0.895 gwt./cm.^{3} **27.** 1,860 lb./ft.^{2} **28.** 20.0 ft. **29.** 1,200 lb. **30.** (a)
1,033 gwt./cm.^{2} (b) 1,033 cm. **31.** (a) 2.50 lb./in.^{2} (b) 200×10^4 gwt./cm.^{2} **32.** 3,050
gwt. **33.** 27.5%. **34.** 38.5 lb. **35.** (a) 37.8 cm.^{3} (b) 398 gwt. (c) 25%.

CHAPTER XVI (pp. 151–152)

1. 370 lb. **2.** 0.0150 gwt. = 15 mgwt. **3.** (a) 244 lb. (b) 188 lb. **4.** (a) 1,006 cm.
(b) 799 cm. **5.** 152 cm. **6.** (a) 44.8 lb. (b) 30 lb. **7.** 33 ft. **8.** 680 gwt./cm.^{2} **9.** 16.7 lb/.in.^{2}

10. 97.5 gwt. **11.** 900 gwt./cm.²; 800 gwt./cm.² **12.** 111,000 cm. **13.** (a) 71.3 cm-of-Hg. (b) 10.8 gwt.

Chapter XVII (p. 158)

1. 980 cm./sec.

Chapter XIX (p. 174)

1. (a) 37°. (b) −39.4°. (c) 20°. (d) 6,093°. **2.** (a) 1,945°F. (b) 675°F. (c) −449°F. (d) −319°F. **3.** −40°F. **4.** 320°F. **5.** 6,000 in.³ **6.** 2,000 cm.³ **7.** 4,000 cm.³ **9.** 4.0 lb./in.² **10.** 1,035 ft.³ **11.** 2.00 cm.³ **12.** 251 cm.³ **13.** 1.54 gm./liter. **14.** 546°C. **15.** −459°F. **16.** 450 gm. **17.** 3,330 ft.³

Chapter XX (p. 181)

1. 0.0416 ft. **3.** 1.003 cm.³ **4.** 0.26 ft. **5.** 0.65 cm. **6.** 0.0000120/C.° **7.** 4.63 cm.³ **8.** (a) 0.30 cm. (b) 920 kgwt. = 2,030 lb.

Chapter XXI (pp. 186–187)

1. 4,000 cal. **2.** 655 cal. **3.** 252 cal. **4.** 443°C. **5.** 533 grams. **6.** 200 grams. **7.** 900 cal./hr. **8.** 0.88. **9.** (a) 8.53 × 10⁶ cal. (b) 2,840 grams. **10.** 1,194 B.t.u. **11.** 0.477 pound. **12.** (a) 212 grams. (b) 1,000 grams. **13.** 11.6 pounds. **14.** 11.1°C. **15.** (a) 62.4 B.t.u. (b) 1.00 cal. **16.** (a) 30.3 C° (b) 33.3 C° (c) 4.71 C° (d) 0.293 C°. **17.** 5,460.

Chapter XXII (pp. 196–197)

1. 320 B.t.u./sec. **2.** (a) 225 × 10⁶ cal. (b) 32.1 kilograms. **3.** 0.060 cal./sec.-cm.² **4.** (a) 1.00 gwt./cm.² (b) 10.0 kgwt. **5.** (a) 3.33 × 10³ cal./sec., 287 × 10⁶ cal./day. (b) 36 kilograms/day. (c) $36. **6.** 31,200 cal./m.²-hr. **7.** 5.34 × 10⁻³ cal./cm-sec-C°. **8.** 130°C. **9.** 11,000 B.t.u./day.

Chapter XXIII (p. 214)

1. 180,000 cal./hr. **2.** 12.5 grams. **3.** 0°C. **4.** 184 cal. **5.** 80 grams. **6.** 18.4 grams. **7.** 79 cal./gram. **8.** 7,180 cal. **9.** 33.7 grams. **10.** 267 grams. **11.** 12.5 grams. **12.** 7.5 pounds.

Chapter XXIV (p. 227)

1. (a) 2,000 ft-lb. (b) 0.0364 hp. (c) 2.57 B.t.u. **2.** (a) 2,000 ft-lb. (b) 2.57 B.t.u. **3.** (a) 405,000 ft-lb. (b) 184 hp. (c) 521 B.t.u. **4.** 31,000 ft. = 5.87 mi. **5.** 7.53 gm./hr.; 15.06 gm./hr. **6.** (a) 1,560,000 ft-lb. (b) 2,000 B.t.u. (c) 2.0 biscuits.

Chapter XXV (p. 241)

1. 12.83 gm./m.³ **2.** (a) 54.4%. (b) 73.3%. **3.** 1.66 km. or 1 mi. **4.** $4.50. **5.** 4.08 × 10⁶ gwt. = 4.08 tons.

Chapter XXVI (p. 247)

1. 1,000 gwt./cm. or 980,000 dynes/cm. **2.** 6.28 sec. **3.** (a) 784,000 dynes/cm. (b) 0.224 sec. **4.** (a) 20,000 lb./ft. (b) 0.236 sec. **5.** (a) 2.0 sec. (b) 0.50/sec. (c) 1.00 ft. **6.** 1.2π ft./sec. **7.** (a) 4.16 cm. (b) 700 cm. **8.** 2.45 sec. **9.** π sec. **10.** 3.27 ft. **11.** 2.09 sec. **12.** 2.40 gwt. = 2,350 dynes.

Chapter XXVII (pp. 256–257)

1. 4,160 ft./sec. **2.** (a) 172 m./sec. (b) 40.2 m./sec. **3.** 2.07 × 10¹⁰ dynes/cm.²

4. 2,180 ft. **5.** 2.00 sec. **6.** 4,800 ft. **7.** 33.3 cm./sec. **8.** 0.43 sec. **9.** 2.31 sec. **10.** 6,300 ft. **11.** 1 bel. **12.** (*a*) 750 ft.² (*b*) 6.66 sec. **13.** (*a*) 1,600 ft.² (*b*) 3.12 sec. **14.** 18 ft.²

Chapter XXVIII (pp. 267–268)

1. 615 rev./min. **2.** 250/sec. **3.** (*a*) 11.0 m. (*b*) 1.65 cm. **5.** (*a*) 8,300 vib./sec. (*b*) 24,900 vib./sec. **6.** 927°C. **7.** 261 vib./sec. **8.** 500 vib./sec. **9.** (*a*) 545/sec. (*b*) 459/sec. **10.** 1.07 ft.; 0.859 ft.; 0.716 ft.; 0.537 ft. **11.** 5.19 m. **12.** 4.2 sec. **13.** (*a*) 40 ft. (*b*) 0.263 ft.

Chapter XXIX (pp. 274–275)

1. 0.50. **2.** 250. **3.** 32. **4.** 31½. **5.** 0.80 ft-candles. **6.** 36. **7.** 2.5 candles. **8.** 1,600,000,000 ft-candles. **9.** 40 ft. **10.** (*a*) 1.00 ft. (*b*) −3.0 ft. **11.** ¾ or 75%. **12.** (*a*) 8,600 ft-candles. (*b*) 5,000 ft-candles. (*c*) 0 ft-candles.

Chapter XXX (p. 279)

1. 25.8 million million mi. **2.** 11.8 tt. **3.** 240 million million mi. **4.** 2.08 mi. **5.** 11.63 mi. **6.** 625 rev./sec.

Chapter XXXI (pp. 289–290)

1. 3.0 ft. **2.** ½ ft. **3.** 2½ ft. **4.** 6 ft./sec. **5.** Below. **6.** Greater. **7.** 2.0. **8.** 60°. **9.** 225,000 km./sec. **10.** 4.0 ft.

Chapter XXXII (pp. 301–302)

7. $D_i = -3.0$ in. **8.** 8 in. $\times$ 10 in. **9.** 6.0 in. **10.** (*a*) 1.00 ft. **11.** (*a*) 1 ft. (*b*) 2 ft. $M_1 = 0.50$; $M_2 = 2.0$. **12.** $F = -4.0$ in. **13.** $F = 2.0$ ft. **14.** −4.0 ft. **15.** −10 cm. **16.** 12 in. **17.** 10 cm. **18.** $D_i = -10$ cm., $M = 5.0$.

Chapter XXXIII (p. 313)

1. 9.68 cm. **2.** 0.20 ft., 2.4 in. **3.** 13 ft. **4.** 0.67 in. **5.** 36 cm. **6.** $F = -200$ cm. **7.** 50 cm. **8.** (*a*) 2.27 cm. (*b*) 11. **9.** (*a*) 0.513 cm. (*b*) 39 and 26. (*c*) 1,014. **10.** 480 mi. **11.** (*a*) 36.5 in. (*b*) 72. **12.** 36.55 in.

Chapter XXXV (p. 335)

1. (*a*) 0.025 cm. (*b*) 40/cm. **2.** 30°. **3.** (*a*) 0.000036 cm. (*b*) 16.

Chapter XXXVIII (p. 358)

1. 20 Ω. **2.** 80 Ω. **3.** 100 Ω. **4.** 224 sec. = 3.73 min. **5.** 2,240 coulombs, 1.40×10^{22} electrons. **6.** 0.216 Ω. **7.** 0.00024 Ω-cm.

Chapter XXXIX (pp. 364–365)

1. 230 Ω. **2.** 5.75 amp. **3.** 130 Ω. **4.** (*a*) 5.00 V. (*b*) 100 V. **5.** 21.7 Ω. **6.** (*a*) 100 V. (*b*) 400 V. (*c*) 300 V. **7.** 1.00 Ω. **8.** (*a*) 3.0 Ω. (*b*) 2.0 Ω. **9.** (*a*) 2.50 V. (*b*) 29.5 V. **10.** 16.0 V. **11.** 0.100 Ω. **12.** (*a*) 6.0 V. (*b*) 5.90 V. (*c*) 5.0 V. (*d*) 4.0 V. **13.** (*a*) 2.00 amp. (*b*) 2.00 V. (*c*) 10.00 V. (*d*) 4.00 V. **14.** 0.273 amp.

Chapter XL (pp. 371–372)

1. 10 Ω. **2.** 230,000 Ω. **3.** 1.00 Ω. **4.** (*a*) 40 V. (*b*) 20 amp. **5.** (*a*) 30 Ω. (*b*) 80 Ω. **6.** 20 lamps. **7.** (*a*) 0.50 amp. (*b*) 3.00 V.; 1.00 V.; 2.00 V. **8.** (*a*) 1.0 amp. (*b*) 2.0 V. **9.** 48 Ω; 2 Ω. **10.** (*a*) 3.5 amp. (*b*) 34.3 Ω. **11.** (*a*) 2.0 Ω. (*b*) 2.50 amp. (*c*) 0.40 Ω. **12.** 0.25 amp. **13.** (*a*) 7.62 amp. (*b*) 1.52 V. (*c*) 30.5 V. **14.** (*a*) 4.0 amp. (*b*) 1.00 amp. **15.** 25 Ω.

Chapter XLI (p. 382)

1. Hydrogen 0.0000209 gm./sec.; oxygen 0.000166 gm./sec. 2. 3.04×10^6 sec. = 35.2 days. 3. 31.76 gm. 4. 29.0 gm. 5. (a) 0.661 gm.; 1.32 cent. (b) 3.8×10^{21}. 6. 0.000304 gm./coulomb. 7. 48.7 gm. 8. (a) 0.00987 gm. (b) 0.01014 gm.

Chapter XLII (p. 386)

1. (a) 60 watts. (b) 480 watts. 2. 0.52 amp. 3. 0.18 cent. 4. (a) 2.80 watts. (b) 0.806×10^6 joule or 0.224 kw.-hr. (c) $1.80. 5. 6.0 V. 6. (a) 13.8 V. (b) 6.9 watts. 7. (a) 5.5 watts. (b) 3.85 kw.-hr. (c) 11.6 cents. 8. 1.0 cent. 9. 10.3 cents. 10. (a) 1.00 watt. (b) 4.00 watts. 11. (a) 2.00 watts. (b) 0.50 watt.

Chapter XLIII (p. 393)

1. 0.30 amp. 2. 120 cal./sec. 3. (a) 101,000 joules. (b) 24,100 cal. 4. (a) 0.25 amp., 1.00 amp. (b) 1.50 watts; 6.00 watts. 5. 836 sec. 6. (a) 6.0 amp. 20 Ω. (b) 3.0 amp. 40 Ω. 7. (a) 22 Ω. (b) 1.65 cents. 8. (a) 1.56×10^6 joules; 3.73×10^5 cal. (b) 6.22 kg. 9. (a) 1,440 watts. (b) 4.32 cents/hr. 10. 1.98 cents. 11. (a) 200×10^4 cal. or 836×10^4 joules or 2.32 kw.-hr. (b) 7.0 cents. 12. 608 sec. 13. 40 lamps. 14. 0.0283 kw.-hr.; $5.35/kw.-hr.

Chapter XLIV (p. 402)

1. 1,980 u.p. 2. 250 dynes. 3. 50 dynes. 4. 98 u.p. 5. 200 u.p. 6. 2,000 dynes/u.p. 7. 4,000 lines. 8. 40,000 dynes. 9. 25 dynes/u.p. 10. 16 dynes/u.p. 11. 1.50 dynes/u.p. 12. 3.18 dynes/u.p. 13. 0.265 dynes/u.p. 14. 25 dynes; −25 dynes; 0 dynes.

Chapter XLV (p. 412)

1. 0.40 dynes/u.p. 2. 0.40 dynes/u.p. 3. 80π dynes/u.p. 4. $3,137/\pi = 1,000$. 5. 0.0050 Ω. 6. 9,950 Ω. 7. 19,800 Ω.

Chapter XLVI (p. 423)

1. 0.0090 V. 2. 40,000 V. 3. 1/1,000 V. 4. (a) 0.020 amp., 12,000 V. (b) 240 watts. 5. (a) 4,000 kw. (b) 160 watts, 0.160 kw. 6. (a) 30 V. (b) 3,000 V. 7. 0.00024 V.

Chapter XLVII (pp. 431–432)

1. (a) 6,000 lines. (b) 3/100,000 V. 2. 4.00 V. 3. (a) 3.33 amp. (b) 11.7 amp. (c) 20.0 amp. 4. 164 watts. 5. (a) 210 watts = 0.282 hp. (b) 1.03 ft. 6. (a) 0.32 kw. (b) $2.30. 7. (a) 36.75 kw. (b) 0.68 cent.

Chapter XLVIII (p. 446)

1. 6.28×10^{-6} sec. 2. 1,890 m. 3. 1.11×10^{-11} farad.

Chapter XLIX (p. 454)

1. 3.13×10^{21} electrons. 2. (a) 900 billion billion ergs, 90,000 billion joules, or 21,500 billion calories. (b) 2.7×10^9 gm. = 2,700 metric tons.

Chapter L (p. 461)

1. (a) 100 watts. (b) 6.25×10^{15} electrons. 2. 10^{-8} cm. 3. (a) 6.0×10^{14} per sec. (b) 39.5×10^{-13} erg, 5.06×10^{18} per sec.

Chapter LI (p. 472)

1. 218 and 84. 2. At. wt. 214, At. no. 84. 4. 30 electron-volts.

INDEX

(References are to pages)

Aberration, chromatic, 316
  spherical, 296, 300
Absorption, coefficients of sounds, 253
  spectra, 318
Acceleration, linear, 48
  of gravity, 101
Accommodation (eye), 306
Achromatic lenses, 316
Action, 59
Adhesion, 111
Age of earth, 465
Air columns, vibrations of, 259
Alpha rays and particles, 463
Alternating currents, 425
Ammeter, 410
Ampere, 354
Amplifier, 441
Aneroid barometer, 145
Angular, momentum, 86
  velocity, 89
Anode, 373
Archimedes' principle, 134
Armature, 426
Astigmatism, 306
Atomic, heat, 185
  mass, 468
  number, 468
Atoms, 103
  disintegration of, 464
  masses of, 452
  nuclei of, 470
  weighing, 378

Barometer, aneroid, 145
  mercury, 144
Barometric, highs and lows, 231
  pressure and altitude, 144
Battery, Edison storage, 380
  lead storage, 379
Beats, 263
Becquerel, 462

Bel, 255
Beta rays and particles, 463
Black body, 192
Boiling point, 204
Bourdon gage, 147
Boyle's law, 168
  and molecular bombardment, 170
Brahe, Tycho, 96
British thermal units, 182
Buoyancy of air, 141

Calorie, 182
Calorimeter, 183
  bomb, 184
Camera, 303
  motion picture, 304
Candle, International, 269
Capacitance, electrical, 434
Capillarity, 114
Carburetor, 155
Carrier radio waves, 439
Cathode rays, 448
Cells, dry, 379
  e.m.f. of, 379
  photoelectric, 458
  voltaic, 377
Center of gravity, 21
Centigrade scale, 167
Centrifugal force, 68
Centripetal force, 66
Charges, electrical, escape from points, 346
  on outside of conductor, 345
Charles' law, 171
Chromatic aberration, 316
Coefficients, of expansion, of gases, 170
  of liquids, 178
  of solids, 176
  of friction, 38
Cohesion, 111

Color, 324
  by scattering, 327
  photography, 326
Colors, complementary, 324
  primary, 324
Combustion, heats of, 184
Commutator, 427
Compass, 394
Components of a force, 15
Concave mirror, 297
Condenser, electric, 435
Conduction, thermal, 188
Conservation, of energy, 77
  of momentum, 80
Convection, 191
Converging lens, 291
Copernicus, 95
Corpuscular theory of light, 458
Cosmic rays, 466
Coulomb, 354
Counter electromotive force of a motor, 429
Cream separator, 67
Critical, angle, 286
  pressure, 210
  temperature, 211
Crystals, 108

Davy safety lamp, 190
Decibel, 255
Declination of the compass, 400
Density,—mass, 127
Density,—weight, 127
Density of water, 180
Detector, radio tube, 440
Deuteron, 470
Dew point, 234
Diatonic scale, 264
Dielectric constant, 436
Diffraction, 326
  grating, 330
  of light, 329
Diffusion, of gases and liquids, 159
  pump, 149
Diverging lens, 295
Doppler effect, 266, 321
Double refraction, 338
Dyes and pigments, 325
Dyne, 10, 58

Earth, age of, 465
  magnetic field of, 399
  weight of, 100
Eddy currents, 422
Efficiency, luminous, 232
  of a machine, 34
  of engines, 223
Elasticity, 120
  limit of, 121
  Young's coefficient or modulus of, 122
Electric, arc, 389
  charge, 342
  current, alternating, 415
    direct, 415
    heating effect of, 388
  "eye," 459
  lighting, 272, 388
  power, 384
Electrical, capacitance, 434
  condenser, 435
Electricity, negative, 342
  positive, 342
Electrochemical equivalent, 376
Electrolysis, 373
  Faraday's laws of, 375
Electrolytic, dissociation, 373
  purification, 375
Electromagnet, 405
Electromotive force, 362
  counter, of a motor, 429
  induced, 415
  of cells, 379
Electron, charge of, 449
  mass of, 450
Electron-volt, 467
Electrophorus, 345
Electroplating, 374
Electroscope, 343
Emissivity, 192
Energy, 74
  conservation of, 77
  degradation of, 222
  kinetic, 74
  matter, a form of, 79
  potential, 76
  subatomic, 470
  transmission of, 417
  unit, electron-volt, 467
    kilowatt-hour, 385

Engines, 216
  Diesel, 221
  efficiency of, 223
  internal-combustion, 219
  steam, 216
Equilibrant, 13
Equilibrium, 13
  conditions of, 21
  of forces, 13
Equivalent window area, 254
Erg, 26
Evaporation, 202
  cooling by, 205
Expansion, linear, 176
  of water, 179
  volume, 178
Eye, 304
Eyepiece, 307

Fahrenheit scale, 167
Falling bodies, 51
Farad, 435
Faraday's laws of electrolysis, 376
Films, strength of, 112
Flow of fluids, 153
Focal lengths, 291, 297
Foot-candle, 271
Foot-pound, 26
Force, and acceleration, 55–58
  centrifugal, 68
  centripetal, 66
  mass, and acceleration, 56
  of molecular attraction, 119
  units, absolute, 58
    gravitational, 58
Force-constant, 243
Forces, resultant of, 10
Franklin, 348
Fraunhofer lines, 320
Freezing mixtures, 201
Friction, and speed, 38
  coefficients of, 38
  fluid, 37, 42
  rolling, 37, 41
  sliding, 37, 38
  starting, 38
Fundamental tone, 259
Fuses, 390
Fusion, 198
  heat of, 199

Galileo, 51
  and telescope, 96
Galvani, 377
Galvanometer, 409
Gamma rays, 464
Gas, ideal, 172
  law, general, 172
  thermometer, 172
Gauss, 397
Generators, 424
Gram-mass, 7
Gram-weight, 10, 58
Grating, diffraction, 330
Gravitation, law of, 97
Gravitational, constant, 99
  units of force, 57
Gravity, acceleration of, 100
  center of, 21
Gyrocompass, 88
Gyroscope, 86

Harmony, 263
Heart, 151
Heat, a form of energy, 215
  conduction, 188
  convection, 191
  equivalent of work, 216
  of combustion, 184
  of fusion, 199
  of vaporization, 206
  produced by electric current, 387
  units, 182
Henry, 421
Hooke's law, 122
Horsepower, the, 26
Humidity, 233
Hydraulic, brakes, 133
  press, 132
Hydrometer, 136
Hygrometer, 234

Ideal gas, 172
Ignition system of a car, 419
Illumination, unit of, 270
Image, equation, 299
  real, 293
    size of, 295
  virtual, 293

Images, formation of, 280
  by lenses, 292
  resolution of, 327
Impulse, 79
Incandescent lamp, 388
Incidence, angle of, 280
Induced, currents, 413
  e.m.f., 415
Inductance, self, 421
Induction, coil, 419
  electromagnetic, 434
Inertia, 55
  rotational, 85
Insulation, thermal, 189
Intensity, luminous, 269
  of sound, 254
Interference, 328
  colors due to, 332
Internal-combustion engine, 219
Inverse square law, 270
Ions, gaseous, 447
  in solution, 373
Isotopes, 469

Jolly, 99
Joule, 25

Kepler, 96
Kilowatt, 27
Kilowatt-hour, 384
Kinetic energy, 74
  molecular, 164
  of rotating body, 89

Lamp, incandescent, 388
Lenses, 291
  achromatic, 316
  thick, 296
Lenz's law, 414
Lever, 19
  arm, 19
Light, 269
  interference of, 329
  polarized, 336
  rectilinear propagation of, 279
  scattering of, 327
  speed of, 276
  waves are transverse, 337
Lightning, 348
Linear expansion, 176

Lines (of force), magnetic, 396
Liquid air, 211
Lodestone, 394
Looming, 288
Loudness of sound, 254
Lubrication, 43
Lumen, 273
Luminous efficiency, 272

Machines, 27
Magnet, 395
Magnetic, compass, 394
  fields, 396
    produced by currents, 403
  induction, 405
  lines (of force), 396
  permeability, 396, 405
  poles, 395
Magnetism, 394
  of earth, 399
Magnetization, due to spinning electrons, 407
  process of, 398
Magnification, 295
  of microscope, 309
  of telescope, 311
Magnifying glass, 307
Manometer, 146
Maps, weather, 232
Mass, 7, 57
  and weight, 57
  of atom, 377
  of earth, 100
Mass-density, 127
Matter, a form of energy, 452
Maxwell color triangle, 324
Measurement, 5
Mechanical advantage, 27
Mercury thermometer, 166
Meter, 6
Meter-candle, 271
Metric system, 5
Michelson's method, 277
Microscope, 309
Mirage, 288
Mirror, curved, 297
  focal length of, 297
  parabolic, 300
  plane, 280
  spherical, 297

Modulation, 439
Molecular kinetic energy, 164
Molecule, 106
Momentum, 79
  angular, 86
  conservation of, 80
Motors, 427
  counter e.m.f. of, 429
  series and shunt, 430
Moving fluids, 153
Music, 258
Musical, intervals, 263
  scales, 264

Neutron, 470
Newcomen steam engine, 217
Newton, 314
Newton's, law of gravitation, 97
  laws of motion, 56, 58, 60
Nicol prism, 339

Oersted, 397
Ohm, 355
Ohm's law, 361
Oil prospecting, 101
Oscillator, electric, 437
Osmosis, 161
Osmotic pressure, 161
Overtone, 259

Parabolic mirror, 300
Parallelogram of forces, 10
Pascal's principle, 131
Pendulum, 245
Period of vibration, 242
Permeability, 396, 405
Phase of vibration, 244
Photoelectricity, 459
Photographic action, 303
Photometer, 271
Photon, 458
Pitch, 262
Polarization, electrolytic, 379
  of light, 336
    by double refraction, 337
    by reflection, 339
Polaroid, 338
Poles, magnetic, 395
Positron, 470

Potential, difference, 359
  energy, 76
Pound-mass, 7
Pound-weight, 10
Power, 26
  electric, 384
  units of, 26
Pressure, 126
  and velocity, 154
  of a gas, and density, 162
    and molecular speed, 162
    formula for, 164
  of a saturated vapor, 203
  of the atmosphere, 142
  osmotic, 161
Principal focus, 293
Principle, of Archimedes, 134
  of Pascal, 131
Projectile, 63
Projection lantern, 303
Protons, 470
Ptolemy, 93
Pumps, 148

Quality of musical sound, 262

Radian, 89
Radiation, 192
  and temperature, 194
Radiations, infra-red, 333
  ultra-violet, 333
Radio, 433
  amplifier, 441
  receiving set, 438, 442
  transmitter, 443
  tubes, 439
Radioactivity, 462
  transformations in, 465
Rainbow, 315
Rays, alpha, 463
  beta, 463
  cathode, 448
  gamma, 463
  infra-red, 333
  ultra-violet, 333
  X-, 455
Reaction, 59
Real image, 523
Rectifier, 438, 440

Reflection, angle of, 280
  diffuse, 281
  laws of, 280
Refraction, double, 338
  index of, 282
Refrigerator, 207
Relative humidity, 233
Resistance, electrical, 355
  and temperature, 356
Resistances, in parallel, 367
  in series, 366
Resonance, electrical, 434
  mechanical, 261
Resultant of forces, 11
Retina, 305
Reverberation, 253
  period of, 254
Rheostat, 357
Right-hand rule, 403
Roemer's method, 276
Roentgen, 455
Rolling friction, 41
Rotational, acceleration, 89
  inertia, 85
Rumford's experiment, 216

Saturated vapor, 203
Scale, musical, chromatic, 264
    diatonic, 264
    equal-tempered, 264
Scattering of light, 327
Science, 4
Scientific method, 2
Second, 8
Self-inductance, 421
Self-induction, 420
Shearing stress and strain, 123
Short radio waves, 444
Shunts, 410
Simple harmonic motion, 242
Siphon, 148
Size of image, 295
Slug, 58
Snell's law, 282
Solar spectrum, 326
Solutions, ions in, 473
Sound, 250
  absorption coefficients, 253
  intensity and loudness, 254
  speed of, 251

Spark coil, 419
Specific, gravity, 128
  heat, 182
    and atomic heat, 185
    of a gas, 185
Spectra, absorption, 318
  continuous, 318
  emission, 318
  of sun, 320
Spectroscope, 319
Speed, 47
  of light, 276
  of sound, 254
Spherical aberration, 296
Standing waves, 258
Steam engine, 216
Storage batteries, 379
Strain and stress, shearing, 123
  stretching, 120
  volume, 123
Streamlining, 43
Sun, spectrum of, 320
Supercooling, 201
Surface, films, 111
  tension, 111
Sympathetic vibrations, 261

Telegraph, relay, 408
  sounder, 407
Telephone, 418
  transmitter, 419
Telescope, astronomical, reflecting, 311
    refracting, 310
  magnification produced by, 311
Temperature, 166
  absolute, 170
  and weather, 228
  centigrade, 167
  critical, 211
  Fahrenheit, 167
  Kelvin, 170
Tempering of metals, 109
Theories, of Copernicus, 93
  of light, 458
  of Ptolemy, 93
Thermal, conduction, 188
  convection, 191
Thermocouple, 392
Thermoelectricity, 390

Thermometer, 166
  gas, 172
  mercury, 166
  of Galileo, 166
  wet and dry bulb, 234
Tides, 101
Tones and semitones, 264
Torque, 19
Total reflection, 286
Trade winds, 236
Transformer, 416
Transverse waves, 249
Tubes, radio, 439
  X-ray, 456
Turbine, steam, 218

Uniform motion, 47, 84
Units, C.G.S., 8
  derived, 8
  F.P.S., 8
  fundamental, 8

Van de Graaf generator, 347
Vapor, density, 202
  pressure, 203
    and volume, 210
Vaporization, heat of, 206
Variation of gravity, 100
Vector, 11
Velocity, angular, 89
  linear, 47
  of a jet, 156
  of stars, 321
  terminal, 43
Vibration, 242
  forced, 261
  period of a, 242
  simple harmonic, 242
  sympathetic, 261
Virtual image, 293

Vision, 304
Volt, 362
Volta, 377
Voltaic cells, 377
  e.m.f. of, 379
Voltmeters, 410

Water equivalent, 183
Watt, 384
Wave, length, 248
  motion, 248
  speed, 248
Waves, compressional, 249
  in air, 249
  polarized, 336
  sound, 250
  standing, 258
  transverse, 249
Weather, 228
  forecasting, 258
  humidity and, 233
  temperature and, 229
  winds and, 229
Weighing the earth, 100
Weight, 10
Weight-density, 127
Wheatstone bridge, 369
White light, 324
Work, 25
  done by an electric current,.383
  units of, 26

X-rays, 455
  "hard" and "soft," 457
  tubes, 456

Young's coefficient or modulus, 122

Zero, Kelvin, 122